THEORY OF THE TRANSMISSION AND PROCESSING OF INFORMATION

PUBLISHER'S NOTICE TO REVIEWERS AND READERS

CONCERNING THE QUALITY OF PRODUCTION AND PUBLISHED PRICE OF THIS WORK

In the interest of speedily making available the information contained in this publication, it has been necessary to produce the text by non-letterpress setting and photo lithography, with the result that the quality of production is not as high as the public have come to associate with and expect from the Pergamon Press.

To have re-set this manuscript by letterpress would have delayed its appearance by many months and the price would have had to be increased further.

The cost of translating scientific and technical works from the Russian in time, money, and publishing effort is very considerable. In the interest of getting the Soviet Authorities eventually to pay the usual authors' royalties to Western authors, the Pergamon Press is voluntarily paying to Russian authors the usual authors' royalties on this publication, in addition to the translators' and editors' fees. This and the somewhat limited market and the lack of any kind of subsidy accounts for what may appear to be a higher than usual published price.

I. R. MAXWELL
Publisher at Pergamon Press

THEORY OF THE TRANSMISSION AND PROCESSING OF INFORMATION

by

A. G. VITUSHKIN

Translated from the Russian by

RUTH FEINSTEIN

Translation Editor

A. D. BOOTH, D.SC., PH.D.

PERGAMON PRESS

NEW YORK · OXFORD · LONDON · PARIS

1961

PERGAMON PRESS INC.
122 East 55th Street, New York 22, N.Y.
1404 New York Avenue N.W., Washington 5 D.C.
Statler Center 640, 900 Wilshire Boulevard,
Los Angeles 17, California

PERGAMON PRESS LTD.
Headington Hill Hall, Oxford
4 & 5 Fitzroy Square, London, W.1

PERGAMON PRESS S.A.R.L.
24 Rue des Écoles, Paris Ve

PERGAMON PRESS G.m.b.H.
Kaiserstrasse 75, Frankfurt am Main

addl.

A translation of the original volume
Otsenka slozhnosti zadachi tabulirovaniya
(Moscow, Fizmatgiz, 1959)

Library of Congress Card Number: 61-14043

Printed in Great Britain by Pergamon Printing and Art Services Limited, London

CONTENTS

PUBLISHER'S NOTICE TO READERS ON THE SUPPLY OF AN ENGLISH TRANSLATION OF ANY RUSSIAN ARTICLE MENTIONED BIBLIOGRAPHICALLY OR REFERRED TO IN THIS PUBLICATION.

The Pergamon Institute has made arrangements with the Institute of Scientific Information of the U.S.S.R. Academy of Sciences whereby they can obtain rapidly a copy of any article originally published in the open literature of the U.S.S.R.

We are therefore in a position to supply readers with a translation (into English or any other language that may be needed) of any article referred to in this publication, at a reasonable price under the cost-sharing plan.

Readers wishing to avail themselves of this service should address their request to the Administrative Secretary, The Pergamon Institute at either 122 East 55th Street, New York 22, N.Y. or Headington Hill Hall, Oxford.

FOREWORD

This monograph is connected with the theory of the transmission and processing of information. The work attempts to define mathematically the concept of the complexity of a tabulation problem (the construction of tables for functions) by using concrete problems as examples. The formal definition of a concept of this kind, apart from its purely theoretical interest, is required in machine mathematics, and, in the first instance, in the automatization of programming.

The "Introduction" is intended for the reader who wishes to acquaint himself quickly with the fundamental results of this work. It assembles together the principles contained in the separate chapters of the book and is, essentially, a resumé. We wish only to add that the first three chapters are concerned with the study of the concept of the ϵ-entropy of metrical space and estimates of the ϵ-entropy of some spaces of analytic and differentiable functions; Chapters IV and V deal with variations of subsets of Euclidean spaces and with the evaluation of the variations of some concrete sets (algebraic surfaces); in the last two chapters we derive estimates of the complexity of constructing tables for some concrete classes of functions (for example, for analytic and differentiable functions).

The author is deeply grateful to A.A. Lyapunov, who has shown great interest in this work, and to A.L. Brudno, who led the author to the fundamental result of this book via a number of concrete problems in the tabulation of functions.

INTRODUCTION

History of the problem. The theme of this monograph was first laid down by work on Hilbert's thirteenth problem. Hilbert's hypothesis, stated in 1900, was as follows. There exist analytic functions of three variables which cannot be represented as the superposition of continuous functions of two variables [Ref. 10]. By raising this problem, which came up in the study of nomography, Hilbert, apparently, wanted to find those characteristics of a function by which it would be possible to differentiate less complex functions from those which were more complex, in the same way, for example, as the topological dimension enables us to classify sets.

Hilbert solved his problem for the class of analytic functions, and, in particular, he proved the existence of analytic functions of several variables which cannot be represented as the superposition of analytic functions of a smaller number of variables. Apparently, by using this theorem, Hilbert also stated his hypothesis which essentially consisted in the statement that the "complexity" of a function is determined firstly by the number of its arguments. Indeed, from Hilbert's theorem, this is obvious for analytic functions.

However, for wider classes of function it is not true. For example, the characteristic of complexity of s-times differentiable functions of n variables is not the number n of its arguments, but the ratio $\frac{n}{s}$. This fact can be put in terms of superpositions as follows: for any n and s there exist s-times differentiable functions of n variables which cannot be represented as superpositions of p-times differentiable functions of m variables, if $\frac{m}{p} < \frac{n}{s}$ [Ref. 12]. From the point of view of the difficulty of tabulating a function (of constructing a table for the function) the same thing can be said in the following way: if there is an algorithm which enables us to decompose any s-times differentiable function of n variables into the superposition of functions of fewer variables, then any table containing the functions which form the superposition cannot be simpler than the table containing, for example, the Fourier coefficients of the decomposed function.

A fuller proof of the theorem that the characteristic of complexity of an s-times differentiable function of n variables is the ratio $\frac{n}{s}$ and the characteristic of complexity of an analytic function is the number n of its arguments, is given by A.N. Kolmogorov's estimates of the ε-entropy for the corresponding functional spaces [Ref. 3]. Using this kind of estimate, it is possible to make an upper estimate of the volume of tables (the total number of binary digits required to write down all the parameters of the table). On the other hand, the improvement of working methods [Ref. 2] has led to the estimates of the complexity of decoding tables which are given here. These estimates again support the view that the ratio $\frac{n}{s}$ is the characteristic of complexity of an s-times differentiable function of n variables, and that the number n is that of an analytic function of n variables.

Concerning the controversy about the solution of Hilbert's thirteenth problem, we must mention that the last word refuting Hilbert's hypothesis was said by a student of Moscow University, V.I. Arnold. A.N. Kolmogorov and V.I. Arnold together proved that any continuous function of n variables (and therefore, also any analytic function) can be represented in the form of the superposition of continuous functions of a single variable and of addition operations [Ref. 4].

Statement of the problem and basic results. Let F be some compact family of real (or complex) functions $f(x)$ defined on some set G (the norm being the upper bound of values of the modulus of the function on the set G). Let Φ be a metrical expansion of the space F, i.e. a space which contains F as its subspace and has the identical metric, and let $T_{\varepsilon}^{\Phi}(f)$ be the table of any function $f(x) \in F$, consisting of the p parameters $y_1, y_2, \ldots, y_p$ and the decoding algorithm $\Gamma(t)$, which represents $f(x)$ (everywhere on G) to an accuracy of ε. By $\Gamma(y)$ we shall understand a real polynomial* $P_x^k(y)$ in p variables $y_1, y_2, \ldots, y_p$, of degree not greater than $k \geqslant 0$, in each variable, whose coefficients depend in an arbitrary way on $x \in G$, and which is such that for any function $f(x) \in F$ we can find a set of values of the parameters $y_1, y_2, \ldots, y_p$, such that for any $x \in G$

$$|f(x) - P_x^k(y)| \leqslant \varepsilon.$$

The index Φ in $T_\varepsilon^\Phi(f)$ indicates that for any y $P_x^k(y)$ is (as a function of x) an element of the space Φ.

Our problem consists in making an upper estimate in some way of the "complexity" of tables of elements in the space F on the basis of the general properties of F. The complexity of a table is characterized by two factors:

(a) its volume (the total number of binary digits required to write down all the parameters of the table).
(b) the complexity of the decoding algorithm for the table (in this case, the magnitude of the numbers p and k).

A.N. Kolmogorov's concept of the ε-entropy of a metrical space enables us to evaluate the order of increase of the volume of the table for an increase in the accuracy of tabulation. We have refined this concept somewhat, namely by defining the relative ε-entropy $H_\varepsilon^\Phi(F)$ and the absolute ε-entropy $H_\varepsilon(F)$ of the space F (see § 3, 4) in terms of which we can prove the following:

1. $H_\varepsilon^\Phi(F)$ is an exact lower bound of the volume of the tables $T_\varepsilon^\Phi(f)$ ($f \in F$, Φ fixed).
2. $H_\varepsilon(F)$ is an exact lower bound of the volume of all possible tables $T_\varepsilon^\Phi(f)$ ($f \in F$ and Φ arbitrary).
3. $H_\varepsilon(F) = \inf\limits_{\Phi \supset F} H_\varepsilon^\Phi(F)$ and therefore the best metrical expansion of any compact metrical space F is the space C of all real functions continuous on [0,1], i.e.

$$H_\varepsilon^C(F) = H_\varepsilon(F).$$

In the second and third chapters of this book

---

* We shall here only consider one of the simplest classes of algorithms. Tables which have decoding algorithms using the simplest logical operations (for example, comparison, taking the maximum, and so on) in addition to arithmetic operations, are also considered in this book.

we evaluate the magnitude of the absolute ε-entropy for some sub-spaces of analytic differentiable functions. The following relations are proved*:

$$2^{H_{4\delta}(4\varepsilon)(G)} + \log\left(\frac{c}{3\varepsilon}\right) \leqslant H_{\varepsilon}\left(F^{G}_{\omega(\delta), c}\right) \leqslant$$

$$\leqslant 2^{H_{\frac{1}{2}\delta}\left(\frac{1}{2}\varepsilon\right)(G)} + \log\left(\frac{3c}{\varepsilon}\right);$$

$$A(s, n)\rho^{n}\left(\frac{L}{\varepsilon}\right)^{\frac{n}{s}} \leqslant H_{\varepsilon}\left(F^{\rho, n}_{s, L, c}\right) \leqslant B(s, n)\rho^{n}\left(\frac{L}{\varepsilon}\right)^{\frac{n}{s}};$$

$$A(G_1, G_2)\left(\log\frac{c}{\varepsilon}\right)^{n+1} \leqslant H_{\varepsilon}\left(F^{G_1, n}_{G_2, c}\right) \leqslant$$

$$\leqslant B(G_1, G_2)\left(\log\frac{c}{\varepsilon}\right)^{n+1};$$

$$H_{\varepsilon}\left(F^{r, n}_{\rho, c}\right) = \frac{2}{(n+1)!}\prod_{k=1}^{n}\left(\frac{1}{\log\rho_k} + \frac{1}{\log r_k}\right)\left(\log\frac{c}{\varepsilon}\right)^{n+1} +$$

$$+ O\left[\left(\log\frac{1}{\varepsilon}\right)^{n}\log\log\frac{1}{\varepsilon}\right];$$

$$H_{\varepsilon}\left(F^{\delta}_{d, c, 2\pi}\right) = \frac{2}{(n+1)!\,(\log e)^{n}}\prod_{k=1}^{n}\left(\frac{1}{d_k} + \frac{1}{\delta_k}\right)\left(\log\frac{c}{\varepsilon}\right)^{n+1} +$$

$$+ O\left[\left(\log\frac{1}{\varepsilon}\right)^{n}\log\log\frac{1}{\varepsilon}\right];$$

$$H_{\varepsilon}(F_{d, c, 2\pi}) = \frac{2}{(n+1)!\,(\log e)^{n}}\prod_{k=1}^{n}\frac{1}{d_k}\left(\log\frac{c}{\varepsilon}\right)^{n+1} +$$

$$+ O\left[\left(\log\frac{1}{\varepsilon}\right)^{n}\log\log\frac{1}{\varepsilon}\right];$$

$$H_{\varepsilon}\left(F^{a, b}_{\rho, c}\right) = \frac{1}{(n+1)!}\prod_{k=1}^{n}\frac{1}{\log\left(\dfrac{2}{b_k - a_k}\rho_k\right)}\left(\log\frac{c}{\varepsilon}\right)^{n+1} +$$

$$+ O\left[\left(\log\frac{c}{\varepsilon}\right)^{n}\log\log\frac{c}{\varepsilon}\right];$$

$$H_{\varepsilon}\left(F^{a, c, n}_{s}\right) = \frac{2}{(n+1)!}\prod_{k=1}^{n}S_k\frac{\left(\log\frac{c}{\varepsilon}\right)^{n+1}}{\left(\log\log\frac{c}{\varepsilon}\right)^{n}} +$$

$$+ o\left[\frac{\left(\log\frac{c}{\varepsilon}\right)^{n+1}}{\left(\log\log\frac{c}{\varepsilon}\right)^{n}}\right]$$

---

* The second and third inequalities were obtained by A.N. Kolmogorov.

(for a definition of the spaces $F^{G}_{\omega(\delta),c}, \dots, F^{\sigma,c,n}_{s}$ see the list of notations at the end of the book), where $A(s, n)$ $B(s, n)$, $A(G_1, G_2)$ and $B(G_1, G_2)$ are positive, and independent of the ε constants.

The fundamental result of the monograph consists in the inequalities which give an estimate of the complexity of the tables for elements of some functional spaces. For some subspaces of analytic functions (for example, for the space $F^{G_1,n}_{G_2,c}$)) we prove in Chapter V that if $T^{\Phi}_{\varepsilon}(f)$ is a table which represents the function $f \in F$ with an accuracy ε, then the numbers p, k and ε must satisfy the inequality

$$p \log\left(\frac{k+1}{\varepsilon}\right) \geqslant A(F) H_{\varepsilon}(F),$$

where $A(F) > 0$ is some constant independent of p, k and ε. In particular, in cases where it is possible to calculate the fundamental term of the ε-entropy of the space F (for example, for the spaces $F^{r,n}_{\rho,c}, \dots, F^{\sigma,c,n}_{s}$) for any table $T^{\Phi}_{\varepsilon}(f)$ $(f \in F)$ the numbers p, k and ε satisfy the more exact inequality

$$p \log\left(\frac{k+1}{\varepsilon}\right) \geqslant H_{\varepsilon}(F) - o\,[H_{\varepsilon}(F)].$$

On the other hand, we prove the existence of methods for constructing the tables $T^{\Phi}_{\varepsilon}(f)$ $(f \in F)$ for which

$$p \log\left(\frac{k+1}{\varepsilon}\right) \leqslant B(F) H_{\varepsilon}(F),$$

where $B(F) > 0$ is a constant. Such methods include, for example, the method based on the representation of the coefficients of a truncated Taylor series for the function.

For spaces which are similar in structure to the space C of real functions continuous on the segment $[0, 1]$ (e.g. for spaces $F^{g}_{\omega(\delta),c}$ and $F^{\rho,n}_{s,L\,c}$) we prove in Chapter VII that the characteristics p and k of the complexity of any table $T^{\Phi}_{\varepsilon}(f)$ $(f \in F)$ must satisfy

$$p \log(1+k) \geqslant c(F) H_{\varepsilon}(F),$$

where $c(F) > 0$ is a constant independent of p, k and ε. On the other hand we prove that for spaces of type C, provided the numbers p and k satisfy the inequality

$$p \log(1+k) \geqslant H_{\frac{1}{2}\varepsilon}(F),$$

we can find a method of constructing the tables of elements $f \in F$ for which the numbers p and k are the characteristics of the complexity of the table.

Chapters IV and V are concerned with the variations of a set, which are a fundamental working tool for deriving these inequalities.

CHAPTER I

THE CONCEPT OF THE ENTROPY OF A METRICAL SPACE

§ 1. A Table and its Volume

Let F be a metrical space, and Φ its metrical expansion, i.e. a metrical space which contains F as a subset and which is such that for any pair of elements f_1, and f_2 of F the equation

$$\rho_F(f_1, f_2) = \rho_\Phi(f_1, f_2)$$

is satisfied, where $\rho_F(f_1, f_2)$ and $\rho_\Phi(f_1, f_2)$ are the distances between f_1, and f_2 in the metrical sense of the spaces F and Φ (respectively).

By a table $T_\varepsilon^\Phi(f)$ of an element f of F, representing f with an accuracy ε using some element φ of Φ, we mean the ordered collection of elements $t = (t_1, t_2, \ldots, t_p)$ of some set ω and the algorithm (rule) $\Gamma(t)$ which puts the collection t in correspondence with some element $\varphi \in \Phi$ such that $\rho_\Phi(\varphi, f) \leqslant \varepsilon$. As regards $\Gamma(t)$ we note that this algorithm must be assumed to be independent of f, i.e. $\Gamma(t)$ can be considered as a mapping of the set ω in the space Φ such that $\Gamma(\omega)$ forms an ε-net* for F in the space Φ.

The elements $t_1, t_2, \ldots, t_p$ will be called the parameters of the table $T_\varepsilon^\Phi(f)$, and $\Gamma(t)$ the decoding algorithm.

The volume of the table $T_\varepsilon^\Phi(f)$ is the number $P(T_\varepsilon^\Phi(f)) = \log_2 n^p$ where n is the number of elements of the set ω.

---

* The set $A \subset \Phi$ is called an ε-net of the space $F \subset \Phi$ if, for any point $f \in F$ we can find an element in A which is not further from f than ε (in the metrical sense of the space Φ).

Henceforth we shall restrict ourselves to the consideration of numerical tables of functions, (i.e. to the case when ω is a set of numbers, and F the space of functions). The volume of tables of this kind can be defined as the minimum number of binary digits* which are required to write down the parameters t_i of the table, since any real number can be represented as exactly as we please using binary numbers.

Let us consider a concrete example of the construction of a table.

Let $f(x)$ be a real function given on the segment $[0, 1]$, and suppose that we know that the maxima of the moduli of $f(x)$ and its first derivative on the segment $[0, 1]$ do not exceed 1. Let the set ω be the totality ω_ε of multiples of ε not exceeding 1 in modulus. Then ω_ε will contain $2\left[\frac{1}{\varepsilon}\right]+1$ elements. As the parameters of our table we take the numbers $t_1, t_2, \ldots, t_{2p}$ of the set ω_ε which are such that

$$|t_k - f(\varepsilon k)| \leqslant \frac{\varepsilon}{2} \quad \text{and} \quad |t_{p+k} - f'(\varepsilon k)| \leqslant \frac{\varepsilon}{2}$$

$$\left(k = 1, 2, \ldots, p;\ p = \left[\frac{1}{\varepsilon}\right]\right)$$

As our decoding algorithm $\Gamma(t)$ which enables us to determine the value of the function $f(x)$ at an arbitrary point x of the segment $[0, 1]$ with an accuracy of $\varepsilon \leqslant \frac{1}{2}$ we take the formula

$$\varphi(x) = t_k + t_{p+k}(x - \varepsilon k)$$

where k is a number depending on x chosen so that

$$|x - \varepsilon k| \leqslant \frac{\varepsilon}{2}$$

The table constructed in this way will result in some function $\varphi(x)$ of the family $\Phi(0, 1)$ of all real functions bounded on the segment $[0, 1]$. We here understand by $F_1 = F \subset \Phi(0,1)$ the space of all functions possessing those properties which $f(x)$ is known to possess, i.e. the space of

---

* A binary number (or digit) is the symbol which denotes an arbitrary element of the set consisting of the two elements +1 and -1 only.

all functions continuously differentiable on $[0, 1]$ which, together with their first derivatives, are bounded by the constant 1. From Lagrange's theorem it is not difficult to prove that, for $\varepsilon \leqslant \frac{1}{2}$, the inequality

$$\|f(x) - \varphi(x)\| \leqslant \varepsilon$$

holds, where

$$\|f(x) - \varphi(x)\| = \max_{x} |f(x) - \varphi(x)|$$

The volume of the table we have constructed is equal to

$$\log_2\left(1 + \left[\frac{2}{\varepsilon}\right]\right)^{2\left[\frac{1}{\varepsilon}\right]} = 2\left[\frac{1}{\varepsilon}\right]\log_2\left(1 + \left[\frac{2}{\varepsilon}\right]\right)$$

Later we shall show that the volume of any table for functions $f(x)$ of this kind, constructed on the basis of only those properties given above, cannot be less than $H_{\varepsilon}(F_1) \geqslant \frac{1}{\varepsilon} + \log_2 \frac{1}{\varepsilon} - 2$ and we shall indicate a more economic method for constructing tables for them whose volume will be equal to $\frac{1}{\varepsilon} + \log_2 \frac{1}{\varepsilon} + 2$.

We note that there is no reasonable method of making an upper estimate of the volume of a table for just any particular function, e.g. for sin x or log x, without laying a restriction on the properties of the function which are to be used in constructing the table. To see this we need only consider the fact that, for example, in writing down the expression "sin x" a very small amount of space is used, while at the same time, this gives the function sin x absolutely exactly. Therefore we can only give the upper estimate "1" of the volume of the table for any particular function. But practical methods of tabulation are, as a rule, based on the use of only a few properties of the function. Therefore we can study more interesting problems, in particular that of estimating the volume of a table and its "complexity" when those properties of the function which exist in a quite broad class of functions are used. This particular question is the one in which we are interested.

§ 2. The Entropy of Discrete Sets

Definition. (C. Shannon). Let X be a set consisting of n elements $x_1, x_2, \ldots, x_n$. The number $H(X) = \log n$* is called the entropy of the set X (see [9]).

Let us consider the meaning of the quantity $H(X)$ from the point of view of the complexity of the numerical representation of an element of the set X.

Suppose that the finite sequence

$$\tau(x) = [\tau_1(x), \tau_2(x), \ldots, \tau_k(x)]$$

of binary digits corresponds according to some criteria to each element $x \in X$ in such a way that different sequences of numbers correspond to different elements of the set X. Since there are only 2^k different sequences of k binary numbers, because of the single-valuedness of the correspondence, $2^k \geqslant n$ and therefore $k \geqslant H(X)$. Thus, to write down an element $x \in X$ (with the condition that nothing is known about x apart from the fact that it belongs to X) not less than $H(X)$ binary digits are required.

On the other hand, there is a method for writing down a element $x \in X$ in which not more than $[H(X)]+1$ binary digits are used. This method consists in the following. By means of some criterion the set X is decomposed into the two subsets X_0 and X_1 $(X_0 + X_1 = X)$ the number of elements of each being equal if n is even and differing by not more than 1 if n is odd. We divide each of the sets X_{τ_1} $(\tau_1 = 0, 1)$ into two subsets X_{τ_1, τ_2} $(\tau_2 = 0, 1)$ differing "in size" by not more than 1, and so on. Continuing this process of dividing the sets into halves (or almost halves) we obtain the sets $X_{\tau_1, \tau_2, \ldots, \tau_k}$ $(\tau_r = 0, 1;\ r = 1, 2, \ldots, k;\ k \leqslant [H(X)]+1)$. When $k = [H(X)]+1$ each of the sets $\{X_{\tau_1, \tau_2, \ldots, \tau_k}\}$ will consist of not more than one element, since otherwise we would have $n > 2^{H(X)} = n$ which is impossible. Thus, each element $x = X_{\tau_1, \tau_2, \ldots, \tau_{[H(X)]+1}}$ can be put in correspondence with a set of indexes $\tau_1, \tau_2, \ldots, \tau_{[H(X)]+1}$. It is not difficult to see that this correspondence is single-valued, and so different

---

* Unless the base of the logarithm is expressly indicated, we shall understand by $\log n$ the logarithm to the base 2.

elements of x correspond to different sequences of indexes τ_i. This gives the required representation.

Thus the number $H(x)$, which is determined by the size of the set X, indicates how many (binary) digits the most economic table for $x \in X$ must contain.

§ 3. The Concept of Relative ε-Entropy

If the set X consists of an infinite number of elements, then $H(X) = \log(+\infty) = +\infty$ and therefore it is impossible to represent an element of X exactly by a finite number of binary digits.

In order to give a reasonable definition of the concept of entropy for infinite sets as well, we have to combine those elements with fairly similar properties into one group so that the resulting set of groups is finite.

Definition. Let F be a compact metrical space, and Φ its metrical expansion. Let $N_\varepsilon^\Phi(F)$ denote the number of elements of the minimum number of points in Φ of the ε-net $S_\varepsilon^\Phi(F)$ of the set F and let

$$H_\varepsilon^\Phi(F) = \log N_\varepsilon^\Phi(F)$$

The number $H_\varepsilon^\Phi(F)$ is called the ε-entropy of the space F with respect to the space Φ or simply the relative ε-entropy of the space F.

At present A.N. Kolmogorov's concept of ε-entropy has taken root, and so we must say a few words to justify the new definition.

In our notation the ε-entropy of a space (in A.N. Kolmogorov's sense) is equal to $H_\varepsilon^F(F)$. Using this quantity we can give an exact upper estimate of the volume of tables only when the element given by the table belongs to the space F. But if, given a table of an element of F, we wish to represent by it elements which approximate to this element but which, in general, do not belong to F, then the only thing we can say about the volume of the table is that $P(T_\varepsilon^\Phi(f)) \geqslant H_{2\varepsilon}^F(F)$. A more obvious disadvantage of the quantity $H_\varepsilon^F(F)$ is that it does not enable us to give the exact lower bound of the volume of tables in the general case. In A.N. Kolmogorov's terminology, this lower bound turns out to be equal to $H^F_{k\varepsilon}(F)$ $(1 \leqslant k \leqslant 2)$ where k, generally speaking, depends on F. In this connexion we remark that the very fact of being able to represent elements of the expansion of the fundamental space in a table leads to concrete, more economic methods of constructing tables.

<u>Theorem 1.</u> The relative ε-entropy $H^\Phi_\varepsilon(F)$ is equal to the lower bound of the quantity $P[T^\Phi_\varepsilon(f)]$ $(f \in F)$ to an accuracy of 1, i.e.

$$-1+\inf_{T^\Phi_\varepsilon(f)} P[T^\Phi_\varepsilon(f)] \leqslant H^\Phi_\varepsilon(F) \leqslant \inf_{T^\Phi_\varepsilon(f)} P[T^\Phi_\varepsilon(f)]$$

Since, by the definition of a table, the algorithm $\Gamma(t)$ in it enables us to put some element $\varphi \in \Phi$ which approximates to any element $f \in F$ with the required accuracy ε in correspondence with f, the whole aggregate of tables of elements from F in the space Φ corresponds to some set Φ_0 which is an ε-net of the space F. Let n denote the number of elements of the set Φ_0. From the definition of a minimal ε-net, $n \geqslant N^\Phi_\varepsilon(F)$. Therefore

$$P[T^\Phi_\varepsilon(f)] \geqslant \log n \geqslant \log N^\Phi_\varepsilon(F) = H^\Phi_\varepsilon(F)$$

We shall now form an algorithm which enables us to construct the ideal (smallest) table representing the element $f \in F$ with an accuracy ε. To do this we choose in the space Φ a set $S^\Phi_\varepsilon(F)$ which is the minimal ε-net (in Φ) of the space F. We denote the elements of this set by $\varphi_1, \varphi_2, \ldots, \varphi_n$ $(n = N^\Phi_\varepsilon(F))$. As the parameters of our ideal table we take the number (suffix) of that element φ which approximates to f with an accuracy ε. Since the suffix in the table can change only between the limits 1 to $n = N^\Phi_\varepsilon(F)$, its binary representation will use

$$[\log N^\Phi_\varepsilon(F)] + 1 = [H^\Phi_\varepsilon(F)] + 1$$

binary digits, i.e. the volume of our ideal table is equal

to $[H_\varepsilon^\Phi(F)]+1$. Q.E.D.

§ 4. The Absolute ε-Entropy of A Metrical Space

If we wish to estimate the volume of tables for elements of F in which elements of all possible metrical expansions of the space F can be represented (as an approximation), then we must introduce a new concept, by analogy with the relative ε-entropy, which is independent of the method of expansion of the space F.

Definition. Let F be a compact metrical space and $\alpha=(\alpha_1, \alpha_2, \ldots, \alpha_n)$ ~~its~~ an arbitrary 2ε-closure* by the sets $\{\alpha_k\}$ of F. We denote by $N_\varepsilon(F)$ the number of elements of the most economic closure (i.e. that which consists of the least number of sets $\{\alpha_k\}$) of the 2ε-closure $S_\varepsilon(F)$. The number

$$H_\varepsilon(F)=\log N_\varepsilon(F)$$

is called the absolute ε-entropy of the space F.**

To justify the name "absolute ε-entropy" we prove the following theorem.

Theorem 1. The absolute ε-entropy $H_\varepsilon(F)$ of any compact metrical space F is equal to the lower bound of the relative ε-entropies of the space for all possible metrical expansions.

$$H_\varepsilon(F)=\inf_{\Phi\supset F} H_\varepsilon^\Phi(F)$$

Proof. We choose some metrical expansion Φ of the space F. We shall show that

$$H_\varepsilon^\Phi(F)\geqslant H_\varepsilon(F)$$

---

* The system of subsets $\alpha_1, \alpha_2, \ldots, \alpha_n$ of the space F is called the 2ε-closure of the space F if the diameter of none of these sets exceeds 2ε and $\sum_{k=1}^{n}\alpha_k=F$. The sets $\{\alpha_k\}$ are then called the elements of the closure.

** A similar characteristic has already been used as an auxiliary concept by A.N. Kolmogorov.

Let $S_\varepsilon^\Phi(F) = (\varphi_1, \varphi_2, \ldots, \varphi_n)$ $(n = N_\varepsilon(F))$ be the minimal ε-net in the space Φ of the space F. Let σ_k denote the closed sphere in $\Phi\{\rho_\Phi(\varphi_k, \varphi) \leqslant \varepsilon\}$ of radius ε and centre at φ_k, and let σ_k^* denote the common part of σ_k and F. Since $S_\varepsilon^\Phi(F)$ approximates to the space F with an accuracy of ε, $\sigma^* = \sum_{k=1}^{n} \sigma_k^* \supset F$. And since the diameter of any of the sets $\{\sigma_k^*\}$ which are subsets of the sphere of radius ε is not greater than 2ε, $N_\varepsilon^\Phi(F) \geqslant N_\varepsilon(F)$, since $N_\varepsilon(F)$ is the number of elements of the most economic 2ε-closure of the space F. Hence

$$H_\varepsilon^\Phi(F) = \log N_\varepsilon^\Phi(F) \geqslant \log N_\varepsilon(F) = H_\varepsilon(F)$$

This proves the first part of the theorem. To complete the proof we need only find a metrical expansion Φ of the space F for which

$$N_\varepsilon^\Phi(F) = N_\varepsilon(F)$$

Lemma 1. (V.D. Erokhin) Given any compact subset of diameter $2r$ of the space C of all functions continuous on the segment $[0, 1]$ we can find an element of C whose distance from any element of the given subset is not greater than r.

Proof of the lemma. Let σ be some compact subset of diameter $2r$ of the space C. Let $\bar{f}(x)$ and $\underline{f}(x)$ denote the functions, given on $[0, 1]$, which are respectively the upper and lower bounds of the family of all functions $f(x)$ of σ. Since σ is a compact subset of the space C, there exists a continuous function $\omega(\delta)$ which is the upper bound of the moduli of continuity for all functions of σ. Therefore the modulus of continuity of $\bar{f}(x)$ and $\underline{f}(x)$ must also be $\omega(\delta)$. If we put

$$f_0(x) = \frac{1}{2}[\bar{f}(x) + \underline{f}(x)]$$

the function $f_0(x)$ has modulus of continuity which also does not exceed $\omega(\delta)$ i.e. $f_0(x)$ is a function which is continuous on $[0, 1]$ and therefore it is an element of the space C.

By the definition of the function $f_0(x)$ it is easy to see that given any x of the segment $[0, 1]$ the value of any function $f(x)$ at this point satisfies the inequality $|f(x)-f_0(x)|\leqslant r$ and therefore $\|f(x)-f_0(x)\|\leqslant r$ for any function of σ. Q.E.D.

Proof of Theorem 1 (continued). On the strength of S. Banach and S. Masure's theorem, any separable (and therefore also compact) metrical space can be isometrically placed in the space C. Therefore we can consider the space F as a subset of C, i.e. we can think of C as a metrical expansion of F. Let σ_k^* $(k=1, 2, \ldots\ldots, N_\varepsilon(F))$ be subsets of F, of diameter 2ε, forming the 2ε-closure of F. From Lemma 1, for any set σ_k^* we can find an element $c_k \in C$ whose distance from all points of the set σ_k^* is not greater than ε. The subset $\sum_{k=1}^{N_\varepsilon(F)} c_k$ of the set C is an ε-net of F. Hence

$$H_\varepsilon(F) \geqslant \log N_\varepsilon^C(F) = H_\varepsilon^C(F)$$

i.e. using the first part of the theorem which has been proved, we have

$$H_\varepsilon(F) = H_\varepsilon^C(F)$$

Q.E.D.

This proof has also given us the following result.

Theorem 2. The space C is the best metrical expansion for any compact metrical space F in the sense that

$$H_\varepsilon^C(F) = H_\varepsilon(F) \leqslant H_\varepsilon^\Phi(F)$$

where Φ is an arbitrary metrical expansion of the space F.

The substance of the concept we have introduced of the absolute ε-entropy of a metrical space leads among other things to the following theorem.

Theorem 3. If $T_\varepsilon^\Phi(f)$ is a table of the element f of the space F then its volume cannot be less than $H_\varepsilon(F)$. Thus for an arbitrary element of F we can construct a table whose volume is equal to $[H_\varepsilon(F)]+1$.

The first part of this theorem is obtained from Theorems 1 of § 3 and 1 of § 4. The second half follows from Theorems 1 of § 3 and 2 of § 4.

§ 5. The ε-capacity of Metrical Spaces

Definition (A.N. Kolmogorov). Let F be a compact metrical space, $s_\varepsilon(F)$ a set of F which consists of the maximum number of elements strictly further apart than 2ε; $n_\varepsilon(F)$ the number of points of the set $s_\varepsilon(F)$. We call the number $h_\varepsilon(F)=\log n_\varepsilon(F)$ the ε-capacity of the space F.

We note first of all two of the simplest properties of the functions

$$H_\varepsilon^\Phi(F),\ H_\varepsilon(F),\ h_\varepsilon(F)$$

Lemma 1. Given an arbitrary compact space F and a metrical expansion of F Φ, for any positive ε and δ such that $\delta\leqslant\varepsilon$,

$$H_\varepsilon^\Phi(F)\leqslant H_\delta^\Phi(F)$$
$$H_\varepsilon(F)\leqslant H_\delta(F)$$
$$h_\varepsilon(F)\leqslant h_\delta(F)$$

Lemma 2. Let F_1 and F_2 be two compact metrical spaces such that F_2 is a metrical expansion of F_1, and Φ is a metrical expansion of F_2 (and therefore also of F_1). Then for any $\varepsilon>0$

$$H_\varepsilon^\Phi(F_2)\geqslant H_\varepsilon^\Phi(F_1)$$
$$H_\varepsilon(F_2)\geqslant H_\varepsilon(F_1)$$
$$h_\varepsilon(F_2)\geqslant h_\varepsilon(F_1)$$

Lemmas 1 and 2 are easily obtained from the definition of the quantities $H_\varepsilon^\Phi(F)$, $H_\varepsilon(F)$ and $h_\varepsilon(F)$.

Lemma 3. (A.N. Kolmogorov). For any compact metrical space F and $\varepsilon>0$

$$H_\varepsilon(F)\geqslant h_\varepsilon(F)$$

where the set $s_\varepsilon(F)$ forms a 2ε-net in F.

Proof. Let $f_1, f_2, f_3, \ldots, f_n$ be elements of F further apart than 2ε, and let $\sigma=(\sigma_1, \sigma_2, \ldots, \sigma_k)$ be an arbitrary 2ε-closure of F. It is clear that any of the elements $f_1, f_2, \ldots\ldots, f_n$

belong to at least one of the sets $\{\sigma_i\}$ and no pair of the $\{f_i\}$ can belong to one and the same element of the closure. Hence $k \geqslant n$, and therefore, putting $n = n_\varepsilon(F)$, we have $H_\varepsilon(F) \geqslant \log n_\varepsilon(F) = h_\varepsilon(F)$. Q.E.D.

Lemma 4. If F is a compact metrical space, and Φ is some metrical expansion of F, then for any $\varepsilon > 0$

$$H_{2\varepsilon}^{\Phi}(F) \leqslant H_\varepsilon(F) \leqslant H_\varepsilon^{\Phi}(F)$$

Proof. We choose the most economic 2ε-closure

$$S_\varepsilon(F) = (\sigma_1, \sigma_2, \ldots, \sigma_n) \quad (n = n_\varepsilon(F))$$

of the space F and in each element of this closure we select one point. The resulting set is denoted by F^*. Since the diameter of no set of $\{\sigma_i\}$ exceeds 2ε, $F^* \subset F \subset \Phi$ approximates in Φ to the space F with an accuracy of 2ε, and therefore the number of elements of the minimal 2ε-net in Φ of F cannot be greater than the number $n_\varepsilon(F)$, i.e. $H_{2\varepsilon}^{\Phi}(F) \leqslant H_\varepsilon(F)$. The second half of the inequality in the lemma was proved in Theorem 1 § 4. Q.E.D.

Lemma 5. In any compact metrical space F we can find $N_{2\varepsilon}(F)$ elements which are further apart than 2ε.

Proof. In the space F we select the set $s_\varepsilon(F)$ consisting of the maximum number of elements further apart than 2ε, $n_{2\varepsilon}(F)$. Let $\sigma_1, \sigma_2, \ldots, \sigma_n$ $(n = n_\varepsilon(F))$ be closed spheres in F of radius 2ε and with centres at $s_\varepsilon(F)$. Since the set $s_\varepsilon(F)$ is maximal, by its very nature $\sum_{i=1}^{n} \sigma_i \supset F$ as otherwise $s_\varepsilon(F)$ could be filled by only one element of $F - \sum_{i=1}^{n} \sigma_i$ strictly further from the set $s_\varepsilon(F)$ than 2ε. Thus $\sigma = (\sigma_1, \sigma_2, \ldots, \sigma_n)$ is a 4ε-closure of the space F and therefore $n_\varepsilon(F) \geqslant N_{2\varepsilon}(F)$, i.e. $h_\varepsilon(F) > H_{2\varepsilon}(F)$. Q.E.D.

Theorem 1. For any F, $\Phi \supset F$ and $\varepsilon > 0$, the relative and absolute ε-entropies of the space F and the ε-capacity of F are connected by the inequalities

$$H_\varepsilon^{\Phi}(F) \geqslant H_\varepsilon(F) \geqslant h_\varepsilon(F) \geqslant H_{2\varepsilon}^{\Phi}(F) \geqslant H_{2\varepsilon}(F)$$

This theorem is a combination of Lemmas 3, 4 and 5 above.

§ 6. The Entropy of Some Simple Sets

Let F_1, and F_2 be two compact metrical spaces, and $F = F_1 \times F_2$ their direct product. We restrict our consideration to those direct products whose metric satisfies the following conditions for any pair of elements

$$f' = (f'_1, f'_2) \text{ and } f'' = (f''_1, f''_2) \text{ of } F$$

$$A \max[\rho_{F_1}(f'_1, f''_1); \rho_{F_2}(f'_2, f''_2)] \leqslant \rho_F(f', f'') \leqslant$$
$$\leqslant B \max[\rho_{F_1}(f'_1, f''_1), \rho_{F_2}(f'_2, f''_2)]$$

where A and B are positive constants.

Lemma 1. For any $\varepsilon > 0$

$$H_\varepsilon(F) \leqslant H_{\frac{\varepsilon}{B}}(F_1) + H_{\frac{\varepsilon}{B}}(F_2)$$

Proof. Put $\delta = \frac{\varepsilon}{B}$ and let

$$S_\delta(F_1) = (\sigma_1^1, \sigma_2^1, \sigma_3^1, \ldots, \sigma_{n_1}^1) \text{ and } S_\delta(F_2) = (\sigma_1^2, \sigma_2^2, \ldots, \sigma_{n_2}^2)$$

$(n_1 = N_\delta(F_1);\ n_2 = N_\delta(F_2))$ be the best 2δ-closures of the spaces F_1 and F_2. It is easy to verify that the sets

$$\sigma_i^1 \times \sigma_k^2 \qquad (i = 1, 2, \ldots, n_1, k = 1, 2, \ldots, n_2)$$

form a 2δ-closure of F, and since there are $n = n_1 n_2$ of these sets

$$H_\varepsilon(F) = H_{B\delta}(F) \leqslant \log n = \log n_1 + \log n_2 =$$
$$= H_\delta(F_1) + H_\delta(F_2) = H_{\frac{\varepsilon}{B}}(F_1) + H_{\frac{\varepsilon}{B}}(F_2)$$

Q.E.D.

Lemma 2. For any $\varepsilon > 0$

$$h_\varepsilon(F) \geqslant h_{\frac{\varepsilon}{A}}(F_1) + h_{\frac{\varepsilon}{A}}(F_2)$$

Proof. Put $\delta = \frac{\varepsilon}{A}$ and let $S_\delta(F_1) = (f_1^1, f_2^1, \ldots, f_{n_1}^1)$

and $S_\delta(F_2)=(f_1^2, f_2^2, \ldots, f_{n_2}^2)$ $(n_1=N_\delta(F_1), \quad n_2=N_\delta(F_2))$ be the maximal sets of elements of F_1, F_2 which are such that

$$\rho_{F_1}(f_i^1, f_k^1)>2\delta \text{ and } \rho_{F_2}(f_i^2, f_k^2)>2\delta$$

It is not difficult to see that, firstly, the set

$$S_\delta(F_1)\times S_\delta(F_2)=\sum_{p=1}^{n_1}\sum_{q=1}^{n_2}(f_p^1, f_q^2)$$

consists of $n=n_1 n_2$ elements and, secondly, the distance (in the metrical sense of the space F) between pairs of elements of this set is not less than $2A\delta>2\varepsilon$. Therefore

$$h_\varepsilon(F)=h_{A\delta}(F)\geqslant \log n_1+\log n_2=$$
$$=h_\delta(F_1)+h_\delta(F_2)=h_{\frac{\varepsilon}{A}}(F_1)+h_{\frac{\varepsilon}{A}}(F_2)$$

Q.E.D.

<u>Theorem 1</u>. If $F=F_1\times F_2$ then

$$H_{\frac{\varepsilon}{B}}(F_1)+H_{\frac{\varepsilon}{B}}(F_2)\geqslant H_\varepsilon(F)\geqslant H_{\frac{2\varepsilon}{A}}(F_1)+H_{\frac{2\varepsilon}{A}}(F_2)$$

This theorem follows from Lemmas 1 and 2, and Theorem 1 § 5.

<u>Corollary 1</u>. If $F=\prod_{k=1}^{n}F_k$ and given any pair of elements $f'=(f_1', \ldots, f_n')$ and $f''=(f_1'', f_2'', \ldots, f_n'')$ of F

$$\rho_F=\max\left(\rho_{F_1}(f_1', f_1''), \rho_{F_2}(f_2', f_2''), \ldots, \rho_{F_n}(f_n', f_n'')\right]$$

then

$$\sum_{k=1}^{n}H_{\alpha\varepsilon}(F_k)\leqslant H_\varepsilon(F)\leqslant\sum_{k=1}^{n}H_\varepsilon(F_k)$$

where $\alpha=2^{n-1}$.

This follows from Theorem 1 putting $A=1$, $B=1$ in the calculation of $H_\delta(\Phi_k\times F_{k+1})$ $(\Phi_k=F_1\times F_2\times\ldots\times F_k)$.

<u>Corollary 2</u>. If $F=\prod_{k=1}^{n}F_k$ and if, given any pair of

elements $f'=(f'_1, f'_2, \ldots, f'_n)$ and $f''=(f''_1, f''_2, \ldots, f''_n)$ of F

$$\rho_F=\left\{\sum_{k=1}^{n}[\rho_{F_k}(f'_k, f''_k)]^2\right\}^{\frac{1}{2}}$$

then

$$\sum_{k=1}^{n} H_{\alpha\varepsilon}(F_k) \leqslant H_\varepsilon(F) \leqslant \sum_{k=1}^{n} H_{\beta\varepsilon}(F_k)$$

where $\alpha=2^{n-1}$, $\beta=\left(\frac{1}{2}\right)^{n-1}$.

This corollary is proved by induction on k taking in this case $A=1$, $B=2$ in the calculation of $H_\delta(\Phi_k \times F_{k+1})$ $(\Phi_k = F_1 \times \times F_2 \times \ldots \times F_k)$.

Lemma 3. Let F be a segment of length r and given $a \in F$ and $b \in F$ let

$$\rho_F(a, b)=|b-a|$$

Then

$$\log\left(\left[\frac{r}{2\varepsilon}\right]-1\right) \leqslant H_\varepsilon(F) \leqslant \log\left(\left[\frac{r}{2\varepsilon}\right]+1\right)$$

Proof. Let c and d be the left- and right-hand ends respectively of the given segment. Let a_k be the point of the segment with co-ordinate

$$x_k=(2\varepsilon+\delta)\times\left(k-\frac{1}{2}\right) \quad \left(k=1, 2, \ldots, n;\ n=\left[\frac{r}{2\varepsilon+\delta}\right]\right)$$

and a_{n+1} the point with co-ordinate $x_{n+1}=d-\varepsilon$. For $\delta=0$ the system of segments $[(x_k-\varepsilon), (x_k+\varepsilon)]$ $(k=1, 2, \ldots, n+1)$ forms a 2ε-closure of the segment $[cd]$. Therefore

$$H_\varepsilon(F) \leqslant \log(n+1)=\log\left(1+\left[\frac{r}{2\varepsilon}\right]\right)$$

For any $\delta>0$ the distance between the points a_k $(k=1, 2, \ldots, n)$ is $2\varepsilon+\delta>2\varepsilon$. Therefore, from Lemma 3 § 5

$$H_\varepsilon(F) \geqslant \log(n-1)=\log\left(\left[\frac{r}{2\varepsilon}\right]-1\right)$$

(inequality does occur, for example, when $\delta = \frac{4\varepsilon^2}{r} \leqslant \frac{2\varepsilon}{\left[\frac{r}{2\varepsilon}\right]}$)).

Q.E.D.

Theorem 2. (A. N. Kolmogorov). Let G be some bounded region of the n-dimensional Euclidean space E_n. Then for sufficiently small $\varepsilon > 0$

$$H_\varepsilon(G) = n \log \frac{1}{\varepsilon} + O_G(1)$$

Proof. We select in E_n two n-dimensional closed cubes J_1, and J_2 of side r_1 and r_2 respectively, such that $J_2 \supset G \supset J_1$. Since an n-dimensional cube is the nth product of a segment, from Corollary 2 to Theorem 1 and Lemma 3

$$n \log\left(\left[\frac{r_1}{2^n\varepsilon}\right] - 1\right) \leqslant H_\varepsilon(J_1) \leqslant n \log\left(\left[\frac{2^{n-2}r_1}{\varepsilon}\right] + 1\right)$$

$$n \log\left(\left[\frac{r_2}{2^n\varepsilon}\right] - 1\right) \leqslant H_\varepsilon(J_2) \leqslant n \log\left(\left[\frac{2^{n-2}r_2}{\varepsilon}\right] + 1\right)$$

i.e. for sufficiently small ε

$$H_\varepsilon(J_1) = n \log \frac{1}{\varepsilon} + O_1(1),$$

$$H_\varepsilon(J_2) = n \log \frac{1}{\varepsilon} + O_2(1).$$

Therefore, from Lemma 2 we have

$$H_\varepsilon(G) = n \log \frac{1}{\varepsilon} + O_G(1)$$

Q.E.D.

CHAPTER II

THE ENTROPY OF ANALYTIC FUNCTION SPACES

In this chapter we calculate the basic term of the absolute ε-entropy for some analytic function spaces. The essence of the calculation consists in the fact that it is possible, by using the rate at which the coefficients in the series for the analytic functions die away, to establish the quality of the functions sufficiently accurately, and, conversely, knowing the region of analyticity of a function it is possible to estimate to the same accuracy the rate of convergence of its series; more exactly, the size of the region of analyticity of a function determines the order of decrease of the coefficients in the series for this function in a one-to-one manner, with a small basic error. Therefore (from the point of view of store economy) the method of approximate representation of analytic functions gives almost the best representation of the coefficients in the expansion of a function. In order to give a better idea of the calculation, let us first study one particular case.

§ 7. The Entropy of Analytic Functions of a Single Real Variable

Let us evaluate the ε-entropy of the space $F_{\rho, c}^{-1,1}$ of all real functions analytic on $[-1, 1]$, for which there exist analytic continuations bounded by the constant $c > 0$ (in modulus) in the region ϑ_ρ, where ϑ_ρ is the region of the complex plane bounded by the ellipse with foci at the ends of the segment $[-1, 1]$ on the real axis, and with semi-major axis $\rho = \frac{a+b}{2}$. For the norm in this space we take the maximum of the modulus of the function $[-1, 1]$.

We choose some function $f(x)$ of the family $F_{\rho, c}^{-1,1}$ and consider its expansion in series by Chebyshev polynomials

$\frac{1}{2}a_0+\sum_{p=1}^{\infty} a_p t_p(x)$. We recall that (see, for example, [6])

$$t_p(x)=\cos(p \arccos x)=\frac{1}{2^{p-1}}x^p+\sum_{k=1}^{p-1}\lambda_k^p x^k \quad (p=1,\ 2,\ \ldots),$$

$$a_p=\frac{2}{\pi}\int_{-1}^{1} f(x)\frac{t_p(x)}{\sqrt{1-x^2}}dx \qquad (p=1,\ 2,\ \ldots),$$

$$a_0=\frac{1}{\pi}\int_{-1}^{1} f(x)\frac{dx}{\sqrt{1-x^2}}.$$

We note also some properties of Chebyshev polynomials and series:

1. The maximum of the polynomial $t_p(x)$ on the segment $[-1,\ 1]$ is equal to 1.

2. The best approximation to the polynomial $t_p(x)$ (in the class of all algebraic polynomials of degree less than p) on the segment $[-1,\ 1]$ is zero identically. From this and property 1, it follows in particular that any polynomial of the form $S_p(x)=\frac{1}{2}a_0+\sum_{r=1}^{p} a_r t_r(x)$ on $[-1,\ 1]$ differs from zero by not less than $|a_p|$ (in the sense of the metric of C).

3. From these properties and the fact that the polynomial $\left(\frac{1}{2}\right)^{p-1} t_p(x)$ differs from zero on the segment $[-1,\ 1]$ less than any other polynomial of degree p with a unit coefficient of x^p, we see that any polynomial of degree p having highest coefficient $c_p=1$ differs from zero by not less than $\left(\frac{1}{2}\right)^{p-1}$.

4. If the function $f(x)$ satisfies the Dini-Lipschitz condition on $[-1,\ 1]$, i.e. if

$$\lim_{n\to\infty} \omega\left(\frac{1}{n}\right)\ln n=0$$

(where $\omega(\delta)$ is the modulus of the function $f(x)$), then on this segment

$$|f(x)-S_p(x)| \leqslant l_p(3+\ln p)$$

where l_p is the deviation from $f(x)$ of the best approximation (in the class of algebraic polynomials of degree p) to the function $f(x)$, and $S_p(x)=\frac{a_0}{2}+\sum_{r=1}^{p} a_r t_r(x)$ is the truncated Chebyshev series of the function.

The proof of this proposition can be found in [6].

Lemma 1. Let an arbitrary real number k be given; and let $\rho > 1$ and $p \geqslant 1$. Then

$$\sum_{m=p}^{\infty} \frac{1}{m^k \rho^m} \leqslant \frac{p^{|k|}}{(\ln \rho)\, \rho^{n-1}}$$

Proof. For

$$\sum_{m=p}^{\infty} \frac{1}{m^k \rho^m} \leqslant \sum_{m=p}^{\infty} \frac{m^{|k|}}{\rho^m} \leqslant \int_p^{\infty} \frac{x^{|k|}}{\rho^{x-1}}\, dx =$$

$$= \frac{p^{|k|}}{(\ln \rho)\, \rho^{p-1}} - \frac{|k|}{\ln \rho} \int_p^{\infty} \frac{x^{|k|-1}}{\rho^{x-1}}\, dx \leqslant \frac{p^{|k|}}{(\ln \rho)\, \rho^{p-1}}$$

Q.E.D.

Lemma 2. If the numbers a_p $(p=0, 1, 2, \ldots)$ are coefficients of a Chebyshev series for some function $f(x)$ of the family $F_{\rho, c}^{-1, 1}$, then

$$|a_p| \leqslant \frac{4c\,(3+\ln p)}{\rho^{p-1}}$$

Proof. We note first of all that from Achieser's theorem (see [7]) the deviation l_p of the function $f(x)$ (of the family $F_{\rho, c}^{-1, 1}$) from its best approximation (in the class of algebraic polynomials of degree p) must satisfy the inequality

$$l_p \leqslant \frac{2c}{\rho^p}$$

From this inequality we have

$$|a_p| = \|a_p t_p(x)\| = \|S_p(x) - S_{p-1}(x)\| \leqslant$$
$$\leqslant \|S_p(x) - f(x)\| + \|f(x) - S_{p-1}(x)\| \leqslant$$
$$\leqslant l_p(3 + \ln p) + l_{p-1}[3 + \ln(p-1)] \leqslant$$
$$\leqslant 2l_{p-1}(3 + \ln p) \leqslant \frac{4c}{\rho^{p-1}}(3 + \ln p).$$

Q.E.D.

Lemma 3. If the coefficients $\{a_p\}$ of the Chebyshev series for the function $f(x)$ satisfy the inequalities

$$|a_0| \leqslant c, \quad |a_p| \leqslant \frac{c}{4p^2\rho^p} \qquad (\rho > 1;\ p = 1,\ 2,\ \ldots)$$

then the function $f(x)$ belongs to the family $F_{\rho, c}^{-1, 1}$.

Proof. We show that the series

$$\frac{1}{2}a_0 + \sum_{p=1}^{\infty} a_p t_p(z)$$

which is the analytic continuation of the function $f(x)$, converges uniformly on $\mathcal{E}_\rho$ and is bounded (in modulus) by the constant c. For

$$\left\| \frac{1}{2}a_0 + \sum_{p=1}^{\infty} a_p t_p(z) \right\| \leqslant \left| \frac{1}{2}a_0 \right| + \sum_{p=1}^{\infty} \|a_p t_p(z)\| \leqslant$$
$$\leqslant \frac{1}{2}c + \sum_{p=1}^{\infty} \frac{c}{4p^2\rho^p}\rho^p = \frac{1}{2}c + \frac{1}{4}c\sum_{p=1}^{\infty}\frac{1}{p^2} \leqslant c$$

since $\|t_p(z)\| \leqslant \rho^p$, $t_p(z)$ being a polynomial of degree p, not exceeding 1 in modulus on $[-1, 1]$. Q.E.D.

Now let $F_{\rho, k, c}$ be the space of series of the form

$$\frac{1}{2}a_0 + \sum_{p=1}^{\infty} a_p t_p(x)$$

such that

$$|a_0| \leqslant c \text{ and } |a_p| \leqslant \frac{c}{p^k\rho^p} \qquad (p = 1,\ 2,\ \ldots)$$

For the norm in $F_{\rho, k, c}$ we take the maximum of the absolute value of the function.

Lemma 4. If $A \leqslant \frac{1}{4} c$ and $B \geqslant 12\rho c$ $(\rho > 1)$, then $F_{\rho, 2, A} \subset F_{\rho, c}^{-1, 1} \subset F_{\rho, -1, B}$. This lemma is easily obtained from the two preceding ones.

Thus, we have reduced the evaluation of the ε-entropy of the space $F_{\rho, c}^{-1, 1}$ to the calculation of the entropy for spaces of the type $F_{\rho, k, c}$ since, from Lemma 4 and Lemma 2 § 5

$$H_\varepsilon(F_{\rho, 2, A}) \leqslant H_\varepsilon(F_{\rho, c}^{-1, 1}) \leqslant H_\varepsilon(F_{\rho, -1, B})$$

Lemma 5. If $\rho > 1$, then

$$H_\varepsilon(F_{\rho, k, c}) = \frac{1}{2 \log \rho}\left(\log \frac{c}{\varepsilon}\right)^2 + O\left[\left(\log \frac{1}{\varepsilon}\right) \log \log \varepsilon\right]$$

Proof. We choose a positive number $\delta \leqslant \frac{c}{2\rho}$, the natural numbers $r \geqslant 1$ and q_p $(p = 0, 1, 2, \ldots, r)$ such that

$$\frac{c}{r^k \rho^r} \geqslant \delta,$$

$$(|q_p| + 1)\delta \geqslant \frac{c}{p^k \rho^p} \geqslant |q_p| \delta \qquad (p = 1, 2, \ldots, r)$$

$$(|q_0| + 1)\delta \geqslant \frac{1}{2} c \geqslant |q_0| \delta.$$

Let us put

$$f^\delta_{k_0, k_1, \ldots, k_r} = k_0 \delta + \sum_{p=1}^{r} k_p \delta \cdot t_p(x) \qquad (k_i \leqslant q_i;\ i = 1, 2, \ldots, r)$$

By counting the number of such functions for two concrete values of the pairs r, δ we obtain the upper and lower estimates for $H_\varepsilon(F_{\rho, k, c})$. Let σ_r^δ be the number of all functions of the type $f^\delta_{k_0, k_1, \ldots, k_r}$. Then

$$\sigma_r^\delta \geqslant \left(\frac{c}{\delta} - 1\right) \prod_{p=1}^{r} \left(\frac{2c}{\delta p^k \rho^p} - 1\right) \geqslant \frac{c}{2\delta} \prod_{p=1}^{r} \frac{c}{\delta p^k \rho^p} =$$

$$= \frac{c^{r+1}}{2\delta^{r+1} (r!)^k \rho^{\frac{r(r+1)}{2}}}$$

On the other hand

$$\sigma_r^\delta=\left(\left[\frac{c}{\delta}\right]+1\right)\prod_{p=1}^{r}\left(\left[\frac{2c}{\delta p^k\rho^p}\right]+1\right)\leqslant$$

$$\leqslant\frac{c}{\delta}\prod_{p=1}^{r}\frac{2c}{\delta p^k\rho^p}=\frac{2^r c^{r+1}}{\delta^{r+1}(r!)^k\rho^{\frac{r(r+1)}{2}}}.$$

Thus we obtain the inequality

$$\frac{c^{r+1}}{2\delta^{r+1}(r!)^k\rho^{\frac{r(r+1)}{2}}}\leqslant\sigma_r^\delta\leqslant\frac{2^r c^{r+1}}{\delta^{r+1}(r!)^k\rho^{\frac{r(r+1)}{2}}}.$$

Put $\delta=3\varepsilon$. We choose two different functions f_1 and f_2 of the type $f_{k_0,k_1,\ldots,k_r}^{3\varepsilon}$. Putting

$$f_1-f_2=\frac{1}{2}a_0+\sum_{p=1}^{r}a_p t_p(x)$$

we note that all the coefficients $\{a_p\}$ of this polynomial must be multiples of 3ε, and at least one of them must be different from zero. Therefore the modulus of the highest non-zero coefficient of this polynomial will be not less than 3ε. Hence, from property 2, f_1-f_2 differs from zero by not less than 3ε, and this means that

$$n_\varepsilon(F_{\rho,k,c})\geqslant\sigma_r^{3\varepsilon}$$

Then, from Lemma 3 § 5,

$$H_\varepsilon(F_{\rho,k,c})\geqslant h_\varepsilon(F_{\rho,k,c})\geqslant\log\sigma_r^{3\varepsilon}$$

Putting

$$r=\left[\log_\rho\left[\frac{c}{\delta}\left(\log_\rho\frac{c}{\delta}\right)^{-2|k|}\right]\right]$$

and remembering that $\delta=3\varepsilon$, from the inequality for σ_r^δ we obtain

$$H_\varepsilon(F_{\rho,k,c})\geqslant\log\sigma_r^{3\varepsilon}\geqslant(r+1)\log c-\log\frac{1}{2}-$$

$$-(r+1)\log\delta-k\log(r!)-\frac{1}{2}r(r+1)\log\rho=$$

$$=\frac{1}{2\log\rho}\left\{\left(\log\frac{c}{\varepsilon}\right)^2+O\left[\left(\log\frac{1}{\varepsilon}\right)\log\log\frac{1}{\varepsilon}\right]\right\}$$

Let us now put $r=\left[\left\{\log_\rho\left(\frac{2c}{\varepsilon \ln\rho}\log_\rho\frac{2c}{\varepsilon\ln\rho}\right)\right\}\right]+1$ and $\delta=\frac{\varepsilon}{r+1}$. We choose the function

$$f(x)=\frac{1}{2}a_0+\sum_{p=1}^{\infty}a_p t_p(x)$$

of the family $F_{\rho,k,c}$, and assemble numbers $k_p (p=0, 1, 2, \ldots, r)$ such that

$$|a_p-k_p\delta|\leqslant\frac{1}{2}\delta=\frac{\varepsilon}{2(r+1)}$$

Then

$$\|f(x)-f^{\delta}_{k_0, k_1, \ldots, k_r}\|\leqslant\sum_{p=0}^{r}|a_p-k_p\delta|\|t_p(x)\|+$$
$$+\sum_{p=r+1}^{\infty}|a_p|\|t_p(x)\|\leqslant\sum_{p=0}^{r}\frac{\varepsilon}{2(r+1)}+\sum_{p=r+1}^{\infty}\frac{c}{p^k\rho^p}\leqslant$$
$$\leqslant\frac{1}{2}\varepsilon+\frac{(r+1)^{|k|}}{(\ln\rho)\rho^{r}}\leqslant\frac{1}{2}\varepsilon+\frac{1}{2}\varepsilon=\varepsilon$$

(see Lemma 1), i.e. the set of functions of the type $f^{\delta}_{k_0, k_1, \ldots, k_r}$ for fixed r and δ forms an ε-net in the space $F_{\rho,k,c}$. And then from the value of the quantity σ^{δ}_{r} we have

$$H_\varepsilon(F_{\rho,k,c})\leqslant\log\left[\frac{2^r c^{r+1}}{\delta^{r+1}(r!)^k\rho^{\frac{r(r+1)}{2}}}\right]=$$
$$=\frac{1}{2\log\rho}\left\{\left(\log\frac{c}{\varepsilon}\right)^2+O\left[\left(\log\frac{1}{\varepsilon}\right)\log\log\frac{1}{\varepsilon}\right]\right\}$$

Q.E.D.

The result of this section is, then, the following theorem.

<u>Theorem 1</u>. The absolute ε-entropy of the space $F^{-1,1}_{\rho,c}$ is equal to

$$H_\varepsilon(F^{-1,1}_{\rho,c})=\frac{1}{2\log\rho}\left\{\left(\log\frac{c}{\varepsilon}\right)^2+O\left[\left(\log\frac{1}{\varepsilon}\right)\log\log\frac{1}{\varepsilon}\right]\right\}$$

The theorem follows from Lemmas 3 and 4.

§ 8. The Entropy of Laurent Series

We are given some compact family Φ_0 of continuous complex functions, defined on some compact A and bounded (in modulus) on A by the constant $c > 0$. For the distance between two functions of Φ_0 we take the maximum of the modulus of their difference (on the set A). We denote by $\Phi^{r_0,\, r_1,\, \Phi_0}_{\rho_0,\, \rho_1,\, m}$ $(0 \leqslant r_1 < r_0 \leqslant \rho_0 < \rho_1 \leqslant +\infty$, m is an arbitrary number) the space of all complex functions of the form

$$f(\alpha, z) = a_0(\alpha) + \sum_{p=1}^{\infty} \frac{a_p(\alpha)\, z^p}{p^m \rho_1^p} + \sum_{p=-1}^{-\infty} \frac{a_p(\alpha)\, z^p}{p^m r_1^p};$$

$$\alpha \in A; \quad a_p(\alpha) \in \Phi_0 \qquad (p = \ldots, -1, 0, 1, \ldots)$$

For the distance between two functions of this family we take the maximum of the modulus of their difference on the set $A \times B^{r_0}_{\rho_0}$, where $B^{r_0}_{\rho_0}$ is the ring of the complex plane given by the inequalities

$$\rho_0 \geqslant |z| \geqslant r_0$$

It is not difficult to see that the series of this form converge absolutely, on the set $A \times \{\rho_1 > |z| > r_1\}$, as well as on $A \times B^{r_0}_{\rho_0}$.

Let Ψ be the transformation $z = e^{iz'}$ of the complex plane $\{z' = x' + iy'\}$ into the complex plane $\{z = x + iy\}$, and let P^d_c be the strip in the $\{z'\}$ plane given by the inequalities $c \leqslant y' \leqslant d$. It is not difficult to verify that the transformation Ψ maps the strip P^d_c into the ring

$$B^{d'}_{c'}\,\{c' \geqslant |z| \geqslant d'\} \quad (c' = e^{-c},\ d' = e^{-d})$$

in such a way that any straight line $y' = \text{const}$ then becomes the circle $|z| = e^{-y}$.

Lemma 1. Let $S_p(z') = \sum_{n=-p}^{p} a_n e^{inz'}$. Then for any fixed y'

$$\max_{x'} |S_p(z')| \geqslant \left(e^{-2py'}|a_p|^2 + e^{2py'}|a_{-p}|^2\right)^{\frac{1}{2}}$$

Proof.

$$
\begin{aligned}
a_n e^{inz'} + a_{-n} e^{-inz'} &= (b_n + ic_n) e^{inz'} + (b_{-n} + ic_{-n}) e^{-inz'} = \\
&= (b_n + ic_n) e^{-ny'} (\cos nx' + i \sin nx') + \\
&\qquad + (b_{-n} + ic_{-n}) e^{ny'} (\cos nx' - i \sin nx') = \\
&= [(-c_n e^{-ny'} + c_{-n} e^{ny'}) \sin nx' + (b_n e^{-ny'} + b_{-n} e^{ny'}) \cos nx'] + \\
&\quad + i [(b_n e^{-ny'} - b_{-n} e^{ny'}) \sin nx' + (c_n e^{-ny'} + c_{-n} e^{ny'}) \cos nx'] \\
&\qquad (n = 1, 2, \ldots, p; \ a_0 = b_0 + ic_0).
\end{aligned}
$$

Therefore the given polynomial can be put in the form

$$
\begin{aligned}
S_p(z') &= \left\{ b_0 + \sum_{n=1}^{p} [(-c_n e^{-ny'} + c_{-n} e^{ny'}) \sin nx' + \right. \\
&\qquad \left. + (b_n e^{-ny'} + b_{-n} e^{ny'}) \cos nx'] \right\} + \\
&\quad + i \left\{ c_0 + \sum_{n=1}^{p} [(b_n e^{-ny'} - b_{-n} e^{ny'}) \sin nx' + \right. \\
&\qquad \left. + (c_n e^{-ny'} + c_{-n} e^{ny'}) \cos nx'] \right\} = \\
&= \left\{ S'_{p-1}(x', y') + \left[\left(-c_p e^{-py'} + c_{-p} e^{py'} \right) \sin px' + \right.\right. \\
&\qquad \left.\left. + \left(b_p e^{-py'} + b_{-p} e^{py'} \right) \cos px' \right] \right\} + \\
&\quad + i \left\{ S''_{p-1}(x', y') + \left[\left(b_p e^{-py'} - b_{-p} e^{py'} \right) \sin px' + \right.\right. \\
&\qquad \left.\left. + \left(c_p e^{-py'} + c_{-p} e^{py'} \right) \cos px' \right] \right\},
\end{aligned}
$$

where $S'_{p-1}(x', y')$ and $S''_{p-1}(x,' y')$ are trigonometric polynomials of order $(p-1)$ (in x'). But it is known that any trigonometric polynomial $\sigma_{p-1}(x) + a \sin px + b \cos px$ ($\sigma_{p-1}(x)$ being a trigonometric polynomial of order $(p-1)$ differs from zero on the real axis by not less than $\sqrt{a^2 + b^2}$ (see [6]). Therefore, taking y' as fixed, we obtain

$$
\max_{x'} |S_p(z')| \geqslant \max_{x'} \left\{ [e^{-2py'} |a_p|^2 + e^{2py'} |a_{-p}|^2 \pm \pm 2 (b_p b_{-p} - c_p c_{-p})]^{\frac{1}{2}} \right\}
$$

where

$$
\begin{aligned}
&[e^{-2py'} |a_p|^2 + e^{2py'} |a_{-p}|^2 + 2 (b_p b_{-p} - c_p c_{-p})] = \\
&\qquad = (-c_p e^{-py'} + c_{-p} e^{py'})^2 + (b_p e^{-py'} + b_{-p} e^{py'})^2, \\
&[e^{-2py'} |a_p|^2 + e^{2py'} |a_{-p}|^2 - 2 (b_p b_{-p} - c_p c_{-p})] = \\
&\qquad = (b_p e^{-py'} - b_{-p} e^{py'})^2 + (c_p e^{-py'} + c_{-p} e^{py'})^2.
\end{aligned}
$$

Hence

$$\max_{x'} |S_p(z')| \geqslant (e^{-2py'} |a_p|^2 + e^{2py'} |a_{-p}|^2)^{\frac{1}{2}}$$

Q.E.D.

Lemma 2. Let $S_p(z') = \sum_{n=-p}^{p} a_n e^{inz}$ and the numbers a_p and a_{-p} be such that either $|a_p| \geqslant \delta e^{cp}$ or $|a_{-p}| \geqslant \delta e^{-dp}$ $(\delta > 0)$. Then in the strip $P_c^d\{c \leqslant y' \leqslant d\}$ the function $|S_p(z')|$ differs from zero by not less than δ.

Proof. From the previous lemma

$$\max_{x} |S_p(z')| \geqslant (e^{-2py'} |a_p|^2 + e^{2py'} |a_{-p}|^2)^{\frac{1}{2}}$$

If $|a_p| \geqslant \delta e^{cp}$, then for $y' = c$ we have

$$\max_{x'} |S_p(z')| \geqslant (e^{2p(c-y')}\delta^2 + e^{2py'} |a_{-p}|^2)^{\frac{1}{2}} \geqslant \delta$$

If $|a_{-p}| \geqslant \delta e^{-dp}$, then for $y' = d$ we have

$$\max_{x'} |S_p(z')| \geqslant (e^{-2py'} (a_p)^2 + e^{2p(y'-d)}\delta^2)^{\frac{1}{2}} \geqslant \delta$$

Lemma 3. Let $S_p(z') = \sum_{n=-p}^{p} a_n e^{inz'}$ and the complex numbers a_p and a_{-p} be such that either $|a_p| \geqslant \delta$, or $|a_{-p}| \geqslant \delta$ $(\delta > 0)$. Then in the strip $P_c^d\{c \leqslant y' \leqslant d\}$

$$\max |S_p(z')| \geqslant \frac{\delta}{\max(e^{cp}, e^{-dp})}$$

Proof. Let us put

$$\delta' = \frac{\delta}{\max(e^{cp}, e^{-dp})}$$

Then either

$$|a_p| \geqslant \delta' \max(e^{cp}, e^{-dp}) \geqslant \delta' e^{cp}$$

or

$$|a_{-p}| \geqslant \delta' \max(e^{cp}, e^{-dp}) \geqslant \delta' e^{-dp}$$

Thus, from the previous lemma

$$\max |S_p(z')| \geqslant \delta' = \frac{\delta}{\max(e^{cp}, e^{-dp})}$$

Q.E.D.

Lemma 4. Let $S_p(z) = \sum_{m=-p}^{p} a_m z^m$ and the coefficients a_p and a_{-p} be such that either $|a_p| \geqslant \delta$ or $|a_{-p}| \geqslant \delta$ ($\delta > 0$). Then on the ring $B_\rho^r \{r \leqslant |z| \leqslant \rho\}$

$$\delta \left[\min\left(\rho, \frac{1}{r}\right)\right]^p \leqslant |S_p(z)|$$

Proof.

$$|S_p(z)| = |S_p(e^{iz'})|$$

($z' \in P_c^d$ where $c = \ln \rho$, $d = -\ln r$). Therefore, from the preceding lemma,

$$\max_{B_\rho^r} |S_p(z)| = \max_{P_c^d} |S_p(e^{iz'})| \geqslant \frac{\delta}{\max(e^{cp}, e^{-dp})} =$$

$$= \delta [\min(e^{-cp}, e^{dp})] = \delta \left[\min\left(\rho^p, \left(\frac{1}{r}\right)^p\right)\right] = \delta \left[\min\left(\rho, \frac{1}{r}\right)\right]^p$$

Q.E.D.

Lemma 5. Let $S_p(z) = \sum_{m=-p}^{p} a_m z^m$ and the coefficients a_p and a_{-p} be such that either $|a_p| \geqslant \frac{\delta}{\rho^p}$ or $|a_{-p}| \geqslant \delta r^p$ ($\delta > 0$) Then in the ring B_ρ^r

$$|S_p(z)| \geqslant \delta$$

The proof of this lemma is easily obtained from Lemma 2.

Let us now evaluate the ε-entropy of the space $\Phi^{r_0, r_1, \Phi_0}_{\rho_0, \rho_1, m}$.
We denote by $D(\Phi_0)$ the one-dimensional diameter of the space Φ_0, i.e.

$$D(\Phi_0) = \sup_{\varphi_1 \in \Phi_0;\ \varphi_2 \in \Phi_0} \rho_{\Phi_0}(\varphi_1, \varphi_2)$$

We choose positive numbers p, q, $\delta \leqslant D(\Phi_0)$, $\delta_q, \delta_{-q+1}, \ldots, \delta_0, \delta_1, \ldots, \delta_p$ in such a way that

$$\left.\begin{aligned} &\delta_0 = \delta; \\ &\delta_i = \frac{\delta \rho_1^i i^m}{\rho_0^i} \qquad (i = 1, 2, \ldots, p); \\ &\delta_{-i} = \frac{\delta r_0^i i^m}{r_1^i} \qquad (i = 1, 2, \ldots, q); \\ &\delta_i \leqslant D(\Phi_0) \qquad (i = -q, -q+1, \ldots, p); \end{aligned}\right\}$$

$$\frac{D(\Phi_0)}{q^m r_1^{-q}} \geqslant \delta r_0^q; \qquad \frac{D(\Phi_0)}{p^m \rho_1^p} \geqslant \frac{\delta}{\rho_0^p}.$$

Lemma 6. The absolute ε-entropy of the space $\Phi^{r_0, r_1, \Phi_0}_{\rho_0, \rho_1, m}$ is equal to

$$H_\varepsilon(\Phi^{r_0, r_1, \Phi_0}_{\rho_0, \rho_1, m}) = \sum_{i=-q(\varepsilon)}^{+p(\varepsilon)} H_{\delta_i^\varepsilon}(\Phi_0)$$

where

$$q(\varepsilon) = \log_r \frac{1}{\varepsilon} + O_q\left(\ln \ln \frac{1}{\varepsilon}\right),$$

$$p(\varepsilon) = \log_\rho \frac{1}{\varepsilon} + O_p\left(\ln \ln \frac{1}{\varepsilon}\right),$$

$$\delta_i^\varepsilon = \varepsilon \rho^i \lambda_p(\varepsilon) \qquad (i = 1, 2, \ldots, p),$$

$$\delta_{-i}^\varepsilon = \varepsilon r^i \lambda_q(\varepsilon) \qquad (i = 0, 1, 2, \ldots, q)$$

$$\rho = \frac{\rho_1}{\rho_0}, \qquad r = \frac{r_0}{r_1};$$

while there exists a positive constant c_0 which does not depend on ε such that

$$c_0 + c_0 \ln \ln \frac{1}{\varepsilon} \geqslant O_p\left(\ln \ln \frac{1}{\varepsilon}\right) \geqslant -c_0 - c_0 \ln \ln \frac{1}{\varepsilon},$$

$$c_0 + c_0 \ln \ln \frac{1}{\varepsilon} \geqslant O_q\left(\ln \ln \frac{1}{\varepsilon}\right) \geqslant -c_0 - c_0 \ln \ln \frac{1}{\varepsilon},$$

$$c_0+c_0\left(\ln\frac{1}{\varepsilon}\right)^{c_0}\geqslant\lambda_p(\varepsilon)\geqslant\left[c_0+c_0\left(\ln\frac{1}{\varepsilon}\right)^{c_0}\right]^{-1},$$
$$c_0+c_0\left(\ln\frac{1}{\varepsilon}\right)^{c_0}\geqslant\lambda_q(\varepsilon)\geqslant\left[c_0+c_0\left(\ln\frac{1}{\varepsilon}\right)^{c_0}\right]^{-1}.$$

Proof. In the space Φ_0 we choose sets $S_{\delta_i}(\Phi_0)$ $(i=-q,\ -q+1,\ \ldots,\ p)$ (see § 5). We then number the functions of the set $S_{\delta_i}(\Phi_0)$ in some way, and denote them by $a_i^j(\alpha)$ $(\alpha\in A;\ j=1,\ 2,\ \ldots,\ n_{\delta_i}(\Phi_0))$.

Put

$$f^{\delta}_{j_1,\,j_2,\,\ldots,\,j_{p+q+1}}(\alpha,\ z)=a_0^{j_0}(\alpha)+\sum_{i=-q}^{-1}\frac{a_i^{j_i}(\alpha)\,z^i}{i^m r_1^i}+\sum_{i=1}^{p}\frac{a_i^{j_i}(\alpha)\,z^i}{i^m\rho_1^i}$$
$$(j_i=1,\ 2,\ \ldots,\ n_{\delta_i}(\Phi_0)).$$

We choose two different functions $f_1(\alpha,\ z)$, $f_2(\alpha,\ z)$ of the type $f^{\delta}_{j_1,\,j_2,\,\ldots,\,j_{p+q+1}}(\alpha,\ z)$ and show that at some point $(\alpha_0,\ z_0)$ $(\alpha_0\in A;\ z_0\in B^{r_0}_{\rho_0})$ these functions differ (in modulus) by not less than δ. For the function $|f_1(\alpha,\ z)-f_2(\alpha,\ z)|$ can be put in the form

$$|f_1(\alpha,\ z)-f_2(\alpha,\ z)|=\left|b_0\alpha+\sum_{i=-q}^{-1}\frac{b_i(\alpha)\,z^i}{i^m r_1^i}+\sum_{i=1}^{p}\frac{b_i(\alpha)\,z^i}{i^m\rho_1^i}\right|$$

where at least one of the coefficients $\{b_i(\alpha)\}$ is not identically equal to zero (in α). Let us choose n so that

$$\max|b_n(\alpha)|+\max|b_{-n}(\alpha)|>0$$

(if $n>q$, then $b_n(\alpha)\equiv 0$; if $n>p$, then $b_n(\alpha)\equiv 0$), and

$$\max|b_{n+k}(\alpha)|+\max|b_{-n-k}(\alpha)|=0$$

for any $k>0$. Then, from the definition of the functions $f^{\delta}_{j_1,\,j_2,\,\ldots,\,j_{p+q+1}}(\alpha,\ z)$ either

$$\max|b_n(\alpha)|\geqslant\delta_n=\frac{\delta\rho_1^n n^m}{\rho_0^n},$$

or

$$\max|b_{-n}(\alpha)| \geqslant \delta_n = \frac{\delta r_0^n n^m}{r_1^n}$$

(see equations 1). For definiteness let $\max|b_n(\alpha)| \geqslant \delta_n$. Then, from the fact that the set A is closed and the family Φ_0 is compact, we know that we can find a point $\alpha_0 \in A$ such that $|b_n(\alpha_0)| \geqslant \delta_n$. Therefore, from Lemma 5, for some $z_0 \subset B_{\rho_0}^{r_0}$

$$|f_1(\alpha_0, z_0) - f_2(\alpha_0, z_0)| \geqslant \delta$$

This means that the functions $\{f^{\delta}_{j_1, j_2, \ldots, j_{p+q+1}}(\alpha, z)\}$ form a set of elements in the space $\Phi^{r_0, r_1, \Phi_0}_{\rho_0, \rho_1, m}$ which are not nearer to one another than δ. Therefore, from Lemma 3 § 5, $H_{\frac{\delta}{2}}(\Phi^{r_0, r_1, \Phi_0}_{\rho_0, \rho_1, m}) \geqslant \log \sigma^{\delta}_{p,q}$, where $\sigma^{\delta}_{p,q}$ is the number of functions of the type $f^{\delta}_{j_1, j_2, \ldots, j_{p+q+1}}(\alpha, z)$.

We shall now show that the set $\{f^{\delta}_{j_1, j_2, \ldots, j_{p+q+1}}\}$ forms a δ'-net in the space $\Phi^{r_0, r_1, \Phi_0}_{\rho_0, \rho_1, m}$, where

$$\delta' = \delta(p+q+1) + c\left[\frac{(q+1)^{|m|}}{r^q \ln r} + \frac{(p+1)^{|m|}}{\rho^p \ln \rho}\right]$$

$$\left(r = \frac{r_0}{r_1}, \quad \rho = \frac{\rho_1}{\rho_0}\right).$$

To do this, we choose some function

$$f(\alpha, z) = a_0(\alpha) + \sum_{i=-1}^{-\infty} \frac{a_i(\alpha) z^i}{i^m r_1^i} + \sum_{i=1}^{\infty} \frac{a_i(\alpha) z^i}{i^m \rho_1^i}$$

of the family $\Phi^{r_0, r_1, \Phi_0}_{\rho_0, \rho_1, m}$, and choose suffixes $j_1, j_2, \ldots, j_{p+q+1}$ such that

$$\max\left|a_i(\alpha) - a_i^{j_i}(\alpha)\right| \leqslant \delta_i \qquad (i = -q, -q+1, \ldots, p)$$

(this is possible, since, from Lemma 3 § 5, for any i the family $\{a_i(\alpha)\}$ forms a δ_i-net in the space Φ_0). Then everywhere on the set $A \times B_{\rho_0}^{r_0}$

$$\left| f(\alpha, z) - f_{j_1, j_2, \ldots, j_{p+q+1}}^{\delta}(\alpha, z) \right| =$$

$$= \left| a_0(\alpha) - a_0^{j_0}(\alpha) + \sum_{i=-q}^{-1} \frac{\left[a_i(\alpha) - a_i^{j_i}(\alpha)\right] z^i}{l^m r_1^i} + \right.$$

$$\left. + \sum_{i=1}^{p} \frac{\left[a_i(\alpha) - a_i^{j_i}(\alpha)\right] z^i}{l^m \rho_1^i} + \sum_{i=-q-i}^{-\infty} \frac{a_i(\alpha) z^i}{l^m r_1^i} + \sum_{i=p+1}^{\infty} \frac{a_i(\alpha) z^i}{l^m \rho_1^i} \right| \leqslant$$

$$\leqslant \delta_0 + \sum_{i=-q}^{-1} \frac{\delta_i r_0^i}{l^m r_1^i} + \sum_{i=1}^{p} \frac{\delta_i \rho_0^i}{l^m \rho_1^i} + \sum_{i=-q-1}^{-\infty} \frac{c r_0^i}{l^m r_1^i} + \sum_{i=p+1}^{\infty} \frac{c \rho_0^i}{\rho_1^i l^m} \leqslant$$

$$\leqslant \delta + \sum_{i=-q}^{-1} \delta + \sum_{i=1}^{p} \delta + \frac{c(q+1)^{|m|}}{\left(\ln \frac{r_0}{r_1}\right)\left(\frac{r_0}{r_1}\right)^q} + \frac{c(p+1)^{|m|}}{\left(\ln \frac{\rho_1}{\rho_0}\right)\left(\frac{\rho_1}{\rho_0}\right)^p} =$$

$$= \delta(p+q+1) + c\left(\frac{(q+1)^{|m|}}{(\ln r) r^q} + \frac{(p+1)^{|m|}}{(\ln \rho) \rho^p}\right) = \delta',$$

where $\rho = \frac{\rho_1}{\rho_0} > 1$, $r = \frac{r_0}{r_1} > 1$ (see Lemma 1 § 7).

Thus we have proved that the set $\{f_{j_1, \ldots, j_{p+q+1}}^{\delta}(\alpha, z)\}$ forms a δ'-net in the space $\Phi_{\rho_0, \rho_1, m}^{r_0, r_1, \Phi_0}$, and hence

$$H_{\delta'}\left(\Phi_{\rho_0, \rho_1, m}^{r_0, r_1, \Phi_0}\right) \leqslant \log \sigma_{p, q}^{\delta}$$

Let us now evaluate the number $\sigma_{p, q}^{\delta}$

$$\sigma_{p, q}^{\delta} = \prod_{i=-q}^{p} n_{\delta_i}(\Phi_0), \qquad \log \sigma_{p, q}^{\delta} = \sum_{i=-q}^{p} h_{\delta_i}(\Phi_0)$$

Put

$$q = q_\varepsilon^1 = \left[\left\{\log_r \left[\frac{D(\Phi_0)}{3\varepsilon}\left(\log_r \frac{D(\Phi_0)}{3\varepsilon}\right)^{-2|m|}\right]\right\}\right]$$

$$p = p_\varepsilon^1 = \left[\left\{\log_\rho \left[\frac{D(\Phi_0)}{3\varepsilon}\left(\log_\rho \frac{D(\Phi_0)}{3\varepsilon}\right)^{-2|m|}\right]\right\}\right]$$

$$\delta_\varepsilon^1 = 3\varepsilon.$$

It is not difficult to verify that for fixed p, q and δ we can find $\varepsilon_0[m, r, \rho, D(\Phi_0)] > 0$ such that for $3\varepsilon < \varepsilon_0[m, r, \rho, D(\Phi_0)]$ the relations (1) hold for p_ε^1, q_ε^1, $\delta = 3\varepsilon$. Therefore

$$H_\varepsilon\left(\Phi_{\rho_0, \rho_1, m}^{r_0, r_1, \Phi_0}\right) \geqslant H_{\frac{\delta}{2}}\left(\Phi_{\rho_0, \rho_1, m}^{r_0, r_1, \Phi_0}\right) \geqslant \log \sigma_{p_\varepsilon^1, q_\varepsilon^1}^{3\varepsilon} = \sum_{i=-q_\varepsilon^1}^{p_\varepsilon^1} h_{\delta_i^1}(\Phi_0).$$

where

$$\delta_i^1 = \frac{3\varepsilon\rho_1^i l^m}{\rho_0^i} \qquad (l = 1,\ 2,\ \ldots,\ p)$$

$$\delta_{-i}^1 = \frac{3\varepsilon r_0^i l^m}{r_1^i} \qquad (l = 1,\ 2,\ \ldots,\ q)$$

Let us now put

$$p = p_\varepsilon^2 = \left[\log_\rho\left[\frac{4c\ln\rho}{\varepsilon}\left(\log_\rho\frac{4c\ln\rho}{\varepsilon}\right)^{2|m|}\right]\right],$$

$$q = q_\varepsilon^2 = \left[\log_r\left[\frac{4c\ln r}{\varepsilon}\left(\log_r\frac{4c\ln r}{\varepsilon}\right)^{2|m|}\right]\right]$$

$$\delta = \delta_\varepsilon^2 = \varepsilon\left[3 + 3p_\varepsilon^2 + 3q_\varepsilon^2 + \frac{4c\ln\rho\left(\log_\rho\frac{4c\ln\rho}{\varepsilon}\right)^{4|m|}}{D(\Phi_0)} + \right.$$
$$\left. + \frac{4c\ln r\left(\log_r\frac{4c\ln r}{\varepsilon}\right)^{4|m|}}{D(\Phi_0)}\right]^{-1}$$

It is easy to see that for sufficiently small ε and for $p = p_\varepsilon^2,\ q = q_\varepsilon^2,\ \delta = \delta_\varepsilon^2$, the relations (1) will hold. Therefore the set of functions $\left\{f_{j_1, j_2, \ldots, j_{p_\varepsilon^2+q_\varepsilon^2+1}}^{\delta_i^2}\right\}$ forms a δ'-net in the space $\Phi_{\rho_0, \rho_1, m}^{r_0, r_1, \Phi_0}$, where

$$\delta' = \delta(p+q+1) + c\left[\frac{(q+1)^{|m|}}{r^q\ln r} + \frac{(p+1)^{|m|}}{\rho^p\ln\rho}\right] \leqslant$$
$$\leqslant \frac{1}{3}\varepsilon + \frac{1}{3}\varepsilon + \frac{1}{3}\varepsilon = \varepsilon$$

i.e.

$$H_\varepsilon\left(\Phi_{\rho_0, \rho_1, m}^{r_0, r_1, \Phi_0}\right) \leqslant H_{\delta'}\left(\Phi_{\rho_0, \rho_1, m}^{r_0, r_1, \Phi_0}\right) \leqslant \sum_{i=-q^2}^{p_\varepsilon^2} h_{\delta_i^2}(\Phi_0)$$

where

$$\delta_i^2 = \frac{\delta_\varepsilon^2\rho_1^i l^m}{\rho_0^i} \qquad (l = 1,\ 2,\ \ldots,\ p),$$

$$\delta_{-i}^2 = \frac{\delta_\varepsilon^2 r_0^i i^m}{r_1^i} \qquad (l = 1,\ 2,\ \ldots,\ q).$$

Thus

$$\sum_{i=-q_\varepsilon^1}^{p_\varepsilon^1} h_{\delta_i^1}(\Phi_0) \leqslant H_\varepsilon(\Phi_{\rho_0,\,\rho_1,\,m}^{r_0,\,r_1,\,\Phi_0}) \leqslant \sum_{i=-q_\varepsilon^2}^{p_\varepsilon^2} h_{\delta_i^2}(\Phi_0)$$

Hence, from Theorem 1 § 5,

$$\sum_{i=-q_\varepsilon^1}^{p_\varepsilon^1} H_{2\delta_i^1}(\Phi_0) \leqslant H_\varepsilon(\Phi_{\rho_0,\,\rho_1,\,m}^{r_0,\,r_1,\,\Phi_0}) \leqslant \sum_{i=-q_\varepsilon^2}^{p_\varepsilon^2} H_{\frac{1}{2}\delta_i^2}(\Phi_0)$$

Using the expressions for

$$q_\varepsilon^1,\ p_\varepsilon^1,\ \delta_\varepsilon^1,\ q_\varepsilon^2,\ p_\varepsilon^2,\ \delta_\varepsilon^2$$

we are justified in writing

$$H_\varepsilon(\Phi_{\rho_0,\,\rho_1,\,m}^{r_0,\,r_1,\,\Phi_0}) = \sum_{i=-q(\varepsilon)}^{p(\varepsilon)} H_{\delta_i^\varepsilon}(\Phi_0)$$

where

$$q(\varepsilon) = \log_r \frac{1}{\varepsilon} + O_q\left(\ln\ln\frac{1}{\varepsilon}\right),$$

$$p(\varepsilon) = \log_\rho \frac{1}{\varepsilon} + O_p\left(\ln\ln\frac{1}{\varepsilon}\right),$$

$$\delta_i^\varepsilon = \varepsilon\rho^i\lambda_p(\varepsilon) \qquad (i = 1,\ 2,\ \ldots,\ p),$$

$$\delta_{-i}^\varepsilon = \varepsilon r^i\lambda_q(\varepsilon) \qquad (i = 0,\ 1,\ 2,\ \ldots,\ q)$$

and moreover

$$c_0 + c_0\ln\ln\frac{1}{\varepsilon} \geqslant O_p\left(\ln\ln\frac{1}{\varepsilon}\right) \geqslant -c_0 - c_0\ln\ln\frac{1}{\varepsilon},$$

$$c_0 + c_0\ln\ln\frac{1}{\varepsilon} \geqslant O_q\left(\ln\ln\frac{1}{\varepsilon}\right) \geqslant -c_0 - c_0\ln\ln\frac{1}{\varepsilon},$$

$$c_0 + c_0\left(\ln\frac{1}{\varepsilon}\right)^{c_0} \geqslant \lambda_p(\varepsilon) \geqslant \left[c_0 + c_0\left(\ln\frac{1}{\varepsilon}\right)^{c_0}\right]^{-1},$$

$$c_0 + c_0\left(\ln\frac{1}{\varepsilon}\right)^{c_0} \geqslant \lambda_q(\varepsilon) \geqslant \left[c_0 + c_0\left(\ln\frac{1}{\varepsilon}\right)^{c_0}\right]^{-1}$$

(c_0 is some positive constant independent of ε). Q.E.D.

Lemma 7. Let the space Φ_0 be such that

$$H_\varepsilon(\Phi_0) = c_n\left(\log\frac{1}{\varepsilon}\right)^n + O_{\Phi_0}\left[\left(\log\frac{1}{\varepsilon}\right)^{n-1}\log\log\frac{1}{\varepsilon}\right]$$

where

$$\left| O_{\Phi_0}\left[\left(\log \frac{1}{\varepsilon}\right)^{n-1} \log\log \frac{1}{\varepsilon}\right]\right| \leqslant c(\Phi_0)\left(\log \frac{1}{\varepsilon}\right)^{n-1} \log\log \frac{1}{\varepsilon}$$

($(c(\Phi_0) > 0$ is some constant not depending upon ε).

Then

$$H_\varepsilon\left(\Phi^{r_0,\, r_1,\, \Phi_0}_{\rho_0,\, \rho_1,\, m}\right) = \frac{c_n}{n+1}\left(\frac{1}{\log \rho} + \frac{1}{\log r}\right)\left(\log \frac{1}{\varepsilon}\right)^{n+1} + $$
$$+ O\left[\left(\log \frac{1}{\varepsilon}\right)^{n} \log\log \frac{1}{\varepsilon}\right] \qquad \left(r = \frac{r_0}{r_1};\ \ \rho = \frac{\rho_1}{\rho_0}\right)$$

Proof. From the previous lemma

$$H_\varepsilon\left(\Phi^{r_0,\, r_1,\, \Phi_0}_{\rho_0,\, \rho_1,\, m}\right) = \sum_{i=-q(\varepsilon)}^{p(\varepsilon)} H_{\delta_i^\varepsilon}(\Phi_0) =$$
$$= \sum_{i=-q(\varepsilon)}^{0} H_{\delta_i^\varepsilon}(\Phi_0) + \sum_{i=1}^{p(\varepsilon)} H_{\delta_i^\varepsilon}(\Phi_0) =$$
$$= \sum_{i=-q(\varepsilon)}^{0} \left\{c_n\left[\log \frac{1}{\delta_i^\varepsilon}\right]^n + O_{\Phi_0}\left[\left(\log \frac{1}{\delta_i^\varepsilon}\right)^{n-1} \log\log \frac{1}{\delta_i^\varepsilon}\right]\right\} +$$
$$+ \sum_{i=1}^{p(\varepsilon)} \left\{c_n\left(\log \frac{1}{\delta_i^\varepsilon}\right)^n + O_{\Phi_0}\left[\left(\log \frac{1}{\delta_i^\varepsilon}\right)^{n-1} \log\log \frac{1}{\delta_i^\varepsilon}\right]\right\} =$$
$$= \sum_{i=-q(\varepsilon)}^{0} \left\{c_n\left(\log \frac{1}{\varepsilon r^{-i}\lambda_q(\varepsilon)}\right)^n + \right.$$
$$\left. + O_{\Phi_0}\left[\left(\log \frac{1}{\varepsilon r^{-i}\lambda_q(\varepsilon)}\right)^{n-1} \log\log \frac{1}{\varepsilon r^{-i}\lambda_q(\varepsilon)}\right]\right\} +$$
$$+ \sum_{i=1}^{p(\varepsilon)} \left\{c_n\left(\log \frac{1}{\varepsilon \rho^{i}\lambda_p(\varepsilon)}\right)^n + \right.$$
$$\left. + O_{\Phi_0}\left[\left(\log \frac{1}{\varepsilon \rho^{i}\lambda_p(\varepsilon)}\right)^{n-1} \log\log \frac{1}{\varepsilon \rho^{i}\lambda_p(\varepsilon)}\right]\right\} =$$

$$= \sum_{i=0}^{q(\varepsilon)} c_n\left(\log \frac{1}{\varepsilon r^{i}\lambda_q(\varepsilon)}\right)^n + \sum_{i=1}^{p(\varepsilon)} c_n\left(\log \frac{1}{\varepsilon \rho^{i}\lambda_p(\varepsilon)}\right)^n +$$
$$+ \sum_{i=0}^{q(\varepsilon)} O_{\Phi_0}\left[\left(\log \frac{1}{\varepsilon r^{i}\lambda_q(\varepsilon)}\right)^{n-1} \log\log \frac{1}{\varepsilon r^{i}\lambda_q(\varepsilon)}\right] +$$
$$+ \sum_{i=1}^{p(\varepsilon)} O_{\Phi_0}\left[\left(\log \frac{1}{\varepsilon \rho^{i}\lambda_p(\varepsilon)}\right)^{n-1} \log\log \frac{1}{\varepsilon \rho^{i}\lambda_p(\varepsilon)}\right]$$

Let us now calculate the first term of the sum. To do this we first evaluate the following:

$$\left|\sum_{i=0}^{q(\varepsilon)}\left(\log\frac{1}{\varepsilon r^i}\right)^k\right| \leqslant (q(\varepsilon)+1)\left|\log\frac{1}{\varepsilon r^0}\right|^k = O\left(\log\frac{1}{\varepsilon}\right)^{k+1}$$

and therefore

$$\sum_{i=0}^{q(\varepsilon)} c_n\left(\log\frac{1}{\varepsilon r^i\lambda_q(\varepsilon)}\right)^n = c_n\sum_{i=0}^{q(\varepsilon)}\sum_{k=0}^{n} C_n^k\left(\log\frac{1}{\varepsilon r^i}\right)^k\left(\log\frac{1}{\lambda_q(\varepsilon)}\right)^{n-k} =$$

$$= c_n\sum_{i=0}^{q(\varepsilon)}\left(\log\frac{1}{\varepsilon r^i}\right)^n + O\left[\left(\log\frac{1}{\varepsilon}\right)^n\log\log\frac{1}{\varepsilon}\right] =$$

$$= c_n\sum_{i=0}^{q(\varepsilon)}\sum_{k=0}^{n} C_n^k\left(\log\frac{1}{\varepsilon}\right)^k\left(\log\frac{1}{r^i}\right)^{n-k} + O\left[\left(\log\frac{1}{\varepsilon}\right)^n\log\log\frac{1}{\varepsilon}\right] =$$

$$= c_n\sum_{k=0}^{n} C_n^k\left(\log\frac{1}{\varepsilon}\right)^k\sum_{i=0}^{q(\varepsilon)}\left(i\log\frac{1}{r}\right)^{n-k} + $$

$$+ O\left[\left(\log\frac{1}{\varepsilon}\right)^n\log\log\frac{1}{\varepsilon}\right] =$$

$$= c_n\sum_{k=0}^{n} C_n^k\left(\log\frac{1}{\varepsilon}\right)^k\left(\log\frac{1}{r}\right)^{n-k}\sum_{i=0}^{q(\varepsilon)} i^{n-k} + $$

$$+ O\left[\left(\log\frac{1}{\varepsilon}\right)^n\log\log\frac{1}{\varepsilon}\right] =$$

$$= c_n\sum_{k=0}^{n} C_n^k\left(\log\frac{1}{\varepsilon}\right)^k\left(\log\frac{1}{r}\right)^{n-k}\frac{q(\varepsilon)^{n-k+1}}{n-k+1} + $$

$$+ O\left[\left(\log\frac{1}{\varepsilon}\right)^n\log\log\frac{1}{\varepsilon}\right] =$$

$$= c_n\sum_{k=0}^{n} C_n^k\left(\log\frac{1}{\varepsilon}\right)^k\left(\log\frac{1}{r}\right)^{n-k}\frac{\left(\log_r\frac{1}{\varepsilon}\right)^{n-k+1}}{n-k+1} + $$

$$+ O\left[\left(\log\frac{1}{\varepsilon}\right)^n\log\log\frac{1}{\varepsilon}\right] =$$

$$= c_n\left(\log\frac{1}{\varepsilon}\right)^{n+1}\sum_{k=0}^{n}\frac{(-1)^{n-k}C_n^k}{(n-k+1)\log r} + $$

$$+ O\left[\left(\log\frac{1}{\varepsilon}\right)^n\log\log\frac{1}{\varepsilon}\right] =$$

$$= \frac{c_n\left(\log\frac{1}{\varepsilon}\right)^{n+1}}{(n+1)\log r} + O\left[\left(\log\frac{1}{\varepsilon}\right)^n\log\log\frac{1}{\varepsilon}\right],$$

since

$$\sum_{k=0}^{n} \frac{(-1)^{n-k} C_n^k}{n-k+1} = \frac{1}{n+1} \sum_{k=0}^{n} (-1)^{n-k} C_{n+1}^k =$$

$$= \frac{1}{n+1} \left[\sum_{k=0}^{n+1} (-1)^{n-k} C_{n+1}^k + C_{n+1}^{n+1} \right] = \frac{1}{n+1}$$

Similarly

$$\sum_{i=1}^{p(\varepsilon)} c_n \left(\log \frac{1}{\varepsilon \rho^i \lambda_p(\varepsilon)} \right)^n = \frac{c_n \left(\log \frac{1}{\varepsilon} \right)^{n+1}}{(\log \rho)(n+1)} + O\left[\left(\log \frac{1}{\varepsilon} \right)^n \log \log \frac{1}{\varepsilon} \right],$$

$$\sum_{i=0}^{q(\varepsilon)} O_{\Phi_0} \left[\left(\log \frac{1}{\varepsilon r^i \lambda_q(\varepsilon)} \right)^{n-1} \log \log \frac{1}{\varepsilon r^i \lambda_q(\varepsilon)} \right] +$$

$$+ \sum_{i=1}^{p(\varepsilon)} O_{\Phi_0} \left[\left(\log \frac{1}{\varepsilon \rho^i \lambda_p(\varepsilon)} \right)^{n-1} \log \log \frac{1}{\varepsilon \rho^i \lambda_p(\varepsilon)} \right] =$$

$$= O_{\Phi} \left[\left(\log \frac{1}{\varepsilon} \right)^n \log \log \frac{1}{\varepsilon} \right].$$

Thus

$$H_\varepsilon(\Phi_{\rho_0, \rho_1, m}^{r_0, r_1, \Phi_0}) = \frac{c_n}{n+1} \left(\frac{1}{\log \rho} + \frac{1}{\log r} \right) \left(\log \frac{1}{\varepsilon} \right)^{n+1} +$$

$$+ O_{\Phi} \left[\left(\log \frac{1}{\varepsilon} \right)^n \log \log \frac{1}{\varepsilon} \right]$$

Q.E.D.

Lemma 8. If the set A contains only one point, and Φ_0 is the set of all real constants not exceeding c (in absolute magnitude) then

$$H_\varepsilon(\Phi_{\rho_0, \rho_1, m}^{r_0, r_1, \Phi_0}) =$$

$$= \frac{1}{2} \left(\frac{1}{\log r} + \frac{1}{\log \rho} \right) \left(\log \frac{c}{\varepsilon} \right)^2 + O\left[\left(\log \frac{1}{\varepsilon} \right) \log \log \frac{1}{\varepsilon} \right]$$

$$\left(r = \frac{r_0}{r_1}; \qquad \rho = \frac{\rho_1}{\rho_0} \right).$$

Proof. From Lemma 3 § 6

$$H_\varepsilon(\Phi_0) = \log \left[\frac{1}{\varepsilon} \right] \pm 1 = \log \frac{1}{\varepsilon} + O\left(\log \log \frac{1}{\varepsilon} \right) .$$

Therefore, from the previous lemma

$$H_{\varepsilon}(\Phi^{r_0,\, r_1,\, \Phi_0}_{\rho_0,\, \rho_1,\, m}) =$$
$$= \frac{1}{2}\left(\frac{1}{\log r} + \frac{1}{\log \rho}\right)\left(\log \frac{1}{\varepsilon}\right)^2 + O\left[\left(\log \frac{1}{\varepsilon}\right)\log\log \frac{1}{\varepsilon}\right] =$$
$$= \frac{1}{2}\left(\frac{1}{\log r} + \frac{1}{\log \rho}\right)\left(\log \frac{c}{\varepsilon}\right)^2 + O\left[\left(\log \frac{1}{\varepsilon}\right)\log\log \frac{1}{\varepsilon}\right]$$

Lemma 9. If the set A contains only one point, and Φ_0 is the set of all complex numbers bounded in modulus by the constant $c > 0$, then

$$H_{\varepsilon}(\Phi^{r_0,\, r_1,\, \Phi_0}_{\rho_0,\, \rho_1,\, m}) = \left(\frac{1}{\log r} + \frac{1}{\log \rho}\right)\left(\log \frac{c}{\varepsilon}\right)^2 + O\left[\left(\log \frac{1}{\varepsilon}\right)\log\log \frac{1}{\varepsilon}\right]$$
$$\left(r = \frac{r_0}{r_1}; \qquad \rho = \frac{\rho_1}{\rho_0}\right).$$

The proof is obtained in the same way as that of the last lemma from Lemma 7 and Theorem 2, § 6.

Theorem 1. Let $\Phi^{r_0,\, r_1}_{\rho_0,\, \rho_1,\, c}$ be the space of all analytic functions in the ring $B^{r_1}_{\rho_1}\{r_1 \leqslant |z| \leqslant \rho_1\}$, bounded in modulus in this ring by the constant $c\,(c > 0)$ (for the norm in this space we take the maximum of the modulus of the function on the ring $B^{r_0}_{\rho_0}$).

Then

$$H_{\varepsilon}(\Phi^{r_0,\, r_1}_{\rho_0,\, \rho_1,\, c}) = \left(\frac{1}{\log r} + \frac{1}{\log \rho}\right)\left(\log \frac{c}{\varepsilon}\right)^2 + O\left[\left(\log \frac{1}{\varepsilon}\right)\log\log \frac{1}{\varepsilon}\right]$$
$$\left(r = \frac{r_0}{r_1}; \qquad \rho = \frac{\rho_1}{\rho_0}\right).$$

Proof. We choose a function $f(z)$ of the given family:

$$f(z) = \sum_{n=0}^{\infty} a_n z^n + \sum_{n=1}^{\infty} b_n z^{-n},$$
$$a_n = \frac{1}{2\pi i}\int_{\gamma} \frac{f(\zeta)\, d\zeta}{\zeta^{n+1}} \qquad (n = 0,\ 1,\ 2,\ \ldots),$$
$$b_n = \frac{1}{2\pi i}\int_{\gamma} f(\zeta)\,\zeta^{n-1}\, d\zeta \qquad (n = 1,\ 2,\ \ldots)$$

(where γ is an arbitrary contour in the ring $B^{r_1}_{\rho_1}$, embracing the point $z = 0$).

Hence

$$|a_n| \leqslant \frac{c}{2\pi\rho_1^{n+1}} \leqslant \frac{c'}{\rho_1^n}$$

and

$$|b_n| \leqslant \frac{cr_1^{n-1}}{2\pi} \leqslant c'r_1^n$$

This means that $f(z)$ belongs to the family $\Phi^{r_0, r_1, \Phi'_0}_{\rho_0, \rho_1, 0}$ (Φ'_0 is the space of complex numbers bounded in modulus by the constant c').

On the other hand, it is not difficult to see that any function of the family $\Phi^{r_0, r_1, \Phi''_0}_{\rho_0, \rho_1, 2}$ (Φ''_0 is the space of complex numbers bounded in modulus by some constant $c'' > 0$) belongs to the space $\Phi^{r_0, r_1}_{\rho_0, \rho_1, c}$.

Thus,

$$\Phi^{r_0, r_1, \Phi'_0}_{\rho_0, \rho_1, 0} \supset \Phi^{r_0, r_1,}_{\rho_0, \rho_1, c} \supset \Phi^{r_0, r_1, \Phi''_0}_{\rho_0, \rho_1, 2}$$

Hence

$$H_\varepsilon\left(\Phi^{r_0, r_1, \Phi'_0}_{\rho_0, \rho_1, 0}\right) \geqslant H_\varepsilon\left(\Phi^{r_0, r_1}_{\rho_0, \rho_1, c}\right) \geqslant H_\varepsilon\left(\Phi^{r_0, r_1, \Phi''_0}_{\rho_0, \rho_1, 2}\right)$$

Therefore, from the preceding lemma we have

$$H_\varepsilon(\Phi^{r_0, r_1}_{\rho_0, \rho_1, c}) = \left(\frac{1}{\log r} + \frac{1}{\log \rho}\right)\left(\log\frac{c}{\varepsilon}\right)^2 + O\left[\left(\log\frac{1}{\varepsilon}\right)\log\log\frac{1}{\varepsilon}\right]$$

Q.E.D.

§ 9. The Entropy of the Space of Analytic Functions of Many Complex Variables

We shall use the following notation:

E^z_n is the space of the n complex variables $(z = z_1, z_2, \ldots, z_n)$; $z_k = x_k + iy_k$, $k = 1, 2, \ldots, n$

$B^{r'}_{\rho'} = B^{r'_1, r'_2, \ldots, r'_n}_{\rho'_1, \rho'_2, \ldots, \rho'_n}$ is the ring of the space E^z_n given by $r'_k \leqslant |z_k| \leqslant \rho'_k$ $(k = 1, 2, \ldots, n)$

$B^{r''}_{\rho''} = B^{r''_1, r''_2, \ldots, r''_n}_{\rho''_1, \rho''_2, \ldots, \rho''_n}$ is the ring of E^z_n given by

$$r''_k \leqslant |z| \leqslant \rho''_k (0 \leqslant r''_k < r'_k \leqslant \rho'_k < \rho''_k \leqslant \infty, \; k = 1, 2, \ldots, n)$$

$F^{r', r''}_{\rho', \rho'', c}$ is the space of functions analytic in the ring $B^{r''}_{\rho''}$, bounded (in modulus) in this ring by the constant $c > 0$ (for the norm in this space we take the maximum of the modulus of the function in the ring $B^{r'}_{\rho'}$).

$\Phi^{r, \Phi_0}_{\rho, m, c} = \Phi^{r_1, r_2, \ldots, r_n, \Phi_0}_{\rho_1, \rho_2, \ldots, \rho_n, m, c}$ is the space of the functions $f(z)$, which can be represented in the form

$$f(z) = \sum_{i_1=-\infty}^{\infty} \sum_{i_2=-\infty}^{\infty} \cdots \sum_{i_n=-\infty}^{\infty} \frac{a_{i_1, i_2, \ldots, i_n} z_1^{i_1} z_2^{i_2} \ldots z_n^{i_n}}{i_1^m i_2^m \ldots i_n^m \mu_1^{i_1} \mu_2^{i_2} \ldots \mu_n^{i_n}} =$$

$$= \sum_{\{i\}=-\infty}^{\infty} \frac{a_{\{i\}, n} z^{\{i\}, n}}{\{i\}_n^m \mu^{\{i\}, n}}$$

(where the second half of the equation must be understood as the conventional representation for $f(z)$), where $a_{\{i\}, n} = a_{i_1, i_2, \ldots, i_n} \in \Phi_0$; $i_k^m = (i_k)^m$ when $i_k \neq 0$, $i_k^m = 1$ when $i_k = 0$ $(k = 1, 2, \ldots, n)$; $\mu_k^{i_k} = (\rho''_k)^{i_k}$ when $i_k > 0$, $\mu_k = 1$ when $i_k = 0$, $\mu_k^{i_k} = (r''_k)^{i_k}$ when $i_k < 0$ $(k = 1, 2, \ldots, n)$. For the norm in the space $\Phi^{r, \Phi_0}_{\rho, m, c}$, we take the maximum of the modulus of the sum in the ring $B^{r'}_{\rho'}$,

$$\rho_k = \frac{\rho''_k}{\rho'_k}; \qquad r_k = \frac{r'_k}{r''_k} \qquad (k = 1, 2, \ldots, n)$$

By Φ_0 in this section we shall mean either the segment $-c \leqslant x_0 \leqslant c$ or the circle of the complex plane $|z_0| \leqslant c$; in the first case, Φ_0 will be denoted by x_0, and in the second by z_0.

Lemma 1. For any real m and $c > 0$

$$H_\varepsilon(\Phi^{r, x_0}_{\rho, m, c}) = \frac{1}{(n+1)!} \prod_{k=1}^{n} \left(\frac{1}{\log r_k} + \frac{1}{\log \rho_k}\right) \left(\log \frac{c}{\varepsilon}\right)^{n+1} +$$

$$+ O_\Phi \left[\left(\log \frac{1}{\varepsilon}\right)^n \log \log \frac{1}{\varepsilon}\right]$$

where

$$A(\rho, r, m, c) + A(\rho, r, m, c)\left(\log\frac{1}{\varepsilon}\right)^n \log\log\frac{1}{\varepsilon} \geqslant$$
$$\geqslant O_\Phi\left[\left(\log\frac{1}{\varepsilon}\right)^n \log\log\frac{1}{\varepsilon}\right] \geqslant$$
$$\geqslant -A(\rho, r, m, c) - A(\rho, r, m, c)\left(\log\frac{1}{\varepsilon}\right)^n \log\log\frac{1}{\varepsilon}$$

(here $\varepsilon \leqslant \frac{1}{2}$, $A(\rho, r, m, c) = A\left(\frac{\rho_1''}{\rho_1'}, \frac{\rho_2''}{\rho_2'}, \ldots, \frac{\rho_n''}{\rho_n'}, \frac{r_1'}{r_1''}, \frac{r_2'}{r_2''}, \ldots, \frac{r_n'}{r_n''}, m, c\right) > 0$ for any m and c does not increase as each of the arguments $\rho_k = \frac{\rho_k''}{\rho_k'}$ and $r_k = \frac{r_k'}{r_k''}$ increases).

Proof. From Lemma 8 § 8, this lemma is true for $n=1$. Further, by induction, (see Lemma 7 § 8) we obtain

$$H_\varepsilon(\Phi^{r, x_0}_{\rho, m, c}) = \frac{c_n}{n+1}\left(\frac{1}{\log\rho_n} + \frac{1}{\log r_n}\right)\left(\log\frac{c}{\varepsilon}\right)^{n+1} + $$
$$+ O_\Phi\left[\left(\log\frac{1}{\varepsilon}\right)^n \log\log\frac{1}{\varepsilon}\right]$$

where $c_n = \frac{1}{n!}\prod_{k=1}^{n-1}\left(\frac{1}{\log\rho_k} + \frac{1}{\log r_k}\right)$ (according to the induction hypothesis). Hence

$$H_\varepsilon(\Phi^{r, x_0}_{\rho, m, c}) = \frac{1}{(n+1)!}\prod_{k=1}^{n}\left(\frac{1}{\log r_k} + \frac{1}{\log\rho_k}\right)\left(\log\frac{c}{\varepsilon}\right)^{n+1} + $$
$$+ O_\Phi\left[\left(\log\frac{1}{\varepsilon}\right)^n \log\log\frac{1}{\varepsilon}\right]$$

Lemma 2. For any real m, $c > 0$,

$$H_\varepsilon(\Phi^{r, z_0}_{\rho, m, c}) = \frac{2}{(n+1)!}\prod_{k=1}^{n}\left(\frac{1}{\log r_k} + \frac{1}{\log\rho_k}\right)\left(\log\frac{c}{\varepsilon}\right)^{n+1} + $$
$$+ O_\Phi\left[\left(\log\frac{1}{\varepsilon}\right)^n \log\log\frac{1}{\varepsilon}\right]$$

By analogy with the previous lemma, the proof is easily obtained from Lemmas 7 and 9, § 8. Let $F^{r, n}_{\rho, c} = F^{r_1, r_2, \ldots, r_n, n}_{\rho_1, \rho_2, \ldots, \rho_n, c}$ be the space of all complex functions analytic inside the region $B^{r''}_{\rho''}$ and bounded in this region (in modulus) by the constant $c > 0$. (For the norm we take the maximum of the modulus of the function on the set $B^{r'}_{\rho'}$).

Lemma 3. Any function of the family $\Phi^{r,\, z_0}_{\rho,\, 2,\, c'_n}$ belongs to the family $F^{r,\, n}_{\rho,\, c}$ $\left(c'_n = \frac{c}{4^n}\right)$.

Proof. We prove the lemma by induction on n. For $n=1$ the space $\Phi^{r,\, z_0}_{\rho,\, 2,\, c'_n}$ $\left(c'_n = \frac{c}{4}\right)$ is the aggregate of functions of the form

$$f(z_1) = a_0 + \sum_{i=1}^{\infty} \frac{a_i z_1^i}{(\rho_1'')^i i^2} + \sum_{i=-1}^{-\infty} \frac{a_i z_1^i}{(r_1'')^i i^2}$$

where

$$|a_i| \leqslant c'_n \qquad (-\infty \leqslant i \leqslant \infty)$$

Therefore

$$|f(z_1)| \leqslant |a_0| + \sum_{i=1}^{\infty} \frac{|a_i|\,|z_1|^i}{(\rho_1'')^i i^2} + \sum_{i=-1}^{-\infty} \frac{|a_i|\,|z_1|^i}{(r_1'')^i i^2} \leqslant \frac{c}{4} + \sum_{i=1}^{\infty} \frac{c}{4i^2} + \sum_{i=-1}^{-\infty} \frac{c}{4i^2} \leqslant c$$

i.e.

$$\Phi^{r,\, z_0}_{\rho,\, 2,\, \left(\frac{c}{4}\right)} \subset F^{r,\, 1}_{\rho,\, c}$$

Suppose that we have proved that $\Phi^{r,\, z_0}_{\rho,\, 2,\, c'_n} \subset F^{r,\, n-1}_{\rho,\, c}$ $\left(c'_n = \frac{c}{4^{n-1}}\right)$

Then for any function $f(z)$ of the family $\Phi^{r,\, z_0}_{\rho,\, 2,\, c'_n}$ $\left(c'_n = \frac{c}{4^n}\right)$ we have

$$f(z) = \sum_{\{i\}=-\infty}^{\infty} \frac{a_{\{i\},\, n} z^{\{i\},\, n}}{\{l\}_n^2 \mu^{\{i\},\, n}} = b_0 \sum_{\{i\}=-\infty}^{\infty} \frac{a_{\{i\},\, n-1,\, 0} z^{\{i\},\, n-1}}{\{l\}_{n-1}^2 \mu^{\{i\},\, n-1}} + \sum_{i_1=1}^{\infty} \frac{b_{i_1} z_1^{i_1}}{i_1^2 (\rho_1'')^{i_1}} \left[\sum_{\{i\}=-\infty}^{+\infty} \frac{a_{\{i\},\, n-1,\, i_1} z^{\{i\},\, n-1}}{\{l\}_{n-1}^2 \mu^{\{i\},\, n-1}} \right] + \sum_{i_1=-1}^{-\infty} \frac{b_{i_1} z_1^{i_1}}{i_1^2 (r_1'')^{i_1}} \left[\sum_{\{i\}=-\infty}^{\infty} \frac{a_{\{i\},\, n-1,\, i_1} z^{\{i\},\, n-1}}{\{l\}_{n-1}^2 \mu^{\{i\},\, n-1}} \right]$$

and so we can assume that $|b_{i_1}| \leqslant \frac{1}{4}$ and $|a_{\{i\},\, n-1,\, i_1}| \leqslant \frac{c}{4^{n-1}}$, since, from the definition of the space $\Phi^{r, z_0}_{\rho, 2, c'_n}\left(c'_n = \frac{c}{4^n}\right)$ $|b_{i_1} \cdot a_{\{i\}, n-1, i_1}| \leqslant \frac{c}{4^n}$. Hence, from the induction hypothesis

$$|f(z)| \leqslant |b_0| \left| \sum_{\{i\}=-\infty}^{\infty} \frac{a_{\{i\}, n-1, 0}\, z^{\{i\}, n-1}}{\{i\}^2_{n-1} \mu^{\{i\}, n-1}} \right| +$$

$$+ \sum_{i_1=1}^{\infty} \left\{ \left| \frac{b_{i_1} z_1^{i_1}}{i_1^2 (\rho''_1)^{i_1}} \right| \left| \sum_{\{i\}=-\infty}^{\infty} \frac{a_{\{i\}, n-1, i_1}\, z^{\{i\}, n-1}}{\{i\}^2_{n-1} \mu^{\{i\}, n-1}} \right| \right\} +$$

$$+ \sum_{i_1=-1}^{-\infty} \left\{ \left| \frac{b_{i_1} z_1^{i_1}}{i_1^2 (r''_1)^{i_1}} \right| \left| \sum_{\{i\}=-\infty}^{\infty} \frac{a_{\{i\}, n-1, i_1}\, z^{\{i\}, n-1}}{\{i\}^2 \mu^{\{i\}, n-1}} \right| \right\} \leqslant$$

$$\leqslant |b_0 c| + \sum_{i_1=1}^{\infty} \left\{ \left| \frac{b_{i_1} z^{i_1}}{i_1^2 (\rho''_1)^{i_1}} \right| c \right\} + \sum_{i_1=-1}^{-\infty} \left\{ \left| \frac{b_{i_1} z_1^{i_1}}{i_1^2 (r''_1)^{i_1}} \right| c \right\} \leqslant$$

$$\leqslant c \left(\frac{1}{4} + \sum_{i_1=1}^{\infty} \frac{1}{4 i_1^2} + \sum_{i_1=-1}^{-\infty} \frac{1}{4 i_1^2} \right) \leqslant c$$

Q.E.D.

<u>Lemma 4</u>. Any function of the family $F^{r, n}_{\rho, c}$ belongs to the space $\Phi^{r, z_0}_{\rho, 0, c''_n}\left(c''_n = c \prod_{k=1}^{n} \frac{r''_k + 1}{r''_k}\right)$.

<u>Proof</u>. For $n = 1$ the lemma is obvious, since any function of the family $F^{r, n}_{\rho, c}$ can be represented in the form

$$f(z_1) = \sum_{i=-\infty}^{+\infty} c_i z_1^i$$

where $c_i = \frac{1}{2\pi i} \int_\gamma \frac{f(\zeta)\, d\zeta}{\zeta^{n+1}}$, $-\infty \leqslant i \leqslant \infty$ (γ is some contour of the complex plane z_1 embracing the point $z_1 = 0$ and lying inside the ring $B^{r''_1}_{\rho''_1}$), i.e.

$$|c_i| \leqslant \frac{c}{2\pi (\rho''_1)^{i+1}} \leqslant \frac{c''_1}{(\rho''_1)^i} \qquad (i = 0, 1, 2, \ldots),$$

$$|c_{-i}| \leqslant \frac{c (r''_1)^{i-1}}{2\pi} \leqslant c''_1 (r''_1)^i \qquad (i = 1, 2, \ldots),$$

where

$$c_1'' = \frac{c}{r_1''}(1 + r_1'')$$

Suppose that the relation

$$F_{\rho, c}^{r, n-1} \subset \Phi_{\rho, 0, c_{n-1}''}^{r, z_0}$$

is proved. We choose a function $f(z)$ of the family $F_{\rho, c}^{r, n}$. Since $f(z)$ is analytic, it can be expanded in a series

$$f(z) = \sum_{\{i\}=-\infty}^{+\infty} \frac{a_{\{i\}, n} z^{\{i\}, n}}{\mu^{\{i\}, n}}$$

which is absolutely convergent in the region $B_{\rho''}^{r''}$. Let us put $f(z)$ in the form

$$f(z) = f_0(z_2, z_3, \ldots, z_n) \frac{(1 + r_1'')}{r_1''} + \\ + \sum_{i=1}^{\infty} \left[\frac{f_i(z_2, z_3, \ldots, z_n)(1 + r_1'')}{r_1''} \frac{z_1^i}{(r_1'')^i} \right] + \\ + \sum_{i=-1}^{-\infty} \left[\frac{f_i(z_2, z_3, \ldots, z_n)(1 + r_1'')}{r_1''} \frac{z_1^i}{(\rho_1'')^i} \right]$$

From the original expansion of $f(z)$ it is not difficult to see that all the functions $\{f_i(z_2, z_3, \ldots, z_n)\}$ are analytic in the region $B_{\rho_2''}^{r_2''} \times B_{\rho_3''}^{r_3''} \times \ldots \times B_{\rho_n''}^{r_n''}$. Since the lemma has been proved for $n = 1$

$$\left| f_i(z_2, z_3, \ldots, z_n) \frac{(1 + r_1'')}{r_1''} \right| \leqslant c_1'' = \frac{c(r_1'' + 1)}{r_1''}$$

i.e. $|f_i(z_2, z_3, \ldots, z_n)| \leqslant c$. Therefore, by the induction hypothesis,

$$|a_{\{i\}, n}| = \left| b_{i_1, \{i\}, n-1} \frac{r_1'' + 1}{r_1''} \right| \leqslant c_{n-1}'' \frac{r_1'' + 1}{r_1''} = \\ = c \prod_{k=1}^{n} \frac{r_k'' + 1}{r_k''}$$

where $\{b_{i_1, \{i\}, n-1}\}$ are coefficients of the expansion

$$f_i(z_2, z_3, \ldots, z_n) = \sum_{i=-\infty}^{+\infty} \frac{b_{i_1\{i\}, n-1} z_2^{i_2} z_3^{i_3} \ldots z_n^{i_n}}{\mu\{i\}, n-1}$$

Q.E.D.

Theorem 1. The ε-entropy of the space $F_{\rho, c}^{r, n}$ is equal to

$$H_{\varepsilon}(F_{\rho, c}^{r, n}) = \frac{2}{(n+1)!} \prod_{k=1}^{n} \left(\frac{1}{\log \rho_k} + \frac{1}{\log r_k}\right)\left(\log \frac{c}{\varepsilon}\right)^{n+1} + \\ + O_F\left[\left(\log \frac{c}{\varepsilon}\right)^n \log\log \frac{c}{\varepsilon}\right]$$

and

$$\left|O_F\left[\left(\log \frac{c}{\varepsilon}\right)^n \log\log \frac{c}{\varepsilon}\right]\right| \leqslant B(r, \rho, c, n)\left(\log \frac{c}{\varepsilon}\right)^n \log\log \frac{c}{\varepsilon} + \\ + B(r, \rho, c, n)$$

The function $B(r, \rho, c, n) = B(r_1, r_2, \ldots, r_n; \rho_1, \rho_2, \ldots, \rho_n, c, n)$ possesses the property that for any fixed values $c > 0$ and $n > 0$ and for any $\delta > 0$ in the region $\{r_k \geqslant \delta, \rho_k \geqslant \delta\}$ $(k = 1, 2, \ldots, n)$ it is uniformly bounded by a constant which depends only on c, n and δ.

Proof. To begin with, we shall assume that all the numbers $r_1'', r_2'', \ldots, r_n''$ are greater than, say, the number 1. Since, from lemmas 3 and 4

$$\Phi_{\rho, 2, c_n'}^{r, z_0} \subset F_{\rho, c}^{r, n} \subset \Phi_{\rho, 0, c_n''}^{r, z_0}$$

from lemma 2 § 6 and lemma 2 § 9 we have

$$\frac{2}{(n+1)!} \prod_{k=1}^{n} \left(\frac{1}{\log \rho_k} + \frac{1}{\log r_k}\right)\left(\log \frac{c_n''}{\varepsilon}\right) + \\ + O\left[\left(\log \frac{c_n''}{\varepsilon}\right)^n \log\log \frac{c_n''}{\varepsilon}\right] \geqslant H_{\varepsilon}(F_{\rho, c}^{r, n}) \geqslant \\ \geqslant \frac{2}{(n+1)!} \prod_{k=1}^{n} \left(\frac{1}{\log \rho_k} + \frac{1}{\log r_k}\right)\left(\log \frac{c_n'}{\varepsilon}\right) + \\ + O\left[\left(\log \frac{c_n'}{\varepsilon}\right)^n \log\log \frac{c_n'}{\varepsilon}\right]$$

i.e.

$$H_\varepsilon(F^{r,\,n}_{\rho,\,c}) = \frac{2}{(n+1)!}\prod_{k=1}^{n}\left(\frac{1}{\log \rho_k} + \frac{1}{\log r_k}\right)\left(\log\frac{c}{\varepsilon}\right)^{n+1} + \\ + O_F\left[\left(\log\frac{c}{\varepsilon}\right)^n \log\log\frac{c}{\varepsilon}\right]$$

From the above lemmas it is not difficult to deduce that

$$\left|O_F\left[\left(\log\frac{c}{\varepsilon}\right)^n \log\log\frac{c}{\varepsilon}\right]\right| \leqslant \\ \leqslant B(r,\ \rho,\ c,\ n)\left(\log\frac{c}{\varepsilon}\right)^n \log\log\frac{c}{\varepsilon} + B(r,\ \rho,\ c,\ n)$$

where

$$B(r,\ \rho,\ c,\ n) = B(r_1,\ r_2,\ \ldots,\ r_n,\ \rho_1,\ \rho_2,\ \ldots,\ \rho_n,\ c,\ n)$$

is a function of the parameters c and n, which depends on $r_1, r_2, \ldots, r_n\ \rho_1, \rho_2, \ldots, \rho_n$ and is independent of the absolute values $r'_1, r'_2, \ldots, r'_n, r''_1, r''_2, \ldots, r''_n, \rho'_1, \rho'_2, \ldots, \rho'_n; \rho''_1, \rho''_2, \ldots, \rho''_n$.

In order to prove the theorem it only remains to lift th restriction $\{r''_k \geqslant 1\}$. To do this, let us consider the (inverse) transformation of the space E^z_n into itself, given by the equations $w_k = \frac{l}{z_k}$ $(k = 1,\ 2,\ \ldots,\ n;\ 0 < l < \infty)$. We put

$$\bar{r}''_k = \frac{l}{\rho''_k}; \quad \bar{r}'_k = \frac{l}{\rho'_k},$$

$$\bar{\rho}'_k = \frac{l}{r'_k}, \quad \bar{\rho}''_k = \frac{l}{r''_k}, \quad \bar{r}_k = \frac{\rho''_k}{\rho'_k}, \quad \bar{\rho}_k = \frac{r'_k}{r''_k},$$

$$\bar{\rho} = (\bar{\rho}_1,\ \bar{\rho}_2,\ \ldots,\ \bar{\rho}_n), \quad \bar{r} = (\bar{r}_1\ \bar{r}_2,\ \ldots,\ \bar{r}_n).$$

In this transformation, the regions $B^{r'}_{\rho'}$, $B^{r''}_{\rho''}$ go into the regi $B^{\bar{r}'}_{\bar{\rho}'}$; $B^{\bar{r}''}_{\bar{\rho}''}$ (respectively), and the space $F^{r,\,n}_{\rho,\,c}$ is then mapped into the space $F^{\bar{r},\,n}_{\bar{\rho},\,c}$, the function $f(z_1, z_2, \ldots, z_n)$ corresponds the function $f(w_1, w_2, \ldots, w_n)$ in such a way that

$$H_\varepsilon(F^{r,\,n}_{\rho,\,c}) = H_\varepsilon\left(F^{\bar{r},\,n}_{\bar{\rho},\,c}\right)$$

And since for any given set of numbers

$$0 \leqslant \bar{r}''_k < \bar{r}'_k \leqslant \bar{\rho}'_k < \bar{\rho}''_k < \infty \qquad (k = 1,\ 2,\ \ldots,\ n)$$

e can find a number l and numbers $1 < r''_k < r'_k \leqslant \rho'_k < \rho''_k \leqslant \infty$ $k = 1, 2, \ldots, n)$ such that

$$H_\varepsilon\left(F^{\bar{r}, n}_{\bar{\rho}, c}\right) = H_\varepsilon\left(F^{r, n}_{\rho, c}\right)$$

e can consider the proof of Theorem 1 to be complete.

orollary. Let $B^{\infty}_{\rho'}$ be the region of E^z_n, given by $|z_k| \leqslant \rho'_k$ $(k = 1, 2, \ldots, n;\ \rho' = (\rho'_1, \rho'_2, \ldots, \rho'_n))$, let $B^{\infty}_{\rho''}$ be the region $\{|z_k| \leqslant \rho''_k\}(\rho'' = (\rho''_1, \rho''_2, \ldots, \rho''_n));\ \rho''_k > \rho'_k$ $(k = 1, 2, \ldots, n)$, $F^{\infty, n}_{\rho, c}$ the space of functions analytic in $B^{\infty}_{\rho''}$, and bounded in this region (in modulus) by the constant c (for the norm in this space we shall take the maximum of the modulus of the function on the set $B^{\infty}_{\rho'}$). Then

$$H_\varepsilon\left(F^{\infty, n}_{\rho, c}\right) = \frac{2}{(n+1)!} \prod_{k=1}^{n} \frac{1}{\log \rho_k} \left(\log \frac{c}{\varepsilon}\right)^{n+1} + $$
$$+ O_F\left[\left(\log \frac{c}{\varepsilon}\right)^n \log\log \frac{c}{\varepsilon}\right],$$

where $\rho_k = \dfrac{\rho''_k}{\rho'_k}$.

roof. Putting $r''_k = 0$ $(k = 1, 2, \ldots, n)$ in Theorem 1, seeing hat value given there does not depend on $\{r'_k\}$, by putting $r'_k = 0$ $(k = 1, 2, 3, \ldots, n)$ we obtain the value we need.

heorem 2. (A.N. Kolmogorov) Let G_1 and G_2 be two bounded regions of E^z_n the first of which lies strictly inside the second, and let $F^{G_1}_{G_2, c}$ be the space of complex functions analytic in G_2, bounded on G_2 by the constant c (for the norm we take the maximum of the modulus of the function in the region G_1). Then for sufficiently small $\varepsilon > 0$

$$A(G_1, G_2)\left(\log \frac{c}{\varepsilon}\right)^{n+1} \leqslant H_\varepsilon\left(F^{G_1}_{G_2, c}\right) \leqslant B(G_1, G_2)\left(\log \frac{c}{\varepsilon}\right)^{n+1}$$

where $A(G_1, G_2)$, $B(G_1, G_2)$ are positive constants, independent of ε.

roof. Let us choose a set of regions in the space E^z_n, $\alpha_2;\ \sigma'_1, \sigma'_2, \ldots, \sigma'_q;\ \sigma''_1, \sigma''_2, \ldots, \sigma''_q$ of the type B^{∞}_{ρ} (see the corollary to Theorem 1), such that

$$\alpha_1 \subset G_1 \subset G_2 \subset \alpha_2$$

$$G_2 \supset \sum_{i=1}^{q} \sigma_i'' \supset \sum_{i=1}^{q} \sigma_i' \supset G_1$$

and such that each pair of regions

$$(\alpha_1, \alpha_2), (\sigma_1', \sigma_1''), (\sigma_2', \sigma_2'') \ldots (\sigma_q', \sigma_q'')$$

is concentric, in the sense that the projections of any pair are concentric circles on each of the co-ordinate planes z_k. By $F^{\alpha_1}_{\alpha_2, c}$ we denote the space of complex function analytic and bounded (in modulus) by the constant c in the region α_2 (the norm being the maximum of the modulus of the function on α_1); by $F_{i,c}$ the space of complex functions, analytic and bounded (in modulus) by the constant c in the region σ_i'' $(i = 1, 2, \ldots, q)$ (the norm being the maximum of the modulus of the function on σ_i', $i = 1, 2, \ldots, q$)). Since $F^{\alpha_1}_{\alpha_2, c} \subset F^{G_1}_{G_2, c}$ and since for any pair of functions $f_1(z)$ and $f_2(z)$ from $F^{\alpha_1}_{\alpha_2, c}$

$$\|f_1(z) - f_2(z)\|_{\alpha_1} \leqslant \|f_1(z) - f_2(z)\|_{G_1}$$

we have $h_\varepsilon(F^{\alpha_1}_{\alpha_2, c}) \leqslant h_\varepsilon(F^{G_1}_{G2, c})$.

By some given method, we establish a correspondence between any point of the region G_1 and the suffix (number) of one of the regions $\{\sigma_i'\}$ which covers the given point. Let σ_i^* be the set of all points of the region σ_i' having suffix i Then, the region G_1 can be decomposed into the subsets $\{\sigma_i^*\}$ $(i = 1, 2, \ldots, q)$ in such a way that $\sigma_i^* \subset \sigma_i'$ $(i = 1, 2, \ldots, q)$ and $\sum_{i=1}^{q} \sigma_i^* = G_1$. We denote by Φ the space of all complex functions defined on the region G_1 (the norm being the upper bound of the values of the modulus of the function on G_1). We choose a function $f(z)$ of the family $F^{G_1}_{G_2, c}$ and set some $\varepsilon > 0$. In each of the spaces $F_{i,c}$ we find the most economi ε-net $S_\varepsilon(F_{i,c})$ consisting of $N_\varepsilon(F_{i,c})$ elements f_j^i $(j = 1, 2, \ldots, N_\varepsilon(F_{i,c}))$ Let $f_{j_1, j_2, \ldots, j_q}$ be the function from the space Φ

which coincides on each of the sets σ_i^* with one of the functions f_j^i and which approximates everywhere on σ_i' (and therefore also on σ_i^*) to $f(z)$ with an accuracy of ε. We know that the functions $\{f_{j_1, j_2, \ldots, j_q}\}$ $(j_i = 1, 2, \ldots, N_\varepsilon(F_{i,c}),$ $i = 1, 2, \ldots, q)$ form an ε-net for the set $F_{G_2 c}^{G_1}$ in Φ. Therefore

$$H_\varepsilon(F_{G_2, c}^{G_1}) \leqslant \log \left[\prod_{i=1}^{q} N_\varepsilon(F_{i,c}) \right] =$$

$$= \sum_{i=1}^{q} H_\varepsilon(F_{i,c}) \leqslant B(G_1, G_2) \left(\log \frac{c}{\varepsilon} \right)^{n+1}$$

since for any i

$$H_\varepsilon(F_{i,c}) \leqslant b(\sigma_i', \sigma_i'') \left(\log \frac{c}{\varepsilon} \right)^{n+1}$$

(see the corollary to Theorem 1).

But it was shown above that

$$h_\varepsilon(F_{\alpha_2, c}^{\alpha_1}) \leqslant h_\varepsilon(F_{G_2, c}^{G_1})$$

i.e.

$$H_\varepsilon(F_{G_2, c}^{G_1}) \geqslant H_{2\varepsilon}(F_{\alpha_2, c}^{\alpha_1}) \geqslant A'(\alpha_1, \alpha_2) \left(\log \frac{c}{\varepsilon} \right)^{n+1} =$$

$$= A(G_1, G_2) \left(\log \frac{c}{\varepsilon} \right)^{n+1}$$

(see Theorem 1 § 6 and the corollary to Theorem 1 in this section). Q.E.D.

§ 10. The Entropy of the Space of Periodic Analytic Functions of Many Complex Variables

Let E_n^w be the space of n complex variables $w = (w_1, w_2, \ldots, w_n)$ $(w_k = u_k + iv_k)$; $P_{\alpha_k}^{\beta_k}$ be the strip of the complex plane w_k, given by $\alpha_k \leqslant v_k \leqslant \beta_k$; $P_\alpha^\beta = P_{\alpha_1, \alpha_2, \ldots, \alpha_n}^{\beta_1, \beta_2, \ldots, \beta_n} = P_{\alpha_1}^{\beta_1} \times P_{\alpha_2}^{\beta_2} \times \ldots \times P_{\alpha_n}^{\beta_n}$ be the closed region of E_n^w, given by $\alpha_k \leqslant v_k \leqslant \beta_k$ $(k = 1, 2, \ldots, n)$; $F_{d, c, 2\pi}^{\delta}$ be the space of all complex functions, analytic in the region $P_{d''}^{\delta''}$, 2π-periodic in the variable $\{u_k\}$, bounded in modulus in the region $P_{d''}^{\delta''}$ by the constant $c > 0$ (for the norm in this space we take the maximum of the modulus of the function in the region $P_{d'}^{\delta'}$) where

$$-\infty \leqslant d_k'' < d_k' \leqslant \delta_k' < \delta_k'' \leqslant +\infty \qquad (k = 1, 2, \ldots, n);$$

$$d' = (d_1', d_2', \ldots, d_n'), \quad d'' = (d_1'', d_2'', \ldots, d_n'');$$

$$d=(d_1, d_2, \ldots, d_n), \quad d_k = d'_k - d''_k \quad (k=1, 2, \ldots, n);$$
$$\delta'=(\delta'_1, \delta'_2, \ldots, \delta'_n), \quad \delta''=(\delta''_1, \delta''_2, \ldots, \delta''_n);$$
$$\delta=(\delta_1, \delta_2, \ldots, \delta_n), \quad \delta_k = \delta''_k - \delta'_k \quad (k=1, 2, \ldots, n).$$

We consider the transformation Ψ of the space E_n^w into the space E_n^z, given by the equations $z_k = e^{iw_k}$ $(k=1, 2, 3, \ldots, n)$. This transformation maps the region $P_{d'}^{\delta'}$ into the region $B_{\rho'}^{r'}$, and the region $P_{d''}^{\delta''}$ into $B_{\rho''}^{r''}$ in such a way that any straight line $v_k = \text{const}$ and $w_l = \text{const}$ $(l=1, 2, \ldots, k-1, k+1, \ldots, n)$ is transformed into a circle, and moreover, any half-interval of this straight line of length 2π is transformed into this circle in a one-to-one manner. $\left(r'_k = e^{-\delta'_k},\ r''_k = e^{-\delta''_k},\ \rho'_k = e^{-d'_k},\ \rho''_k = e^{-d''_k},\ r_k = e^{\delta_k},\ \rho_k = e^{d_k}\right)$. The transformation Ψ produces a linear, one-to-one mapping of the space $F_{d,c,2\pi}^{\delta}$ into the space $F_{\rho,c}^{r,n}$ (see notation of § 9) and, in particular, the function

$$f(e^{iw}) = f(e^{iw_1}, e^{iw_2}, \ldots, e^{iw_n})$$

corresponds to the function $f(x)$ of the family $F_{\rho,c}^{r,n}$.

It is not difficult to verify that in this correspondence

$$\|f(z)\|_{B_{\rho'}^{r'}} = \|f(e^{iw})\|_{P_{d'}^{\delta'}}$$

Therefore $H_\varepsilon(F_{d,c,2\pi}^{\delta}) = H_\varepsilon(F_{\rho,c}^{r,n})$, i.e. from Theorem 1 of the last section,

$$H_\varepsilon(F_{d,c,2\pi}^{\delta}) = \frac{2}{(n+1)!}\prod_{k=1}^{n}\left(\frac{1}{\log\rho_k}+\frac{1}{\log r_k}\right)\left(\log\frac{c}{\varepsilon}\right)^{n+1} +$$
$$+ O_F\left[\left(\log\frac{c}{\varepsilon}\right)^n \log\log\frac{c}{\varepsilon}\right] =$$
$$= \frac{2}{(n+1)!\,(\log e)^n}\prod_{k=1}^{n}\left(\frac{1}{d_k}+\frac{1}{\delta_k}\right)\left(\log\frac{c}{\varepsilon}\right)^{n+1} +$$
$$+ O_F\left[\left(\log\frac{c}{\varepsilon}\right)^n \log\log\frac{c}{\varepsilon}\right].$$

Thus, taking into account the value of the remainder term

$$O_F\left[\left(\log\frac{c}{\varepsilon}\right)^n \log\log\frac{c}{\varepsilon}\right]$$

(see Theorem 1 § 9) we obtain the following theorem:

Theorem 1. The absolute ε-entropy of the space $F^{\delta}_{d,c,2\pi}$ is equal to

$$H_\varepsilon\left(F^{\delta}_{d,c,2\pi}\right) = \frac{2}{(n+1)!\,(\log e)^n}\prod_{k=1}^{n}\left(\frac{1}{d_k}+\frac{1}{\delta_k}\right)\left(\log\frac{c}{\varepsilon}\right)^{n+1} + \\ + O_F\left[\left(\log\frac{c}{\varepsilon}\right)^n \log\log\frac{c}{\varepsilon}\right]$$

where

$$\left|O_F\left[\left(\log\frac{c}{\varepsilon}\right)^n \log\log\frac{c}{\varepsilon}\right]\right| \leqslant B'(d,\delta,c,n) + \\ + B'(d,\delta,c,n)\left(\log\frac{c}{\varepsilon}\right)^n \log\log\frac{c}{\varepsilon}$$

(Here $B'(d,\delta,c,n) = B(e^d, e^\delta, c, n)$, see Theorem 1 § 9).

§ 11. The Entropy of the Space of Real Analytic Periodic Functions of Many Variables

Let $F_{d,c,2\pi}$ denote the space of real functions of n real variables $u_1, u_2, \ldots, u_n$, 2π-periodic (in each of the variables) and analytic (in the space E_n), having analytic continuations in the regions

$$P_d = P^{d}_{-d} = P^{d_1}_{-d_1}\times P^{d_2}_{-d_2}\times P^{d_3}_{-d_3}\times \ldots \times P^{d_n}_{-d_n}$$

(where $P^{d_k}_{-d_k}$ is the strip of the complex plane $w_k = u_k + iv_k$, given by $-d_k \leqslant v_k \leqslant d_k$), bounded (in absolute magnitude) in P_d by the constant $c > 0$; let $F^{+}_{d,c,2\pi}$ denote the subspace of all even* functions of $F_{d,c,2\pi}$; and $\Phi_{d,m,c}$ the space of

---

* In this case a function is said to be even if, for any

$$f(u_1, u_2, \ldots u_{k-1}, u_k, u_{k+1}, \ldots, u_n) \equiv \\ \equiv f(u_1, u_2, \ldots u_{k-1}, -u_k, u_{k+1}, \ldots, u_n)$$

The Fourier series of an even function has non-zero coefficients for the expressions $\cos l_1u_1 \cos l_2u_2 \ldots \cos l_nu_n$ only.

functions which can be represented on E_n in the form

$$f(u)=\sum_{p=0}^{\infty}\sum_{i_1\geq 0}^{i_1+i_2+\ldots+i_n=p}\sum_{i_2\geq 0}\cdots\sum_{i_n\geq 0}\frac{a_{i_1,i_2,\ldots,i_n}g_1^{i_1}g_2^{i_2}\cdots g_n^{i_n}}{(p+1)^m e^{d_1i_1}e^{d_2i_2}\cdots e^{d_ni_n}}$$

where $\{a_{i_1,i_2,\ldots,i_n}\}$ are real numbers bounded in absolute magnitude by the constant c, and $g_k^{i_k}$ is either $\sin l_k u_k$ or $\cos l_k u_k$.

As the norm in each of these spaces, we take the maximum of the modulus of the function for all real values of its arguments.

We first consider the evaluation of the absolute ε-entropy of the space $F^+_{d,c,2\pi}$.

<u>Lemma 1</u>. Any function of the space $F^+_{d,c,2\pi}$ belongs to the space $\Phi^+_{d_1-n,c''_n}$, where

$$c''_n=c\prod_{k=1}^{n}\frac{e^{-d_k}+1}{e^{-d_k}}$$

<u>Proof</u>. We choose a function $f(u)$ of the space $F^+_{d,c,2\pi}$, and consider its Fourier series

$$\sum_{p=0}^{\infty}\sum_{i_1\geq 0}^{i_1+i_2+\ldots+i_n=p}\sum_{i_2\geq 0}\cdots\sum_{i_n\geq 0}\frac{a'_{i_1,i_2,\ldots,i_n}\cos l_1u_1\cos l_2u_2\ldots\cos l_nu_n}{e^{d_1i_1}e^{d_2i_2}\ldots e^{d_ni_n}}$$

where

$$a_{i_1,i_2,\ldots,i_n}=b_{i_1,i_2,\ldots,i_n}e^{d_1i_1}e^{d_2i_2}\ldots e^{d_ni_n}$$

($b_{i_1,i_2,\ldots,i_n}$ is the corresponding Fourier coefficient). Since $f(u)$ is analytic, its Fourier series converges absolutely to itself everywhere on E_n (see [11]). The transformation Ψ (see § 10) will make the function $\varphi(z)=\varphi(e^{iw})=f(w)$, which is analytic in the region

$$B^{r''}_{\rho''}=B^{r''_1}_{\rho''_1}\times B^{r''_2}_{\rho''_2}\times\ldots\times B^{r''_n}_{\rho''_n}\qquad(\rho''_k=e^{d_k};\ r''_k=e^{-d_k})$$

nd bounded in this region by the constant c, correspond o $f(u)'$. From Lemma 4 § 9,

$$\varphi(z)=\sum_{\{i\}=-\infty}^{+\infty}\frac{a'_{\{i\},n}z^{\{i\},n}}{\mu^{\{i\},n}}$$

see § 9), where

$$|a'_{\{i\},n}|\leqslant c''_n=c\prod_{k=1}^{n}\left(\frac{r''_k+1}{r''_k}\right)$$

.e.

$$\varphi(z)=\sum_{i_1=-\infty}^{+\infty}\sum_{i_2=-\infty}^{+\infty}\cdots\sum_{i_n=-\infty}^{+\infty}\frac{a'_{i_1,i_2,\ldots,i_n}z_1^{i_1}z_2^{i_2}\ldots z_n^{i_n}}{\rho_1^{i_1}\rho_2^{i_2}\ldots\rho_n^{i_n}}$$

ince in this case $\rho'_k=r'_k=1$ and $\rho_k=\frac{1}{r_k}$. But since $_k=\rho''_k=e^{d_k}$,

$$f(w)=\sum_{\{i\}=-\infty}^{\infty}\frac{a'_{\{i\},n}(e^{iw})^{\{i\},n}}{(e^{d})^{\{i\},n}}=$$

$$=\sum_{i_1=-\infty}^{+\infty}\sum_{i_2=-\infty}^{+\infty}\cdots\sum_{i_n=-\infty}^{+\infty}\frac{a'_{i_1,i_2,\ldots,i_n}e^{ii_1w_1}e^{ii_2w_2}\ldots e^{ii_nw_n}}{e^{i_1d_1}e^{i_2d_2}\ldots e^{i_nd_n}}$$

Using Euler's formula, we replace $e^{ii_kw_k}$ by $\cos i_kw_k+i\sin i_kw_k$ nd collect similar terms, obtaining

$$f(w)=\sum_{p=0}^{\infty}\sum_{i_1\geqslant 0}\sum_{i_2\geqslant 0}\cdots\sum_{i_n\geqslant 0}^{i_1+i_2+\ldots+i_n=p}\frac{c_{i_1,i_2,\ldots,i_n}g_1^{i_1}g_2^{i_2}\ldots g_n^{i_n}}{e^{d_1i_1}e^{d_2i_2}\ldots e^{d_ni_n}}+$$

$$+i\sum_{p=0}^{\infty}\sum_{i_1\geqslant 0}\sum_{i_2\geqslant 0}\cdots\sum_{i_n\geqslant 0}^{i_1+i_2+\ldots+i_n=p}\frac{c_{i_1,i_2,\ldots,i_n}g_1^{i_1}g_2^{i_2}\ldots g_n^{i_n}}{e^{d_1i_1}e^{d_2i_2}\ldots e^{d_ni_n}}$$

here $|c_{i_1,i_2,\ldots,i_n}|\leqslant c''_n(p+1)^n$. But since on E_n the function $(w)=f(u)$ is real,

$$f(u)=\sum_{p=0}^{\infty}\sum_{i_1\geqslant 0}\sum_{i_2\geqslant 0}\cdots\sum_{i_n\geqslant 0}^{i_1+i_2+\ldots+i_n=p}\frac{c_{i_1,i_2,\ldots,i_n}g_1^{i_1}(u_1)\,g_2^{i_2}(u_2)\ldots g_n^{i_n}(u_n)}{e^{d_1i_1}e^{d_2i_2}\ldots e^{d_ni_n}}=$$

$$=\sum_{p=0}^{\infty}\sum_{i_1\geqslant 0}\sum_{i_2\geqslant 0}\cdots\sum_{i_n\geqslant 0}^{i_1+i_2+\ldots+i_n=p}\frac{a_{i_1,i_2,\ldots,i_n}\cos i_1u_1\cos i_2u_2\ldots\cos i_nu_n}{e^{d_1i_1}e^{d_2i_2}\ldots e^{d_ni_n}}$$

(from the theorem about the unique expansion of a function in a series of orthogonal functions). And since

$$|c_{i_1, i_2, \dots, i_n}| = |a_{i_1, i_2, \dots, i_n}| \leqslant c''_n (p+1)^n$$

$$f(u) = \sum_{p=0}^{\infty} \sum_{i_1 \geqslant 0} \sum_{i_2 \geqslant 0} \cdots \sum_{i_n \geqslant 0}^{i_1+i_2+\dots+i_n=p} \frac{a''_{i_1, i_2, \dots, i_n} \cos l_1 u_1 \cos l_2 u_2 \dots \cos l_n u_n}{(p+1)^{-n} e^{d_1 i_1} e^{d_2 i_2} \dots e^{d_n i_n}}$$

where $a''_{i_1, i_2, \dots, i_n}$ are real numbers bounded in absolute magnitu by the constant c''_n. But

$$c''_n = c \prod_{k=1}^{n} \frac{r''_k + 1}{r''_k} = c \prod_{k=1}^{n} \frac{e^{-d_k} + 1}{e^{-d_k}}$$

Q.E.D.

Lemma 2. Any function of the space $\Phi^+_{d, n+2, \frac{c}{2}}$ belongs to th family $F^+_{d, c, 2\pi}$.

Proof. We choose a function $f(u)$ of the family $\Phi^+_{d, n+2, \frac{c}{2}}$, and evaluate the modulus of its analytic continuation $f(w)$: the region P_d. We have

$$|f(w)| = \left| \sum_{p=0}^{\infty} \sum_{i_1 \geqslant 0} \sum_{i_2 \geqslant 0} \cdots \sum_{i_n \geqslant 0}^{i_1+i_2+\dots+i_n=p} \frac{a_{i_1, i_2, \dots, i_n}}{(p+1)^{n+2}} \prod_{k=1}^{n} \frac{\cos l_k w_k}{e^{d_k i_k}} \right| \leqslant$$

$$\leqslant \sum_{p=0}^{\infty} \sum_{i_1 \geqslant 0} \sum_{i_2 \geqslant 0} \cdots \sum_{i_n \geqslant 0}^{i_1+i_2+\dots+i_n=p} \frac{a_{i_1, i_2, \dots, i_n}}{(p+1)^{n+2}} \prod_{k=1}^{n} \frac{|e^{i i_k w_k}|}{e^{d_k i_k}} \leqslant$$

$$\leqslant \sum_{p=0}^{\infty} \sum_{i_1 \geqslant 0} \sum_{i_2 \geqslant 0} \cdots \sum_{i_n \geqslant 0}^{i_1+i_2+\dots+i_n=p} \frac{|a_{i_1, i_2, \dots, i_n}|}{(p+1)^{n+2}} \leqslant \sum_{p=0}^{\infty} \frac{c}{2(p+1)^2} \leqslant c$$

It is easily seen from the definition of $f(u)$ that it is an even function. Q.E.D.

Lemma 3. The absolute ε-entropy of the space $\Phi_{d, m, c}$ is equal to

$$H_{\varepsilon}(\Phi_{d,m,c}) = \frac{1}{(n+1)!\,(\log e)^n} \prod_{k=1}^{n} \frac{1}{d_k} \left(\log \frac{c}{\varepsilon}\right)^{n+1} + O_{\Phi}\left[\left(\log \frac{c}{\varepsilon}\right)^n \log\log \frac{c}{\varepsilon}\right]$$

The proof of this lemma is almost a word-for-word repetition of the reasoning used in calculating the ε-entropy of the space $\Phi^{r,\Phi_0}_{\rho,m,c}$ of Laurent series (see § §8,9). Therefore we shall only spend time on the essential parts of the proof. Let $\Phi^{\Phi_0}_{d,m,c}$ denote the space of series of the form

$$f(u_0\alpha) = \sum_{p=0}^{\infty} \frac{a_p(\alpha)\cos pu_0}{e^d\,(p+1)^m}$$

where Φ_0 is some space of functions defined on the set A $(\alpha \in A)$ and a_p is a function of Φ_0.

Just as in Lemma 6 § 8, we can show that

$$H_{\varepsilon}(\Phi^{\Phi_0}_{d,m,c}) = \sum_{i=0}^{p(\varepsilon)} H_{\delta_i^{\varepsilon}}(\Phi_0)$$

where $p(\varepsilon) = \log_{e^d}\left(\frac{c}{\varepsilon}\right) + O_p\left(\log\log\frac{c}{\varepsilon}\right)$ and $\delta_i^{\varepsilon} = \varepsilon e^{d,i}\lambda_p(\varepsilon)$ is a function whose orders of increase and decrease are as $\left(\log\frac{1}{\varepsilon}\right)^{4m}$ and $\left(\log\frac{1}{\varepsilon}\right)^{-4m}$. To prove this, we need only make use of two properties of the function $\cos ku_0$, namely, in calculating the lower estimate for the quantity $H_{\varepsilon}(\Phi_{d,m,c})$) we need only know that any trigonometric polynomial of order p of the form $\sum_{k=0}^{p} a_k \cos ku_0$ differs from zero by not less than $|a_p|$ on the u_0-axis, and in calculating the upper estimate for the quantity $H_{\varepsilon}(\Phi^{\Phi}_{d,m,c})$ it is sufficient to know that for real u_0 $|\cos ku_0| \leqslant 1$. Taking the equation

$$H_{\varepsilon}(\Phi^{\Phi_0}_{d,m,c}) = \sum_{i=0}^{p(\varepsilon)} H_{\delta_i^{\varepsilon}}(\Phi_0)$$

as proved as in the lemma of § 9, we can show that

$$H_\varepsilon(\Phi_{d,m,c}) = \frac{1}{(n+1)!\,(\log e)^n} \prod_{k=1}^{n} \frac{1}{d_k} \left(\log \frac{c}{\varepsilon}\right)^{n+1} + \\ + O_\Phi\left[\left(\log \frac{c}{\varepsilon}\right)^n \log\log \frac{c}{\varepsilon}\right]$$

Collecting the results of Lemmas 1, 2, 3 we obtain the following theorem:

Theorem 1. The absolute ε-entropy of the space $F^+_{d,c,2\pi}$ is equal to

$$H_\varepsilon(F^+_{d,c,2\pi}) = \frac{1}{(n+1)!\,(\log e)^n} \prod_{k=1}^{n'} \frac{1}{d_k} \left(\log \frac{c}{\varepsilon}\right)^{n+1} + \\ + O_F\left[\left(\log \frac{c}{\varepsilon}\right)^n \log\log \frac{c}{\varepsilon}\right]$$

By proving assertions analogous to Lemmas 1, 2, and 3 for the spaces $\Phi_{d,m,c}$ and $F_{d,c,2\pi}$, i.e. by repeating almost word-for-word the proof of Theorem 1, we obtain:

Theorem 2. The absolute ε-entropy of the space $F_{d,c,2\pi}$ is equal to

$$H_\varepsilon(F_{d,c,2\pi}) = \frac{2^n}{(n+1)!\,(\log e)^n} \prod_{k=1}^{n} \frac{1}{d_k} \left(\log \frac{c}{\varepsilon}\right)^{n+1} + \\ + O_F\left[\left(\log \frac{c}{\varepsilon}\right)^n \log\log \frac{c}{\varepsilon}\right]$$

(see the notation at the beginning of this section).

§ 12. The Entropy of the Space of Real Analytic Functions of Many Variables

Let $F^{-1,1}_{\rho,c} = F^{-1,1}_{\rho_1,\rho_2,\dots,\rho_n,c}$ denote the space of functions analytic on the n-dimensional closed cube $J_n \subset E_n \subset E^z_n$ $\{-1 \leqslant x_k \leqslant 1\}$ $(k = 1, 2, \dots, n)$ having analytic continuations in the region $\partial_\rho = \partial_{\rho_1} \times \partial_{\rho_2} \times \dots \times \partial_{\rho_n} \subset E^z_n$, which are bounded in modulus in this region by the constant $c > 0$, where ∂_{ρ_k} i the region of the complex plane $z_k = x_k + iy_k$ bounded by the ellipse with semi-major axis ρ_k and with foci at the points —1, 1 of the real axis ($k=1,2,\ldots,n$).

Theorem 1. The absolute ε-entropy of the space $F_{\rho, c}^{-1, 1}$ is equal to

$$H_{\varepsilon}(F_{\rho, c}^{-1, 1})=\frac{1}{(n+1)!}\prod_{k=1}^{n}\frac{1}{\log\rho_k}\left(\log\frac{c}{\varepsilon}\right)^{n+1}+ \\ +O_F\left[\left(\log\frac{c}{\varepsilon}\right)^{n}\log\log\frac{c}{\varepsilon}\right]$$

Proof. Consider the transformation Ψ' of the space E_n^w into the space E_n^z, given by the equations

$$z_k=\cos w_k \qquad (k=1, 2, \ldots, n)$$

This transformation maps the region $P_d = P_{d_1}\times P_{d_2}\times \ldots \times P_{d_n}$ (see the notation of § 10) into the region $\mathcal{E}_\rho=\mathcal{E}_{\rho_1}\times\mathcal{E}_{\rho_2}\times \ldots \times\mathcal{E}_{\rho_n}$ (where $\rho_k=e^{d_k}$), and the real plane E_n of E_n^w into the cube J_n. The mapping Ψ' is not single-valued: the point $z=\cos w=\cos(-w)$ corresponds to the points w and $-w$. However, the transformation Ψ' maps any pair of points a, b, for which, for some k $|v_k(a)|\neq|v_k(b)|$, into different points of E_n^z. We note further that Ψ' is 2π-periodic along each of the axes $u_1, u_2, \ldots, u_n$. It produces a linear mapping of the space $F_{d, c, 2\pi}^{+}$ (see § 11) into the space $F_{\rho, c}^{-1, 1}$ ($\rho_k=d^{d_k}$, $k=1, 2, \ldots, n$) with the same norm

$$\|f(z)\|_{J_n}=\|f(w)\|_{E_n}$$

Hence

$$H_{\varepsilon}(F_{\rho, c}^{-1, 1})=H_{\varepsilon}(F_{d, c, 2\pi}^{+})=$$
$$=\frac{1}{(n+1)!}\prod_{k=1}^{n}\frac{1}{\log\left(e^{d_k}\right)}\left(\log\frac{c}{\varepsilon}\right)^{n+1}+O_F\left[\left(\log\frac{c}{\varepsilon}\right)^{n}\log\log\frac{c}{\varepsilon}\right]=$$
$$=\frac{1}{(n+1)!}\prod_{k=1}^{n}\frac{1}{\log\rho_k}\left(\log\frac{c}{\varepsilon}\right)^{n+1}+O_F\left[\left(\log\frac{c}{\varepsilon}\right)^{n}\log\log\frac{c}{\varepsilon}\right]$$

Q.E.D.

Let $J_n^{a, b}$ denote the n-dimensional parallelepiped in E_n^z, given by $a_k \leqslant x_k \leqslant b_k$ $(k=1, 2, \ldots, n)$. Let $\mathcal{E}_{\rho_k}^{a_k, b_k}$ be the region of the complex plane z_k bounded by the ellipse with semi-major axis ρ_k and with foci at the points a_k, b_k of the real axis; let $F_{\rho, c}^{a, b}$ be the space of real functions, analytic on $J_n^{a, b}$, and such that the modulus of their analytic continuations in the region $\mathcal{E}_{\rho}^{a, b} = \mathcal{E}_{\rho_1}^{a_1, b_1} \times \mathcal{E}_{\rho_2}^{a_2, b_2} \times \ldots \times \mathcal{E}_{\rho_n}^{a_n, b_n}$ is bounded by the constant $c > 0$ (for the norm in this space we take the maximum of the modulus of the function on the parallelepiped $J_n^{a, b}$).

<u>Theorem 2</u>. The absolute ε-entropy of the space is equal to

$$H_{\varepsilon}(F_{\rho, c}^{a, b}) = \frac{1}{(n+1)!} \prod_{k=1}^{n} \frac{1}{\log\left(\frac{2}{b_k - a_k}\rho_k\right)} \left(\log \frac{c}{\varepsilon}\right)^{n+1} + \\ + O_F\left[\left(\log \frac{c}{\varepsilon}\right)^n \log\log \frac{c}{\varepsilon}\right]$$

Theorem 2 reduces to Theorem 1 by the linear transformation (with the same norm) of the space $F_{\rho, c}^{a, b}$ into $F_{\rho', c}^{-1, 1}$, given as follows: the function

$$f\left(\frac{2(z-a)}{b-a} - 1\right) \quad \left(z'_k = \frac{2(z_k - a_k)}{b_k - a_k} - 1, \quad k = 1, 2, \ldots, n\right)$$

of $F_{\rho, c}^{a, b}$ corresponds to $f(z)'$ of $F_{\rho', c}^{-1, 1}$.

§ 13. <u>The Entropy of the Space of Integral Functions</u>

Let A be a set, and Φ_0 some compact space, consisting of complex functions defined on the set A (the norm being the maximum of the modulus of the function on A). Let $\Phi_{l, m}^{\rho, \Phi_0}$ the the space of functions of the form

$$f(\alpha, z_1) = a_0(\alpha) + \sum_{p=1}^{\infty} \frac{a_p(\alpha)\rho^p}{p^{lp+m}} z_1^p$$

(where $\alpha \in A$; $l > 0$, $\rho > 0$ and m is an arbitrary real number) defined on the set $A \times E_1^{z_1}$, where $\{a_p(\alpha)\}$ are functions from Φ_0 (for the norm in the space $\Phi_{l, m}^{\rho, \Phi_0}$ we take the maximum of the modulus of the function on the set $A \times B_1^0$, where B_1^0 is the circle of the complex plane $E_1^{z_1}$ $(0 \leqslant |z| \leqslant 1)$.

Lemma 1. The modulus of any polynomial

$$f(z_1) = \sum_{i=0}^{p} a_i z_1^i$$

(where $\{a_i$ are complex numbers) on the circle $B_r^0 \{0 \leqslant |z_1| \leqslant r\}$ differs from zero by not less than $|a_p| r^p$.

Proof. The transformation Ψ (see § 8) maps the circle B_r^0 into the half-plane $y' \geqslant -\ln r$. On this half-plane the modulus of the function $f(e^{i, z'}) = \sum_{k=0}^{p} a_k e^{ikz'}$ differs from zero by not less than $\sqrt{|a_p|^2 e^{2p \ln r}} = |a_p| e^{p \ln r}$ (see Lemma 1 § 8).

Hence, on the circle B_r^0 $|f(z_1)|$ differs from zero by not less than $|a_p| r^p$.

Q.E.D.

Lemma 2. For sufficiently small ε, the absolute ε-entropy of the space $\Phi_{l, m}^{\rho, \Phi_0}$ is equal to

$$H_\varepsilon(\Phi_{l, m}^{\rho, \Phi_0}) = \sum_{i=0}^{p(\varepsilon)} H_{\delta_i^\varepsilon}(\Phi_0)$$

where

$$p(\varepsilon) = \frac{\log \frac{c}{\varepsilon}}{l \log \log \frac{c}{\varepsilon}} (1 + O_\Phi) \qquad (\lim_{\varepsilon \to 0} O_\Phi = 0)$$

$$\delta_i^\varepsilon = \frac{\varepsilon l^{li+m}}{\rho^i} \lambda(\varepsilon)$$

$\left(3 \geqslant \lambda(\varepsilon) \geqslant \frac{l \log \log \frac{c}{\varepsilon}}{\log \frac{c}{\varepsilon}} B\right.$, where B is an absolute constant$\left.\right)$.

Proof. Let us choose the numbers $p, \delta_0, \delta_1, \ldots, \delta_p$ so that

$$\delta_i \leqslant D(\Phi_0); \quad \delta_i = \frac{\delta l^{li+m}}{\rho^i} \qquad (l = 0, 1, 2, \ldots, p)$$

and the number

$$\delta < \frac{D(\Phi_0)\rho^p}{p^{lp+m}}$$

where $D(\Phi_0)$ is the one-dimensional diameter of the space Φ_0 Let $a_i^j(\alpha)$ $\left(j = 1, 2, \ldots, n_{\frac{\delta_i}{2}}(\Phi_0)\right)$ be a collection of functions of Φ_0 which form in Φ_0 the maximal set $S_{\frac{\delta_i}{2}}(\Phi_0)$ of elements which are further apart than δ_i from one another. We put

$$f_{j_0, j_1, j_2, \ldots, j_p}(\alpha, z) = a_0^{j_0}(\alpha) + \sum_{i=1}^{p} \frac{a_i^{ji}(\alpha)\rho^i z_1^i}{l^{li+m}}$$

$$\left(j_i = 1, 2, \ldots, n_{\frac{\delta_i}{2}}(\Phi_0); \quad i = 0, 1, 2, \ldots, p\right)$$

It is not difficult to see that the number σ_p^δ of functions $\{f_{j,j_1,j_2,\ldots,j_p}(\alpha, z)\}$ is equal to

$$\sigma_p^\delta = \prod_{i=0}^{p} n_{\frac{\delta_i}{2}}(\Phi_0)$$

Taking two concrete values of the pair δ and p, we then obtain the required estimates for the ε-entropy of the space $\Phi_{l,m}^{\rho,\Phi_0}$.

In order to obtain a lower estimate for $H_\varepsilon(\Phi_{l,m}^{\rho,\Phi_0})$ we put $\delta = 3\varepsilon$, and take p to be the maximum whole number satisfying the inequality

$$3\varepsilon \leqslant \frac{D(\Phi_0)\rho^p}{p^{lp+m}}$$

We can show that

$$p = \frac{\log \frac{c}{\varepsilon}}{l \log\log \frac{c}{\varepsilon}}[1 + \mu(\varepsilon)]$$

where $\mu(\varepsilon)$ is a function of ε which tends to zero as $\varepsilon \to 0$.

Let $f_1(\alpha, z_1)$ and $f_2(\alpha_1, z_2)$ be two different functions of the type

$$f_{j_0, j_1, j_2, \ldots, j_p}(\alpha, z)$$

Then their difference can be put in the form

$$f_1(\alpha, z_1) - f_2(\alpha, z_1) = b_0(\alpha) + \sum_{i=1}^{p} \frac{b_i(\alpha)\rho^i z_1^i}{i^{li+m}}$$

and, moreover, the coefficients $\{b_i(\alpha)\}$ are such that for any i $\max_A |b_i(\alpha)|$ is either equal to zero, or greater than $\delta_i = \frac{\delta i^{li+m}}{\rho^i}$. Therefore we can find a point $\alpha_0 \in A$ such that for some $k \leqslant p$ $|b_k(\alpha_0)| \geqslant \delta_k$ and $|b_i(\alpha_0)| = 0$ for any $i > k$. And since the coefficient of z_1^k in the polynomial $f_1(\alpha_0, z_1) - f_2(\alpha_0, z_1)$ is equal to $\frac{b_k(\alpha_0)\rho^k}{k^{lk+m}} \geqslant 3\varepsilon$, then, from Lemma 1,

$$\max_{B_1^0} |f_1(\alpha_0, z_1) - f_2(\alpha_0, z_1)| \geqslant 3\varepsilon$$

i.e. the functions $\{f_{j_0, j_1, j_2, \ldots, j_p}(\alpha, z)\}$ form a set of elements in $\Phi_{l, m}^{\rho, \Phi_0}$ which are further than 2ε apart (in pairs). Hence (see Lemma 3 § 5 and Theorem 1 § 5)

$$H_\varepsilon(\Phi_{l, m}^{\rho, \Phi_0}) \geqslant \sum_{i=0}^{p} \log \left[n_{\frac{\delta_i}{2}}(\Phi_0) \right] = \sum_{i=0}^{p} h_{\frac{\delta_i}{2}}(\Phi_0) \geqslant \sum_{i=0}^{p} H_{\delta_i}(\Phi_0)$$

where

$$\delta_i = \frac{3\varepsilon i^{li+m}}{\rho^i} \left(i = 0, 1, 2, \ldots, p, \ p = \frac{\log \frac{c}{\varepsilon}}{l \log\log \frac{c}{\varepsilon}} (1 + \mu(\varepsilon)) \right)$$

Let us now find the least whole number p such that $\sum_{i=p+1}^{\infty} \frac{c\rho^i}{i^{li+m}} \leqslant \frac{1}{2}\varepsilon$ and put $\delta = \frac{\varepsilon}{2(p+1)}$. In this case it is not too difficult to show that

$$p = \frac{\log \frac{c}{\varepsilon}}{l \log\log \frac{c}{\varepsilon}} (1 + \nu(\varepsilon))$$

where $\nu(\varepsilon)$ is a function of ε, tending to zero as $\varepsilon \to 0$. For fixed δ and p the functions $\{f_{j_0, j_1, j_2, \ldots, j_p}(\alpha, z)\}$ form an ε-net in the space $\Phi_{l, m}^{\rho, \Phi_0}$.

Hence

$$H_{\varepsilon}\left(\Phi_{l,\,m}^{\rho,\,\Phi_0}\right) \leqslant \log \sigma_p^{\delta} \leqslant \sum_{i=0}^{p} H_{\delta_i}(\Phi_0)$$

where $\delta_i = \dfrac{\varepsilon^{li+m}}{2(p+1)\rho^i}$. Combining the estimates we have obtained we have

$$H_{\varepsilon}\left(\Phi_{l,\,m}^{\rho,\,\Phi_0}\right) = \sum_{i=0}^{p(\varepsilon)} H_{\delta_i^{\varepsilon}}(\Phi_0)$$

where

$$p(\varepsilon) = \frac{\log \frac{c}{\varepsilon}}{l \log\log \frac{c}{\varepsilon}}(1 + O_{\Phi}) \qquad \left(\lim_{\varepsilon \to 0} O_{\Phi} = 0\right)$$

and

$$\delta_i^{\varepsilon} = \frac{\varepsilon^{li+m}}{\rho^i}\lambda(\varepsilon)$$

$\left(3 \geqslant \lambda(\varepsilon) \geqslant \dfrac{l \log\log \frac{c}{\varepsilon}}{\log \frac{c}{\varepsilon}} B\right.$ where B is an absolute constant).

Q.E.D.

Lemma 3. If A is a set consisting of one point, and Φ_0 is the set of complex numbers whose modulus does not exceed the constant c, then

$$H_{\varepsilon}\left(\Phi_{l,\,m}^{\rho,\,\Phi_0}\right) = \frac{\left(\log \frac{c}{\varepsilon}\right)^2}{l \log\log \frac{c}{\varepsilon}} + O_{\Phi}\left[\frac{\left(\log \frac{c}{\varepsilon}\right)^2 \log\log\log \frac{c}{\varepsilon}}{\left(\log\log \frac{c}{\varepsilon}\right)^2}\right]$$

Proof. From the previous lemma

$$H_{\varepsilon}\left(\Phi_{l,\,m}^{\rho,\,z_0}\right) = \sum_{i=0}^{p(\varepsilon)} H_{\delta_i^{\varepsilon}}(z_0) = \sum_{i=1}^{p(\varepsilon)} = 2\log\frac{1}{\delta_i^{\varepsilon}} + O\left(\log\frac{1}{\varepsilon}\right)$$

(see Theorem 2 § 6). But

$$\delta_i^{\varepsilon} = \frac{\varepsilon^{li+m}}{\rho^i}$$

(see Lemma 2), and hence

$$H_\varepsilon(\Phi_{l,\,m}^{\rho,\,z_0}) = \frac{2\left(\log\frac{c}{\varepsilon}\right)^2}{l\log\log\frac{c}{\varepsilon}} + 2\sum_{i=1}^{p(\varepsilon)}\log\frac{\rho^i}{i^{li+m}} + O\left(\log\frac{1}{\varepsilon}\right)$$

We evaluate the second term:

$$\sum_{i=1}^{p(\varepsilon)}\log\frac{\rho^i}{i^{li+m}} = \sum_{i=1}^{p(\varepsilon)}\log\frac{1}{i^{li}} + \sum_{i=1}^{p(\varepsilon)} i\log\rho + \sum_{i=1}^{p(\varepsilon)} m\log\frac{1}{i} =$$

$$= l\sum_{i=1}^{p(\varepsilon)} i\log\frac{1}{i} + (\log\rho)\frac{p(\varepsilon)+1}{2}p(\varepsilon) - m\log[p(\varepsilon)!] =$$

$$= l\sum_{i=1}^{p(\varepsilon)} i\log\frac{1}{i} + O\left[\frac{\left(\log\frac{1}{\varepsilon}\right)^2}{\left(\log\log\frac{1}{\varepsilon}\right)^2}\right] =$$

$$= -l\int_2^{p(\varepsilon)} x\log x\,dx + O\left[\frac{\left(\log\frac{1}{\varepsilon}\right)^2}{\left(\log\log\frac{1}{\varepsilon}\right)^2}\right] =$$

$$= -\frac{l}{2}[p(\varepsilon)]^2\log p(\varepsilon) + O\left[\frac{\left(\log\frac{1}{\varepsilon}\right)^2}{\left(\log\log\frac{1}{\varepsilon}\right)^2}\right] =$$

$$= -\frac{1}{2l}\frac{\left(\log\frac{c}{\varepsilon}\right)^2}{\log\log\frac{c}{\varepsilon}} + O\left[\frac{\left(\log\frac{c}{\varepsilon}\right)^2\log\log\log\frac{c}{\varepsilon}}{\log\log\frac{c}{\varepsilon}}\right].$$

i.e.

$$H_\varepsilon(\Phi_{l,\,m}^{\rho,\,z_0}) = \frac{\left(\log\frac{c}{\varepsilon}\right)^2}{l\log\log\frac{c}{\varepsilon}} + O_\Phi\left[\frac{\left(\log\frac{c}{\varepsilon}\right)^2\log\log\log\frac{c}{\varepsilon}}{\left(\log\log\frac{c}{\varepsilon}\right)^2}\right]$$

Q.E.D.

Let $F_s^{\sigma,\,c}$ be the space of all complex functions $f(z_1)$ of the one complex variable z_1, such that everywhere on the complex plane

$$|f(z_1)| \leqslant ce^{\sigma|z_1|^s}$$

(the norm being the maximum of the modulus of the function on the unit circle $|z_1| \leqslant 1$). Such functions are usually called integral functions of order σ and type s

<u>Lemma 4</u>. If $f(z_1)=\sum\limits_{k=0}^{\infty} a_k z_1^k$ belongs to the family $F_s^{\sigma, c}$, then for any k

$$|a_k| \leqslant \frac{c}{2\pi}\left(\frac{e\sigma s}{k+1}\right)^{\frac{k+1}{s}}$$

<u>Proof</u>. We choose a function

$$f(z_1)=\sum_{k=0}^{\infty} a_k z_1^k$$

of the family $F_s^{\sigma, c}$. From Cauchy's theorem

$$a_n=\frac{1}{2\pi i}\int\limits_{\gamma} \frac{f(\varphi)}{\varphi^{n+1}}\, d\varphi$$

Let γ be a circle of radius $r_n=\sqrt[s]{\frac{n+1}{\sigma s}}$. Then

$$a_n \leqslant \frac{c e^{\sigma r_n^s}}{2\pi r_n^{n+1}}=\frac{c}{2\pi}\left(\frac{e\sigma s}{n+1}\right)^{\frac{n+1}{s}}$$

<u>Lemma 5</u>. Any function of the family $\Phi_{l, m}^{\rho, z_0}$ is an integral function of order σ and type s, where $s=\frac{1}{l}$, and σ is some constant, determined by the parameters c, m, ρ, l.

<u>Proof</u>. We choose the function

$$f(z_1)=\sum_{k=0}^{\infty} a_k z_1^k$$

of the family $\Phi_{l, m}^{\rho, z_0}$. Then

$$|f(z_1)| \leqslant \sum_{k=0}^{\infty} |a_k|\,|z_1|^k \leqslant \sum_{k=1}^{\infty} \frac{c\rho^k |z_1|^k}{k^{lk+m}}+c=$$

$$=\sum_{k=1}^{\infty} \frac{c\rho^{\frac{p-m}{l}} |z_1|^{\frac{p-m}{l}}}{\left(\frac{p-m}{l}\right)^p}+c \leqslant c+\sum_{p} \frac{r^p |w|^{p+q}}{p^p}=$$

$$= c + |w|^2 \sum_p \frac{r^p |w|^p}{p^p}$$

where $p = lk + m$, $r > 1$, $q > 0$, $w = z_1^{\frac{1}{l}}$. Further, we take $|z_1|$ to be so large that $|w| > 1$. Then, putting $n = [p] + 1$, we obtain:

$$|f(z_1)| \leqslant c + |w|^q \sum_p \frac{r^p |w|^p}{p^p} \leqslant$$

$$\leqslant c + |w|^q \sum_p \frac{r^n |w|^n}{(n-1)^{n-1}} \leqslant c + |w|^q \sum_{n=1}^{\infty} \frac{(r')^n |w|^n}{n^n} <$$

$$< c + |w|^q e^{r'|w|} e^{r'|w|} \leqslant c + |z_1|^{\frac{q}{l}} e^{r'|z_1|^{\frac{1}{l}}}$$

Therefore we can find a constant σ such that for any z_1,

$$|f(z_1)| \leqslant e^{\sigma |z_1|^{\frac{1}{l}}} = e^{\sigma |z_1|^8}$$

Q.E.D.

<u>Theorem 1.</u> The absolute ε-entropy of the space $F_s^{\sigma, c}$ is equal to

$$H_\varepsilon(F_s^{\sigma, c}) = \frac{s\left(\log \frac{c}{\varepsilon}\right)^2}{\log\log \frac{c}{\varepsilon}} + O_F\left[\frac{\left(\log \frac{c}{\varepsilon}\right)^2 \log\log\log \frac{c}{\varepsilon}}{\left(\log\log \frac{c}{\varepsilon}\right)^2}\right]$$

This theorem is obtained from Lemmas 3, 4 and 5.

Let $\Psi_s^{\sigma, c}$ denote the space of real analytic functions, whose analytic continuations are integral functions of order σ and type $s > 0$ (the norm being the maximum of the absolute magnitude of the function on the segment $[-1, 1]$).

<u>Theorem 2.</u> The absolute ε-entropy of the space $\Psi_s^{\sigma, c}$ is equal to

$$H_\varepsilon(\Psi_s^{\sigma, c}) = \frac{s\left(\log \frac{c}{\varepsilon}\right)^2}{2\log\log \frac{c}{\varepsilon}} + O_\psi\left[\frac{\left(\log \frac{c}{\varepsilon}\right)^2 \log\log\log \frac{c}{\varepsilon}}{\left(\log\log \frac{c}{\varepsilon}\right)^2}\right]$$

The proof is similar to that of Theorem 1, where, instead of Lemma 1, we use Chebyshev's theorem, which states that any polynomial of degree n with leading coefficient equal to 1, differs from zero by not less than $\frac{1}{2^{n-1}}$ on $[-1, 1]$.

Corollary to Theorem 2. Let $\Psi_{1, T}^{\sigma; c}$ be the space of real integral functions on the real axis, of order σ and type 1 (the norm being the maximum of the absolute magnitude of the function on the segment $0 \leqslant x \leqslant T$; $\sigma > 0$, $c > 0$)). Then for sufficiently small ε

$$H_{\varepsilon}(\Psi_{1, T}^{\sigma; c}) = \frac{\left(\log \frac{c}{\varepsilon}\right)^2}{2 \log\log \frac{c}{\varepsilon}} + O_{\Psi}\left[\frac{\left(\log \frac{c}{\varepsilon}\right)^2 \log\log\log \frac{c}{\varepsilon}}{\left(\log\log \frac{c}{\varepsilon}\right)^2}\right]$$

The proof of the corollary is easily obtained from Theorem 2. To do this we need only make a change of variable (shift by $\frac{T}{2}$ and then multiply by $\frac{T}{2}$).

Further, let $F_s^{\sigma, c, n}$ be the space of complex integral function which are of order σ_k and type s_k $(k = 1, 2, \ldots, n)$ in z_k (the norm being the maximum of the modulus of the function on the set $B_1^0\{|z_k| \leqslant 1\}, k = 1, 2, \ldots, n)$), and let $\Psi_s^{\sigma, c, n}$ be the aggregate of functions of $F_s^{\sigma, c, n}$ which are real on the real part of the space E_n^z (the norm being the maximum of the absolute magnitude of the function on the cube

$$J_n\{-1 \leqslant u_k \leqslant 1\}, \quad k = 1, 2, \ldots, n)$$

Theorem 3. The absolute ε-entropy of the space $F_s^{\sigma, c, n}$ is equal to

$$H_{\varepsilon}(F_s^{\sigma, c, n}) = \frac{2}{(n+1)!} \prod_{k=1}^{n} s_k \frac{\left(\log \frac{c}{\varepsilon}\right)^{n+1}}{\left(\log\log \frac{c}{\varepsilon}\right)^n} + o\left[\frac{\left(\log \frac{c}{\varepsilon}\right)^{n+1}}{\left(\log\log \frac{c}{\varepsilon}\right)^n}\right]$$

Theorem 4. The absolute ε-entropy of the space $\Psi_s^{\sigma, c, n}$ is equal to

$$H_{\varepsilon}(\Psi_s^{\sigma, c, n}) = \frac{1}{(n+1)!} \prod_{k=1}^{n} s_k \frac{\left(\log \frac{c}{\varepsilon}\right)^{n+1}}{\left(\log\log \frac{c}{\varepsilon}\right)^n} + o\left[\frac{\left(\log \frac{c}{\varepsilon}\right)^{n+1}}{\left(\log\log \frac{c}{\varepsilon}\right)^n}\right]$$

These theorems are proved by induction on n, using the method we have demonstrated more than once in this chapter.

CHAPTER III

THE ENTROPY OF SOME SUBSPACES OF CONTINUOUS FUNCTIONS

§ 14. The Entropy of the Space of Lipschitz Functions

Let $F^{\rho}_{L,\varepsilon}$ be the space (with metric C) of functions $f(x)$ defined on the segment $(0 \leqslant x \leqslant \rho)$ of length ρ, which satisfy the Lipschitz condition with constant L and such that $|f(0)| \leqslant \varepsilon$, and let $\Phi^{\rho}_{L,\varepsilon}$ denote the aggregate of functions $\varphi(x)$ which can be represented on the segment r in the form

$$\varphi(x) = L \int_0^x \varphi^*(t)\, dt$$

where $\varphi^*(t)$ is a function taking the two values $+1$ and -1 only, constant on each interval of the form

$$\frac{(k-1)\,\varepsilon}{L} < t < \frac{k\varepsilon}{L} \qquad \left(k = 1,\, 2,\, \ldots,\, \left[\frac{\rho L}{\varepsilon}\right]\right)$$

Theorem 1. For any function $f(x)$ of the family $F^{\rho}_{L,\varepsilon}$, we can find a function $\varphi(x)$ of the family $\Phi^{\rho}_{L,\varepsilon}$ such that everywhere on the segment r

$$|f(x) - \varphi(x)| \leqslant \varepsilon$$

Proof. Put

$$x_k = \frac{(k-1)\,\varepsilon}{L} \qquad \left(k = 1,\, 2,\, \ldots,\, h;\ h = \left[\frac{\rho L}{\varepsilon}\right]\right)$$

and $x_{h+1} = \rho$. The points $\{x_k\}$ divide the segment r into $h+1$ segments $\delta_1, \delta_2, \ldots, \delta_{h+1}$, the length of each one not exceeding $\delta = \frac{\varepsilon}{L}$. We shall look for the function $\varphi(x)$ in the form

$$\varphi(x) = L \int_0^x \varphi^*(t)\, dt$$

We shall set the function $\varphi^*(t)$ by passing successively from one segment δ_x to the next. The first step of the induction, as we shall see, is no different from any of the later ones. Hence we shall select the sign of the function $\varphi^*(t)$ on the segment δ_k at once, taking it to be already fixed on all previous segments, and taking a function which is already fixed to be such that for any $j<k$ everywhere on δ_j

$$|f(x)-\varphi(x)|\leqslant\varepsilon$$

We denote by $\varphi^*_+(t)$ (or $\varphi^*_-(t)$) the function which is equal to $\varphi^*(t)$ on all the segments preceding δ_k and equal to $+1$ (or -1) inside the segment δ_k. Put

$$\varphi_+(x)=L\int_0^x\varphi^*_+(t)\,dt;\qquad \varphi^*(x)=L\int_0^x\varphi^*_-(t)\,dt;$$

$$\varphi_+(x_k)=L\int_0^{x_k}\varphi^*_+(t)\,dt=L\int_0^{x_{k-1}}\varphi^*_+(t)\,dt+L\int_{\delta_k}dt=$$
$$=\varphi(x_{k-1})+L\,|\delta_k|.$$

Similarly

$$\varphi_-(x_k)=\varphi(x_{k-1})-L\,|\delta_k|$$

i.e.

$$\varphi_+(x_k)-\varphi_-(x_k)=2L\,|\delta_k|\leqslant 2\varepsilon$$

Since, by the induction hypothesis

$$|f(x_{k-1})-\varphi(x_{k-1})|\leqslant\varepsilon\ *$$

and since $f(x)$ satisfies the Lipschitz condition with constant L

$$f(x_k)-\varphi\ (x_k)\leqslant\varepsilon\quad\text{and}\quad\varphi_-(x_k)-f(x_k)\leqslant\varepsilon$$

---

* When $k=1$, i.e. when constructing the function $\varphi^*(t)$ on δ_1, this inequality comes at once from the definition of the family $F^{\rho}_{L,\varepsilon}$ and of $\Phi^{\rho}_{L,\varepsilon}$.

The easiest way of seeing the truth of the last two inequalities is by means of a geometric picture: if the value of $f(x_k)$ falls in the segment $\varphi(x_{k-1}) \pm L|\delta_k|$, then the inequalities are obvious, since their left-hand sides will then be negative; if the value of $f(x_k)$ does not fall in this segment, then it cannot differ by more than ε from the nearest end of it, since

$$|f(x_{k-1}) - \varphi(x_{k-1})| \leqslant \varepsilon$$

and because $\varphi_+(x)$ and $\varphi_-(x)$ vary on the segment δ_k (on different sides) with the maximum speeds allowed by the Lipschitz constant.

It follows from the last two inequalities and

$$\varphi_+(x_k) - \varphi_-(x_k) \leqslant 2\varepsilon$$

that at least one of the two inequalities

$$|\varphi_+(x_k) - f(x_k)| \leqslant \varepsilon$$

and

$$|\varphi_-(x_k) - f(x_k)| \leqslant \varepsilon$$

holds. If the first holds, then we put $\varphi^*(t) = +1$ on the segment δ_k, and in the contrary case $\varphi^*(t) = -1$. Then the sign of the function $\varphi^*(t)$ is fixed on the segment δ_k in such a way that

$$|\varphi(x_k) - f(x_k)| \leqslant \varepsilon,$$
$$|\varphi(x_{k-1}) - f(x_{k-1})| \leqslant \varepsilon$$

(the second inequality is obtained immediately from the induction hypothesis).

From these two inequalities, together with the fact that the function $f(x)$ satisfies the Lipschitz condition with constant L, we immediately see that

$$|\varphi(x) - f(x)| \leqslant \varepsilon$$

everywhere on δ_k. Let us suppose the contrary. Then at some point x

$$|\varphi(x') - f(x')| > \varepsilon$$

For simplicity, let us suppose that

$$f(x') > \varphi(x')$$

and that on the segment δ_k

$$\varphi(x) = \varphi_-(x)$$

Since $f(x') - \varphi_-(x') > \varepsilon$ and $f(x_k) - \varphi_-(x_k) \leqslant \varepsilon$, we have

$$f(x') - f(x_k) > \varphi_-(x') - \varphi_-(x_k) = L|x' - x_k|$$

i.e.

$$f(x') - f(x_k) > L|x' - x_k|$$

which contradicts the Lipschitz condition.

By using this construction $h+1$ times, we define the function $\varphi(x)$ such that

$$|\varphi(x) - f(x)| \leqslant \varepsilon$$

Q.E.D.

By $F^{\rho}_{L,c}$ we denote the space of functions defined on the segment r (of length ρ) which satisfy the Lipschitz condition with constant L on this segment, and not exceeding the constant c (in absolute magnitude) at the point $x=0$.

From Theorem 1, it follows that any function of $F^{\rho}_{L,c}$ can be approximated to with an accuracy of ε by a function of the form

$$f(0) + L\int_0^x f^*(t)\,dt$$

where $f^*(x)$ is a function of the family $\Phi^{\rho}_{L,\varepsilon}$, and $f(0)$ is a multiple of 2ε. Hence the sequence of $\left[\frac{\rho L}{\varepsilon}\right] + \left[\log\frac{c}{\varepsilon}\right] + 2$ binary digits

$$\alpha_1, \alpha_2, \ldots, \alpha_{k_1}, \beta_1, \beta_2, \ldots, \beta_{k_2};$$

$$\left(k_1 = \left[\frac{\rho L}{\varepsilon}\right] + 1, \quad k_2 = \left[\log\frac{c}{\varepsilon}\right] + 1\right)$$

can serve as a table for a function of $F^{\rho}_{L,c}$, these digits, which depend on the function $f(x)$, being chosen as follows: $\alpha_p = 0$ if $f^*(x)$ (see Theorem 1) is negative on the corresponding segment δ_p, and, in the contrary case, $\alpha_p = 1$ $(p = 1, 2, \ldots, k_1)$; $\beta_1, \beta_2, \ldots, \beta_k$ are the coefficients of the binary expansion of the number $f(0)$, which are computed inductively from the formulae:

$$\beta_1 = \begin{cases} 0, & \text{if } f(0) \leqslant 0, \\ 1, & \text{if } f(0) > 0. \end{cases}$$

$$\beta_q = \begin{cases} 0, & \text{if } \left| f(0) - \sum_{m=1}^{q-1} \frac{\beta_m c}{2^m} \right| \leqslant 0, \\ 1, & \text{if } \left| f(0) - \sum_{m=1}^{q-1} \frac{\beta_m c}{2^m} \right| > 0 \end{cases}$$

The formula $f(x) \approx f(0) + L \int_0^x f^*(t)\,dt$ enables us to compute the function $f(x)$ at any point x of the segment r from the constructed table.

The volume of the constructed table is equal to

$$\left[\frac{\rho L}{\varepsilon}\right] + \left[\log \frac{c}{\varepsilon}\right] + 2$$

for a function satisfying the Lipschitz condition. In order to show that for functions satisfying the Lipschitz condition there is no way of constructing considerably smaller tables, we prove the following theorem.

Theorem 2. The absolute ε-entropy of the space $F^{\rho}_{L,c}$ satisfies the inequality

$$\frac{\rho L}{\varepsilon} + \log \frac{c}{\varepsilon} + 2 \geqslant H_{\varepsilon}(F^{\rho}_{L,c}) \geqslant \frac{\rho L}{\varepsilon} + \log \frac{c}{\varepsilon} - 2 \qquad (\varepsilon \leqslant c)$$

Proof. Since the aggregate of functions of the form

$$f(0) + L \int_0^x f^*(t)\,dt$$

forms an ε-net of the space $F^{\rho}_{L,c}$ and there are more than $2^{k_1+k_2} = 2^{\left(\left[\frac{\rho L}{\varepsilon}\right] + \left[\log \frac{c}{\varepsilon}\right] + 2\right)}$ of them,

$$H_{\varepsilon}(F^{\rho}_{L,c}) \leqslant \left[\frac{\rho L}{\varepsilon}\right] + \left[\log \frac{c}{\varepsilon}\right] + 2 \leqslant \frac{\rho L}{\varepsilon} + \log \frac{c}{\varepsilon} + 2$$

This gives us the first half of the inequality.

We choose $\delta > 0$ and put $\varepsilon' = \varepsilon + \delta$. We shall show that any two different functions $f_1(x)$ and $f_2(x)$, which can be put in the form

$$f(x) = f_0 + L\int_0^x f^*(t)\,dt$$

($f^*(t) \in \Phi^{\rho}_{L,\varepsilon'}; f_0$ is a multiple of $2\varepsilon'$) differ by more than 2ε at one point at least of the segment r. If $f_1(0) \neq f_2(0)$, then

$$|f_1(0) - f_2(0)| \geqslant 2\varepsilon' = 2\varepsilon + 2\delta > 2\varepsilon$$

Hence, to complete the proof, we shall assume that $f_1(0) = f_2(0)$.

Since $f_1(x) \neq f_2(x)$ on r, we can find $k \leqslant \left[\frac{\rho L}{\varepsilon}\right]$ such that

$$|f_1^*(t) - f_2^{*\prime}(t)| = 2$$

everywhere inside the corresponding interval δ_k, and $f_1^*(t) - f_2^*(t)$ keeps the same sign on the segment δ_k. Let us choose the smallest k satisfying these conditions. Then

$$|f_1(x_k) - f_2(x_k)| = \left|L\int_0^{x_k} (f_1^*(t) - f_2^*(t))\,dt\right| =$$

$$= L\int_{\delta_k} 2\,dt = 2L|\delta_k| = 2L\frac{\varepsilon'}{L} = 2\varepsilon' > 2\varepsilon$$

From this, and the fact that functions of the form $f_0 + L\int_0^x f^*(t)\,dt$ satisfy the Lipschitz condition with constant L, we find that there are in $F^{\rho}_{L,c}$ not less than $2^{\left(\left[\frac{\rho L}{\varepsilon'}\right] + \left[\log\frac{c}{\varepsilon'}\right]\right)}$ elements which are further apart than 2ε. But since this is true for any $\delta > 0$, however small, from Lemma 3 (§ 5)

$$H_\varepsilon(F^{\rho}_{L,c}) \geqslant \left[\frac{\rho L}{\varepsilon'}\right] + \left[\log\frac{c}{\varepsilon}\right] \geqslant \frac{\rho L}{\varepsilon'} + \log\frac{c}{\varepsilon} - 2$$

Q.E.D.

§ 15. The Entropy of the Space of Differentiable Functions of One Variable

We fix the natural number $s \geqslant 1$ and arbitrary numbers $L > 0,\ c > 0,\ \rho > 0,\ \delta > 0$. $F^{\rho}_{s, L, c}$ denotes the spaces of functions $f(x)$ given on the segment $r\,(0 \leqslant x \leqslant \rho)$ of length ρ, which have an $(s-1)$-th derivative everywhere on r, satisfying the Lipschitz condition with constant L on r, and are such that

$$|f^{(k)}(0)| \leqslant c \qquad (k = 0,\ 1,\ 2,\ \ldots,\ s-1)\ *$$

$\Phi^{\rho, \delta}_{s, L, c}$ denotes the space of functions of the form

$$\varphi(x) = \sum_{k=0}^{s-1} a_k x^k + \frac{L}{(s-1)!} \int_0^x (x-t)^{s-1} \varphi^*_{\delta}(t)\, dt \qquad (x \in r)$$

where the a_k are multiples of δ^{s-k} $(k = 0,\ 1,\ 2,\ \ldots,\ s-1)$ and bounded in absolute magnitude by the constant c, and $\varphi^*_{\delta}(t)$ is a function which takes the two values $+1$ and -1 only and is constant on the intervals

$$(\delta_q\ (q-1)\delta < t < q\delta) \qquad \left(q = 1,\ 2,\ \ldots,\ h;\ h = \left[\frac{\rho}{\delta}\right]\right)$$

and on the interval

$$\delta_{h+1} \qquad (h\delta < t < \rho)$$

In this section we wish to evaluate the ε-entropy of the space $F^{\rho}_{s, 1, c}$, and at the same time to prove that the functions $\varphi(x)$ of $\Phi^{\rho, \delta}_{s, L, c}$ approximate sufficiently well to functions of the space $F^{\rho}_{s, L, c}$.

Theorem 1. For any function $f(x)$ of the space $F^{\rho}_{s, L, c}$ we can find a function $\varphi(x)$ of the family $\Phi^{\rho, \delta}_{s, L, c} (L > 1)$ such that

$$\|\varphi(x) - f(x)\| \leqslant A\delta^s$$

where $A > 0$ is some constant, depending neither on δ nor on the function $f(x)$ (A depends only on s and L). Before proving this theorem we first prove several lemmas.

---

* By a derivative of order zero we mean the function itself.

Lemma 1. Let $f(x)$ be some function of $F^{\rho}_{1,1,c}$, and $\varphi(x)$ be a function of $\Phi^{\rho,\delta}_{1,L,c}$ $(L>1)$ such that at the point $x_q = q\delta$

$$|f(x_q) - \varphi(x_q)| \leqslant \delta(L+1)$$

Then for any number a we can find a whole number

$$q(|\alpha|) \leqslant A(L) + \frac{\alpha}{\delta^3}$$

and a function $\psi(x)$ of the family $\Phi^{\rho,\delta}_{1,L,c}$ equal to $\varphi(x)$ for $x \leqslant x_q$ and such that

$$|f(x_{q+q(|\alpha|)}) - \psi(x_{q+q(|\alpha|)})| \leqslant (L+1)\delta$$
$$(x_{q+q(|\alpha|)} = (q + q(|\alpha|) + 1)\delta),$$
$$\int_{x_q}^{x_{q+q(|\alpha|)}} [f(x) - \psi(x)]\,dx = \alpha + \varepsilon_f,$$

where $|\varepsilon_f| \leqslant B(L)\delta^2$, and $A(L)$ and $B(L)$ are positive constants, depending only on L *.

Proof. Put $g(x) = f(x) - \psi(x)$, where $\psi(x)$ is the function we wish to find. We note that if $\psi(x) \in \Phi^{\rho,\delta}_{1,L,c}$, then on each of the intervals δ_p the function $g(x)$ either increases strictly monotonically, or decreases strictly monotonically, depending on the function $f(x)$ and the sign of $\psi^*_\delta(x)$ $\left(\psi^*_\delta(x) = \frac{d\psi(x)}{dx}\right)$, and at any point x not coinciding with either end of any of the intervals $\{\delta_p\}$, $g'(x)$ exists, where, since $|\psi'(x) = L$ and $|f'(x) \leqslant 1$

$$L - 1 \leqslant g'(x) \leqslant L + 1$$

From this it follows that for any $p < h$

$$\delta_p(L-1) \leqslant g(x_p) - g(x_{p-1})| \leqslant \delta_p(L+1)$$

(x_{p-1}, x_p are the ends of the interval δ_p), and that the sign of $g(x_p) - g(x_{p-1})$ (for a fixed function $f(x)$ is determined

---

* The numbers q, $|\alpha|$ and δ are assumed in this lemma to be so small that $x_{q+q(|\alpha|)} < \rho$. Similar conditions will be assumed in Lemmas 2 and 3 below.

in a one-to-one manner by the sign of the function $\psi_\delta^*(x)$ on the interval δ_p.

For definiteness we shall assume from now on that the number α given in the lemma is non-negative. The essence of the rest of the proof consists in defining the function $\psi_\delta^*(x)$ in such a way that the function $g(x)$ corresponding to it increases monotonically (after x_q) on the first few intervals $\{\delta_p\}$, then remains positive and greater than δ on a group of standard intervals, and then decreases to zero on a subsequent group of intervals.

We shall choose the sign of $\psi_\delta^*(x)$ on the intervals δ_{q+1}, $\delta_{q+2}, \ldots, \delta_{q+q_1}$ (the number q_1 will be determined below) so that the corresponding function $g(x)$ increases monotonically on all these intervals. We choose q_1 so that

$$\delta \leqslant g[\delta(q+q_1+1)] \leqslant 2(L+1)\delta$$

This is possible, since for an arbitrary choice of values of the function $\psi_\delta^*(x)$ the oscillations of the corresponding function $g(x)$ on each of the intervals $\{\delta_p\}$ do not exceed $(L+1)\delta$ and are not less than $(L-1)\delta$. Since for any $i \leqslant q_i$

$$g[\delta(q+i+1)] - g[\delta(q+i)] \geqslant (L-1)\delta$$

and since, by hypothesis,

$$|g(q\delta)| = |f(q\delta) - \varphi(q\delta)| \leqslant (L+1)\delta$$

we have

$$q_1 \leqslant \left[\frac{L+2}{L-1}\right] + 1$$

On the intervals after δ_{q+q_1}, i.e. $\delta_{q+q_1+1}, \delta_{q+q_1+2}, \ldots, \delta_{q+q_1+q_2}$, the signs of ψ_δ^* are chosen successively so that for any i $(q+q_1+1 \leqslant i \leqslant q+q_1+q_2)$ and for any $x \in \delta_i$

$$\delta \leqslant g(x) \leqslant (3L+3)\delta$$

q_2 is chosen so that

$$\int_{\delta(q+q_1)}^{\delta(q+q_1+q_2-1)} g(x)\,dx \leqslant \alpha \leqslant \int_{\delta(q+q_1)}^{\delta(q+q_1+q_2)} g(x)\,dx$$

Taking the limits of $g(x)$ on the intervals $\delta_{q+q_1+1}, \ldots, \delta_{q+q_1+q_2}$ into account, we have

$$q_2 \leqslant \left[\frac{\alpha}{\delta^2}\right]+1$$

On the next group of intervals $\delta_{q+q_1+q_2+1}, \ldots, \delta_{q+q_1+q_2+q_3}$ the signs of the function $\psi_\delta^*(x)$ are so chosen that the function $g(x)$ decreases monotonically on each of these intervals and at some point of the interval $\delta_{q+q(\alpha)}$ $(q(\alpha)=q_1+q_2+q_3)$ becomes zero. Since $g[\delta(q+q_1+q_2+1)] \leqslant (3L+3)\delta$ and since on the last group of intervals $g(x)$ decreases at a rate not less than $L-1$, $q_3 \leqslant \left[\frac{3L+3}{L-1}\right]+1$.

Combining the inequalities for q_1, q_2, q_3 which we have obtained, we have

$$q(\alpha)=q_1+q_2+q_3 \leqslant \left[\frac{L+2}{L-1}\right]+\left[\frac{\alpha}{\delta^2}\right]+\left[\frac{3L+3}{L-1}\right]+3 \leqslant$$
$$\leqslant 3+\frac{4L+5}{L-1}+\frac{\alpha}{\delta^2}=A(L)+\frac{\alpha}{\delta^2}.$$

We now evaluate the difference between α and the integral of $g(x)$. From the above inequalities, putting $a=q\delta$ and $b=(q+q(\alpha)+1)\delta$ we have

$$\left|\int_a^b [f(x)-\psi(x)]\,dx-\alpha\right|=\left|\int_a^b g(x)\,dx-\alpha\right| \leqslant$$
$$\leqslant (2L+2)\delta q_1\delta+(3L+3)\delta\delta+(3L+3)\delta\delta q_3 \leqslant$$
$$\leqslant (3L+3)(q_1+1+q_3)\delta^2<(3L+3)A(L)\delta^2=B(L)\delta^2$$

Since $g(x)$ becomes zero at some point of the interval $\delta_{q+q(\alpha)}$ and everywhere on this interval

$$\overline{\lim_{\delta x \to 0}}\left|\frac{\delta g(x)}{\delta(x)}\right| \leqslant L+1$$

therefore

$$|g[\delta(q+q(\alpha)+1)]| \leqslant (L+1)\delta$$

i.e.

$$|f[\delta(q+q(\alpha)+1)]-\psi[\delta(q+q(\alpha)+1)]| \leqslant (L+1)\delta$$

Q.E.D.

Lemma 2. Let $f(x)$ be a function, defined for all real values of x, possessing an $(s-1)$th derivative $(s>0)$ which satisfies the Lipschitz condition with constant L over a complete straight line segment, and such that at some point $x=c$

$$f(c) \geqslant B_0\delta^s, \quad \left|\frac{d^k f(c)}{dx^k}\right| \leqslant B_k\delta^{s-k}$$

$$(k=1, 2, \ldots, s-1;\ \delta>0;\ B_k>0,\ k=0, 1, 2, \ldots, s-1)$$

Then on the interval (a, b)

$$\left(a = c - \frac{B_0\delta}{B+B_0},\ b = c + \frac{B_0\delta}{B+B_0}\right) \qquad f(x) > 0$$

and

$$\int_a^b f(x)\,dx \geqslant c(s, L)\,B_0\delta^{s+1}$$

where $c(s, L) > 0$ and $B > 0$ are two constants, independent of both B_0 and δ.

Proof. Since the $(s-1)$th derivative of the function $f(x)$ satisfies the Lipschitz condition

$$f(x) = \sum_{k=0}^{s-1} \frac{d^k f(c)}{dx^k}\frac{1}{k!}(x-c)^k + \frac{1}{(s-1)!}\int_c^x (x-t)^{s-1}\frac{d^s f(t)}{dt^s}\,dt$$

i.e.

$$f(x) \geqslant f(c) - \sum_{k=1}^{s-1}\left|\frac{d^k f(c)}{dx^k}\right|\frac{1}{k!}|x-c|^k -$$

$$-\frac{L}{S!}|x-c|^s \geqslant B_0\delta^s - \sum_{k=1}^{s-1} B_k\delta^{s-k}|x-c|^k - L|x-c|^s$$

Put $y = \frac{x-c}{\delta}$. Then when $y<1$

$$f(x) \geqslant B_0\delta^s - \sum_{k=1}^{s-1} B_k\delta^s|y|^k - L\delta^s|y|^s \geqslant$$

$$\geqslant \delta^s(B_0 - B_y) \geqslant \delta^s[B_0 - (B+B_0)y] =$$

$$= \delta^s\left[B_0 - (B+B_0)\frac{|x-c|}{\delta}\right],$$

where B is some positive constant, depending only on S and L. Put $a = c - \frac{B_0\delta}{B + B_0}$ and $b = c + \frac{B_0\delta}{B + B_0}$. Since a and b are the roots of the equation

$$B_0 - (B - B_0)\frac{|x - c|}{\delta} = 0$$

inside the interval (a, b)

$$f(x) \geqslant \delta^s \left[B_0 - (B + B_0)\frac{|x - c|}{\delta}\right] > 0,$$

$$\int\limits_a^b f(x)\,dx \geqslant \int\limits_a^b \delta^s \left[B_0 - (B + B_0)\frac{|x - c|}{\delta}\right] dx =$$

$$= 2\delta^s \int\limits_c^b \left[B_0 - (B + B_0)\frac{|x - c|}{\delta}\right] dx =$$

$$= 2\delta^s \left[B_0(b - c) - \frac{B_0 + B}{2\delta}(b - c)^2\right] = \frac{B_0^2}{B + B_0}\delta^{s+1} =$$

$$= \frac{B_0\delta^{s+1}}{1 + \frac{B}{B_0}} \geqslant \frac{B_0\delta^{s+1}}{1 + B} = c(s, L)\,B_0\delta^{s+1}$$

Q.E.D.

Lemma 3. There exists a whole number $q_s \geqslant 1$ and a set of positive constants $B_k^s \geqslant 1$ $(k = 0, 1, \ldots, s - 1)$ which possess the following property: given any functions $f(x) \in F^{\rho}_{s, 1, c}$ and $\varphi(x) \in \Phi^{\rho, \delta}_{s, L, c}$ $(L > 1)$ such that at some point $x_q = \delta_q \geqslant 0$

$$\left|\frac{d^k f(x_q)}{dx^k} - \frac{d^k \varphi(x_q)}{dx^k}\right| \leqslant B_k^s \delta^{s-k} \qquad (k = 0, 1, \ldots, s - 1)$$

and given $\eta = \pm 1$ we can find a function $\psi(x)$ of the same family $\Phi^{\rho, \delta}_{s, L, c}$ which is equal to $\varphi(x)$ when $x \leqslant x_q$ and such that

$$\left|\frac{d^k f(x_{q+q_s})}{dx^k} - \frac{d^k \psi(x_{q+q_s})}{dx^k}\right| \leqslant B_k^s \delta^{s-k}$$

$$(x_{q+q_s} = \delta(q + q_s), \qquad k = 0, 1, \ldots, s - 1)$$

$$\operatorname{sign} \int\limits_{x_q}^{x_{q+q_s}} [f(x) - \psi(x)]\,dx = \operatorname{sign} \eta;$$

$$\delta^{s+1} \leqslant \left| \int_{x_q}^{x_{q+q_s}} [f(x) - \psi(x)]\, dx \right| \leqslant B(s, L)\, \delta^{s+1}$$

where $B(s, L)$ is a positive parameter, depending only on s and L.

Proof. The lemma is proved by induction on s. By putting $\alpha = (B(L) + 1)\, \eta\delta^2)$ in Lemma 1, it is seen to be true for $s = 1$. We prove it for the general case.

Let the functions $f(x) \in F^{\rho}_{s,1,c}$ and $\varphi(x) \in \Phi^{\rho,\delta}_{s,L,c}$, satisfying the conditions of the lemma, be given. For definiteness we shall put $\eta = +1$. Since $f(x) \in F^{\rho}_{s-1,1,c}$ and $\varphi(x) \in \Phi^{\rho,\delta}_{s-1,L,c}$, the lemma holds for them, from the induction hypothesis, but since $[f^{(k)}(x)]' = f^{(k+1)}(x)$ and $[\varphi^{(k)}(x)]' = \varphi^{(k+1)}(x)$

$$B^{k+1}_{s+1} = B^k_s$$

We put

$$\psi^{s-1}_1(x) = \varphi'(x) = \sum_{k=0}^{s-2} a_k x^k + \frac{L}{(s-2)!} \int_0^x (x-t)^{s-2}\, \psi^{*,\, s-1}_{\delta,\,1}(t)\, dt$$

and construct the sequence

$$\psi^{s-1}_1,\ \psi^{s-1}_2,\ \ldots,\ \psi^{s-1}_n$$

(which we can do, according to the induction hypothesis), such that

1. $\psi^{s-1}_1(x) = \varphi'(x)$ when $x \leqslant x_q = \delta q$,

$\psi^{s-1}_m(x) = \psi^{s-1}_{m-1}(x)$ when $x \leqslant y_m = \delta(q + mq_{s-1} - 1)$

$$(m = 2,\ 3,\ \ldots,\ n).$$

2. $$\int_{y_{m-1}}^{y_m} [f'(x) - \psi^{s-1}_m(x)]\, dx \geqslant \delta^s$$

when $m = 1,\ 2,\ \ldots,\ p\,(p \leqslant n)$.

3. $$\int_{y_{m-1}}^{y_m} [f'(x) - \psi^{s-1}_m(x)]\, dx \leqslant -\delta^s$$

when $m = p+1,\ p+2,\ \ldots,\ n.$

$$4. \qquad \left| \frac{d^k f(y_m)}{dx^k} - \frac{d^k \psi_m^{s-1}(y_m)}{dx^k} \right| \leqslant B_k^s \delta^{s-k}$$

when $m = 1,\ 2,\ \ldots,\ n;\ k = 1,\ 2,\ \ldots,\ s-2$ (the numbers p and n will be given below).

By the induction hypothesis

$$\delta^s \leqslant \left| \int_{y_{m-1}}^{y_m} [f'(x) - \psi_m^{s-1}(x)]\, dx \right| \leqslant B(s-1,\ L)\,\delta^s$$

Put

$$\psi_m^s(x) = \frac{L}{(s-1)!} \int_0^x (x-t)^{s-1} \psi_{\delta, m}^{*s-1}(t)\, dt \qquad (m = 1,\ 2,\ \ldots,\ n),$$

$$\psi(x) = \psi_n^s(x), \qquad g(x) = f(x) - \psi(x).$$

From the inequalities we have obtained it follows that

$$\delta^s \leqslant | g(y_m) - g(y_{m-1}) | \leqslant B(s-1,\ L)\,\delta^s$$

and from conditions 2 and 3 we have

$$g(y_m) - g(y_{m-1}) \geqslant \delta^s \quad \text{when} \quad m < p,$$

$$g(y_m) - g(y_{m-1}) \leqslant -\delta^s \quad \text{when} \quad m > p$$

Let us now choose some $m \leqslant n$ and some point x' of the segment $[y_{m-1},\ y_m]$, and make a lower estimate of the modulus of the increment $|g(x') - g(y_{m-1})|$. We have

$$| g(x') - g(y_{m-1}) | \leqslant$$

$$\leqslant \int_{y_{m-1}}^{x_1} \left| \frac{dg(t)}{dt} \right| dt = (x' - y_{m-1}) \left| \frac{dg(x'')}{dx} \right| \leqslant$$

$$\leqslant \sum_{k=0}^{s-2} \frac{1}{k!} \left| \frac{d^k g'(y_{m-1})}{dx^k} \right| (x' - y_{m-1})^k + \frac{L+1}{s!} (x' - y_{m-1})^s \leqslant$$

$$\leqslant \sum_{k=1}^{s-1} \frac{1}{(k-1)!} \left| \frac{d^k g(y_{m-1})}{dx^k} \right| (x' - y_{m-1})^{k-1} + \frac{L+1}{s!} (x' - y_{m-1})^s \leqslant$$

$$\leqslant \delta^s \left[(1 + q_{s-1}) \sum_{k=1}^{s-1} B_k^s + (L+1) \right] = B'(s,\ L)\,\delta^s$$

$(B'(s, L) > 0)$, since by hypothesis q_{s-1} is constant. Since

$$|q(x) - q(y_{m-1})| \leqslant B(s, L)\delta^s$$

the oscillation $g(x)$ on any of the segments $\{[y_{m-1}, y_m]\}$ is not greater than $2B'(s, L)\delta^s$.

Let us now put $B_0^s = 2B'(s, L) + 1$. We shall find the value of p below. But here we note that n is chosen as near p as possible, so that at some point of the segment $[y_{n-1}, y_n]$ the function becomes zero. This is possible, since on the segments $[y_{m-1}, y_m]$ $(m > p)$ the function $g(x)$ decreases sufficiently fast on going from the point y_{m-1} to y_m. With this value of n

$$|g(x_{q+q_s})| = |f(x_{q+q_s}) - \psi(x_{q+q_s})| \leqslant B_0^s\delta^s \quad (q_s = nq_{s-1}),$$

$$\left|\frac{d^k g(x_{q+q_s})}{dx^k}\right| = \left|\frac{d^k f(x_{q+q_s})}{dx^k} - \frac{d^k \psi(x_{q+q_s})}{dx^k}\right| \leqslant B_k^s\delta^{s-k}$$

$$(k = 1, 2, \ldots, s-1)$$

(see condition 4). a' and b' are the ends of the maximum interval of the x-axis containing the point $c = y_p$, lying inside the segment $[x_q, x_{q+q_s}]$ and such that everywhere inside the interval (a', b') $g(x) > 0$. Then, from Lemma 2

$$\int_{a'}^{b'} g(x)\,dx \geqslant \int_{a}^{b} g(x)\,dx \geqslant c(s, L-1)\,g(y_p)\,\delta$$

But since $|g(x_q)| \leqslant B_0^s\delta^s$ and $|g(x_{q+q_s})| \leqslant B_0^s\delta^s$, and since the oscillation of $g(x)$ on each of the segments $\{[y_{m-1}, y_m]\}$ does not exceed $B_0^s\delta^s$, ,

$$\int_{x_q}^{x_{q+q_s}} g(x)\,dx \geqslant$$

$$\geqslant \int_{a'}^{b'} g(x)\,dx - \int_{x_q}^{a'} |g(x)|\,dx - \int_{b'}^{x_{q+q_s}} |g(x)|\,dx \geqslant$$

$$\geqslant c(s, L-1)\,g(y_p)\,\delta - 2B_0^s\delta^s\left[|x_q - a'| + |b' - x_{q+q_s}|\right]$$

But from the fact that on the set of points $\{y_m\}$ $g(x)$ first increases strictly (for $m \leqslant p$)) and then decreases strictly monotonically at a rate (along the axis of function values) not less than δ^s, we know that

$$a' - x_q \leqslant \{[2B_0^s] + 1\}(y_m - y_{m-1}) = B_1\delta$$

and

$$x_{q-q_s} - b' \leqslant \{[2B_0^s] + 1\}(y_m - y_{m-1}) = B_1\delta$$

Therefore

$$\int_{x_q}^{x_{q+q_s}} g(x)\,dx \geqslant c(s, L-1)\,g(y_p)\,\delta - B_0^s B_1 \delta^{s+1} = \\ = \delta^{s+1}\left(\frac{c(s, L-1)\,g(y_p)}{\delta^s} - 4B_0^s B_1\right)$$

Now let us put

$$p = \left[\frac{1 + 4B_0^s B_1}{c(s, L-1)} + 2B_0^s\right] + 1$$

Then

$$g(y_p) \geqslant p\delta^s - 2B_0^s\delta^s \geqslant \left(\left[\frac{1 + 4B_0^s B_1}{c(s, L-1)} + 2B_0^s\right] + 1\right)\delta^s - 2B_0^s\delta^s \geqslant \\ \geqslant \frac{(1 + 4B_0^s B_1)\,\delta^s}{c(s, L-1)}$$

Hence

$$\int_{x_q}^{x_{q+q_s}} g(x)\,dx \geqslant \delta^{s+1}\left(\frac{c(s, L)\,g(y_p)}{\delta^s} - 4B_0^s B_1\right) \geqslant \delta^{s+1}$$

On the other hand, since for any m

$$|g(y_m) - g(y_{m-1})| \leqslant B(s-1, L)\,\delta^s$$

on the segment $[x_q, x_{q+q_s}]$

$$\max|g(x)| \leqslant pB(s-1, L)\,\delta^s + 2B_0^s\delta^s = \\ = \delta^s(pB(s-1, L) + 2B_0^s).$$

Hence

$$\left|\int_{x_q}^{x_{q+q_s}} g(x)\,dx\right| = \left|\int_{x_q}^{x_{q+q_s}} [f(x)-\psi(x)]\,dx\right| \leqslant$$

$$\leqslant (x_{q+q_s}-x_q)\,\delta^s\left(pB(s-1,\ L)+2B_0^s\right)=$$

$$=\delta_{q_s-1}n\delta^s\left(pB(s-1,\ L)+2B_0^s\right)=B(s,\ L)\,\delta^{s+1}$$

Thus, we can consider the lemma as proved for $\eta=+1$ The proof for $\eta=-1$ is similar.

Proof of Theorem 1. Let the function $f(x)$ of the family $F^{\rho}_{s,1,c}$ be given. We choose a set of constants $\{a_k\}$(a_k a multiple of δ^{s-k}) such that

$$|a_k|\leqslant c,\ \left|a_k-\frac{d^k f(0)}{dx^k}\right|\leqslant \delta^{s-k} \qquad (k=0,\ 1,\ 2,\ \ldots,\ s-1)$$

It follows from Lemma 3 that there exists a function $\psi_1(x)$ of the family $\Phi^{\rho,\delta}_{s,L,c}$ such that $\frac{d^k\psi_1(0)}{dx^k}=a_k$ and

$$\left|\frac{d^k f(\delta q_s)}{dx^k}-\frac{d^k\psi_1(\delta q_s)}{dx^k}\right|\leqslant B_k^s\delta^{s-k} \qquad (k=0,\ 1,\ \ldots,\ s-1)$$

By Lemma 3, there exists a function $\psi_2(x)$ of the family $\Phi^{\rho,\delta}_{s,L,c}$ which is equal to $\psi_1(x)$ when $x\leqslant\delta q_s$ and such that

$$\left|\frac{d^k f(2\delta q_s)}{dx^k}-\frac{d^k\psi_2(2\delta q_s)}{dx^k}\right|\leqslant B_k^s\delta^{s-k} \quad (k=0,\ 1,\ \ldots,\ s-1)$$

In a similar way we define the functions

$$\psi_3(x),\ \psi_4(x),\ \ldots,\ \psi_h(x) \quad \left(h=\left[\frac{\rho}{q_s\delta}\right]\right)$$

of the family $\Phi^{\rho,\delta}_{s,L,c}$ such that $\psi_m(x)$ is equal to $\psi_{m-1}(x)$ when $x\leqslant(m-1)\,\delta q_s$ and

$$\left|\frac{d^k f(m\delta q_s)}{dx^k}-\frac{d^k\psi_m(m\delta q_s)}{dx^k}\right|\leqslant B_k^s\delta^{s-k}$$

$$(k=0,\ 1,\ 2,\ \ldots,\ s-1;\quad m=1,\ 2,\ \ldots,\ h)$$

Let

$$\psi(x)=\sum_{k=0}^{s-1}a_kx^k+\frac{L}{(s-1)!}\int_0^x (x-t)^{s-1}\psi^*(t)\,dt$$

be the function of the family $\Phi^{\rho,\delta}_{s,L,c}$ which is identically equal to $\psi_h(x)$ when $x \leqslant h\delta q_s$, and, when $x \geqslant h\delta q_s$ $\psi^*(x) = +1$. Let us evaluate the quantity $\|f(x) - \psi(x)\|$. We choose the point x of the segment r and denote the smallest number which is a multiple of δq_s and such that

$$|x - p\delta q_s| \leqslant \delta q_s$$

by $p\delta q_s$. Then

$$|f(x) - \psi(x)| = \left| \sum_{k=0}^{s-1} \left(\frac{d^k f(p\delta q_s)}{dx^k} - \frac{d^k \psi(p\delta q_s)}{dx^k} \right) \frac{(x - p\delta q_s)^k}{k!} + \right.$$

$$\left. + \frac{1}{(s-1)!} \int_0^x (x-t)^{s-1} \left[\frac{d^s f(t)}{dt^s} - \frac{d^s \psi(t)}{dt^s} \right] dt = \right.$$

$$= \left| \sum_{k=0}^{s-1} \left(\frac{d^k f(p\delta q_s)}{dx^k} - \frac{d^k \psi_q(p\delta q_s)}{dx^k} \right) \frac{(x - p\delta_{q_s})^k}{k!} + \right.$$

$$\left. + \frac{1}{(s-1)!} \int_0^x (x-t)^{s-1} \left[\frac{d^s f(t)}{dt^s} - \frac{d^s \psi(t)}{dt^s} \right] dt \right| =$$

$$= \left| \sum_{k=0}^{s-1} \left(\frac{d^k f(p\delta q_s)}{dx^k} - \frac{d^k \psi_p(p\delta q_s)}{dx^k} \right) \frac{(x - p\delta q_s)^k}{k!} + \right.$$

$$\left. + \frac{1}{(s-1)!} \int_0^x (x-t)^{s-1} \left[\frac{d^s f(t)}{dt^s} - \frac{d^s \psi(t)}{dt^s} \right] dt \right| \leqslant$$

$$\leqslant \left| \sum_{k=0}^{s-1} B_k^s \delta^{s-k} \frac{(x - p\delta q_s)^k}{k!} + \frac{1}{(s-1)!} \int_0^x (x-t)^{s-1} 2L\, dt \right| \leqslant$$

$$\leqslant \sum_{k=0}^{s-1} B_k^s \delta^{s-k} \frac{(q_s\delta)^k}{k!} + \frac{2L}{s!} (q_s\delta)^s =$$

$$= \left(\sum_{k=0}^{s-1} \frac{q_s^k}{k!} B_k^s + \frac{2Lq_s^s}{s!} \right) \delta^s = A\delta^s.$$

Q.E.D.

Lemma 4. Let $\varphi_1(x)$ and $\varphi_2(x)$ be two functions of the family $\Phi^{\rho,\delta}_{s,1,0}$ such that at some point

$$x_0 \leqslant \rho - 4s\delta \quad \varphi_1(x_0) \neq \varphi_2(x_0)$$

Then at some point x' of the segment r

$$|\varphi_1(x') - \varphi_2(x')| \geqslant c^s \delta^s$$

where $c > 0$ is an absolute constant.

Proof. Let q be the smallest whole number such that in the corresponding interval δ_q the functions

$$\varphi_1^*(x) = \frac{d^s \varphi_1(x)}{dx^s}, \quad \varphi_2^*(x) = \frac{d^s \varphi_2(x)}{dx^s}$$

take different values, i.e. $|\varphi_1^*(x) - \varphi_2^*(x)| = 2$. Then when $x \leqslant x_{q-1} = \delta(q-1)$ we have $\varphi_1(x) \equiv \varphi_2(x)$. Put

$$g(x) = \varphi_2(x) - \varphi_1(x) = \frac{1}{(s-1)!} \int_0^x (x-t)^{s-1} g^*(t)\, dt$$

If $x_{q-1} = 0$, then, by hypothesis

$$\frac{d^k g(0)}{dx^k} = \frac{d^k \varphi_2(0)}{dx^k} - \frac{d^k \varphi_1(0)}{dx^k} = 0$$

But if $x_{q-1} > 0$, $g(x) \equiv 0$ on the segment $[0, x_{q-1}]$, and hence

$$\frac{d^k g(x_{q-1})}{dx^k} = 0$$

i.e. for any x_{q-1}

$$\frac{d^k g(x_{q-1})}{dx^k} = 0 \qquad (k = 0, 1, \ldots, s-1)$$

Since, by hypothesis, $g(x_0) \neq 0$

$$x_{q-1} \leqslant x_0 \leqslant \rho - 4s\delta$$

Let $x \geqslant x_{q-1}$. Then

$$|g(x)| = \frac{1}{(s-1)!} \left| \int_{x_{q-1}}^{x} (x-t)^{s-1} g^*(t)\, dt \right| \geqslant$$

$$\geqslant \frac{1}{(s-1)!} \int_{x_{q-1}}^{x_q} (x-t)^{s-1} |g^*(t)|\, dt -$$

$$-\frac{1}{(s-1)!}\int_{x_q}^{x}(x-t)^{s-1}\,|\,g^*(t)\,|\,dt \geqslant$$

$$\geqslant \frac{1}{(s-1)!}\int_{x_{q-1}}^{x_q}(x-t)^{s-1}2\,dt - \frac{1}{(s-1)!}\int_{x_q}^{x}(x-t)^{s-1}2\,dt =$$

$$= \frac{2}{s!}\,[(x-x_{q-1})^s - 2\,(x-x_q)^s].$$

Put

$$x' = \delta\,(q-1) + \delta\,\frac{2^{\frac{1}{s-1}}}{2^{\frac{1}{s-1}}-1}$$

Then it is not difficult to verify that $x' \leqslant \rho$ and

$$|\,g(x')\,| \geqslant \frac{2}{s!}\,[(x'-x_{q-1})^s - 2\,(x'-x_q)^s] =$$

$$= \frac{2\delta^s}{s!}\left(\frac{2^{\frac{s}{s-1}}-2}{\left(2^{\frac{s}{s-1}}-1\right)^s}\right) = \frac{4\delta}{s!}\,\frac{1}{\left(2^{\frac{1}{s-1}}-1\right)^{s-1}} \geqslant$$

$$\geqslant \frac{4\delta^s}{s!}\,\frac{1}{\left[\left(1+\frac{2}{3}\right)^{\frac{1}{s-1}}-1\right]^{s-1}} = \frac{2^{3-s}s^{s-1}}{s!}\,\delta^s \geqslant \delta^s$$

i.e. at the point $x' \leqslant \rho$

$$\varphi_1(x') - \varphi_2(x')\,| \geqslant \delta^s$$

Q.E.D.

Theorem 2. (A.N. Kolmogorov). For any $s \geqslant 1$, $L > 0$, $c > 0$ there exist two positive constants A' and A'', depending only on s, such that for sufficiently small $\varepsilon > 0$

$$A'\rho\left(\frac{L}{\varepsilon}\right)^{\frac{1}{s}} \leqslant H_{\varepsilon}(F^{\rho}_{s,\,L,\,c}) \leqslant A''\rho\left(\frac{L}{\varepsilon}\right)^{\frac{1}{s}}$$

Proof. We prove the theorem first for $L=1$. Put $\delta = (3\varepsilon)^{\frac{1}{s}}$. Then, from Lemma 4, any two functions $\varphi_1(x)$ and $\varphi_2(x)$ which are not equal on the segment $[0,\ \rho - 4s\delta]$, differ by $\delta^s_{h_s} = 3\varepsilon$ on r. But there are obviously not less than 2^{h_s} such functions, where $h_s = \left[\frac{\rho - 4s\delta}{\delta}\right] \geqslant \frac{\rho}{\delta} - 5s$.

Therefore, from Lemma 3 § 5

$$H_{\varepsilon}(F^{\rho}_{s,1,c}) \geqslant \frac{\rho}{\delta} - 5s = \rho\left(\frac{1}{3\varepsilon}\right)^{\frac{1}{s}} - 5s$$

Now put $\delta = \left(\frac{\varepsilon}{A}\right)^{\frac{1}{s}}$. Then, by Theorem 1, we can approximate to any function $f(x)$ of the family $F^{\rho}_{s,1,c}$ by a function $\varphi(x)$ of the family $\Phi^{\rho,\delta}_{s,L,c}$ to an accuracy of $(A\delta)^s = \varepsilon$ (L can be taken equal to 2 for example; $\delta = \left(\frac{\varepsilon}{A}\right)^{\frac{1}{s}}$, $A > 0$ depends only on s).

But the number of functions of the family $\Phi^{\rho,\delta}_{s,2,c}$ does not exceed $\left(\left[\frac{2c}{\delta}\right]+1\right)^s 2^h$, where $h = \left[\frac{\rho}{\delta}\right]+1$, i.e.

$$H_{\varepsilon}(F^{\rho}_{s,1,c}) \leqslant H_{\varepsilon}^{\Phi^{\rho,\delta}_{s,2,c}}(F^{\rho}_{s,1,c}) \leqslant \log\left\{\left(\left[\frac{2c}{\delta}\right]+1\right)^s 2^h\right\} \leqslant$$

$$\leqslant \rho\left(\frac{A}{\varepsilon}\right)^{\frac{1}{s}} + 1 + \log\left(1 + \frac{cA^{\frac{1}{s}}}{\varepsilon^{\frac{1}{s}}}\right).$$

Hence, for sufficiently small ε

$$H_{\varepsilon}(F^{\rho}_{s,1,c}) \leqslant 2A^{\frac{1}{s}}\rho\left(\frac{1}{\varepsilon}\right)^{\frac{1}{s}},$$

$$H_{\varepsilon}(F^{\rho}_{s,1,c}) \geqslant \rho\left(\frac{1}{3\varepsilon}\right)^{\frac{1}{s}} - 5s \geqslant \frac{1}{2\cdot 3^{\frac{1}{s}}}\rho\left(\frac{1}{\varepsilon}\right)^{\frac{1}{s}}$$

i.e. we can find two positive constants, depending only on s, such that for sufficiently small ε

$$A'\rho\left(\frac{1}{\varepsilon}\right)^{\frac{1}{s}} \leqslant H_{\varepsilon}(F^{\rho}_{s,1,c}) \leqslant A''\rho\left(\frac{1}{\varepsilon}\right)^{\frac{1}{s}}$$

It is not difficult to verify that

$$H_{\varepsilon}(F^{\rho}_{s,L,c}) = H_{\frac{\varepsilon}{L}}\left(F^{\rho}_{s,1,\frac{c}{L}}\right)$$

Thus, for any $L > 0$

$$A'\rho\left(\frac{L}{\varepsilon}\right)^{\frac{1}{s}} \leqslant H_{\varepsilon}(F^{\rho}_{s,L,c}) \leqslant A''\rho\left(\frac{L}{\varepsilon}\right)^{\frac{1}{s}}$$

Q.E.D.

§ 16. A.N. Kolmogorov's Theorem

Let E_n be an n-dimensional Euclidean space, J_n^ρ the n-dimensional closed cube in E_n given by

$$0 \leqslant x_i \leqslant \rho \qquad (i = 1, 2, \ldots, n)$$

We choose the natural number p and $0 < \alpha \leqslant 1$, and denote by $F_{s, L, c}^{\rho, n}$ $(s = p + \alpha)$ the space of the real functions $f(x) = f(x_1, x_2, \ldots, x_n)$ defined on the cube J_n^ρ, all of whose partial derivatives of order p satisfy the Golder* condition on the cube J_n^ρ with constant $L > 0$ and index α, and such that

$$\left| \frac{\partial^{k_1 + k_2 + \ldots + k_n} f(0)}{\partial x_1^{k_1}\, \partial x_2^{k_2}, \ldots, \partial x_n^{k_n}} \right| \leqslant c \qquad \left(\sum_{i=1}^{n} k_i \leqslant p \right)$$

In this section we shall prove that the value of the ε-entropy of $F_{s, L, c}^{\rho, n}$ obtained by A.N. Kolmogorov is correct, and, in particular, that for sufficiently small ε

$$A\rho^n \left(\frac{L}{\varepsilon} \right)^{\frac{n}{s}} \leqslant H_\varepsilon \left(F_{s, L, c}^{\rho, n} \right) \leqslant B\rho^n \left(\frac{L}{\varepsilon} \right)^{\frac{n}{s}}$$

where A and B are positive parameters, depending only on s and n.

We choose $\delta > 0$ such that the number $\frac{\rho}{\delta}$ is an integer. We divide the cube J_n^ρ into $\left(\frac{\rho}{\delta}\right)^n$ n-dimensional cubes ω_i^δ $\left(i = 1, 2, \ldots, \left(\frac{\rho}{\delta}\right)^n\right)$ by hyperplanes, parallel to its $(n-1)$-dimensional edges. Each of the cubes ω_i^δ has side of length δ, and the edges of these cubes are parallel to those of J_n^ρ. Let C_i denote the centre of the cube ω_i^δ and σ_i^δ the n-dimensional closed sphere (inscribed in ω_i^δ) of radius $\frac{\delta}{2}$ and centre

---

* The function $g(x)$ is said to satisfy the Golder condition with constant L and index α if, for any pair of points x', x'' of J_n^ρ

$$| g(x') - g(x'') | \leqslant L \left[\rho_{E_n}(x', x'') \right]^\alpha$$

at the point C_i. Put

$$\varphi_i^{A,\delta}(x)=\varphi_i^{A,\delta}(x_1, x_2, \ldots, x_n)=\begin{cases} 0, \text{ if } x\in J_n^{\rho}-\sigma_i^{\delta}, \\ A\left\{\cos\left[\frac{\pi}{\delta}\rho(c_i, x)\right]\right\}^s, \\ \qquad\qquad \text{if } x\in\sigma_i^{\delta}, \end{cases}$$

where $\rho(C_i, x)=\rho_{E_n}(C_i, x)$ is the distance from the point x to the centre C_i of the sphere σ_i^{δ}. Put, further,

$$\varphi^{A,\delta}_{\eta_1,\eta_2,\ldots,\eta_h}(x)=\sum_{i=1}^{h}\eta_i\varphi_i^{A,\delta}(x)$$

$$\left(\eta_i=\pm 1;\ i=1, 2, \ldots, h;\ h=\left(\frac{\rho}{\delta}\right)^n\right)$$

Lemma 1. We can find a positive number $A(s, L, n)$, such that when $A=A(s, L, n)\delta^s$ and given any set of numbers $\eta_i\,(i=1, 2, \ldots, h)$ the corresponding function $\varphi^{A,\delta}_{\eta_1,\eta_2,\ldots,\eta_n}(x)$ belongs to $F^{\rho,n}_{s,L,c}$.

Proof. By differentiating $\varphi_i^{A,\delta}(x)$ it is not difficult to see that inside the sphere σ_i^{δ} its partial derivatives of all orders exist. And the modulus of any partial derivative of order k is bounded inside σ_i^{δ} by $AB(s, k, n)\delta^{-k}$, where $B(s, k, n)>0$ is some constant, depending only on s, k, n. In particular, any derivative of the function $\varphi_i^{A,\delta}(x)$ of order $p+1$ is bounded in the sphere σ_i^{δ} by the constant

$$AB(s, p+1, n)\delta^{-p-1}=\frac{A(s, L, n)B(s, p+1, n)}{\delta^{1-\alpha}}$$

Let $g(x)$ be any pth order partial derivative of the functions $\varphi_i^{A,\delta}(x)$. We take two points a and b belonging to the sphere σ_i^{δ}. Then $g(b)-g(a)=\rho_{E_n}(a, b)\frac{\partial g(C)}{\partial r}$ where $\frac{\partial g(C)}{\partial r}$ is the derivative of $g(x)$ along the direction (a, b), taken at some point C of $[a, b]$. Since any $p+1$th order partial derivative of $\varphi_i^{A,\delta}(x)$ is bounded inside the sphere by the constant

$$\frac{A(s, L, n)B(r, p+1, n)}{\delta^{1-\alpha}}, \quad \text{we have} \quad \left|\frac{\partial g(c)}{\partial r}\right|\leqslant n\frac{A(s, L, n)B(s, p+1, n)}{\delta^{1-\alpha}}$$

And then

$$|g(b)-g(a)| \leqslant \left|\rho \frac{\partial g C}{\partial r}\right| \leqslant \rho n \frac{A(s, L, n) B(s, p+1, n)}{\delta^{1-\alpha}} \leqslant$$
$$\leqslant \rho^{\alpha} n A(s, L, n) B(s, p+1, n)$$

Put

$$A(s, L, n)=\frac{L}{2nB(s, p+1, n)}$$

Then

$$|g(b)-g(a)| \leqslant \frac{1}{2} L\rho^{\alpha}$$

Now let $\psi(x)$ be any of the p-x partial derivatives of the function $\varphi^{A\,\delta}_{\eta_1, \eta_2, \ldots, \eta_h}(x)$. We choose two points x' and x'' of $J^{\rho}_{n}\left(x' \in \sigma^{\delta}_{i},\ x'' \in \sigma^{\delta}_{j}\right)$ and let $g_1(x)$ and $g_2(x)$ be the partial derivatives of the same kind as $\psi(x)$ of the functions $\varphi^{A,\delta}_{i}(x)$ and $\varphi^{A,\delta}_{j}(x)$ (respectively). It is easy to verify that $g_1(x)$ and $g_2(x)$ are continuous on J^{ρ}_{n} and identically equal to zero on the sets $J^{\rho}_{n}-\sigma^{\delta}_{i}$ and $J^{\rho}_{n}-\sigma^{\delta}_{j}$ (respectively). We select some point x_0 belonging to the boundary of the sphere σ^{δ}_{i} and lying on the segment $[x', x'']$. Then

$$|\psi(x'')-\psi(x')| \leqslant |g_1(x'')-g_1(x')|+|g_2(x'')-g_2(x')| =$$
$$=|g_1(x')-g_1(x_0)|+|g_2(x'')-g_2(x_0)| \leqslant$$
$$\leqslant \frac{1}{2} L[\rho(x', x_0)]^{\alpha}+\frac{1}{2} L[\rho(x'', x_0)]^{\alpha} \leqslant L[\rho(x', x'')]^{\alpha}$$

If one of the points x', x'' (or both) belongs to the set $J^{\rho}_{n}-\sum_{i=1}^{h}\sigma^{\delta}_{i}$, then we can prove similarly that

$$|\psi(x'')-\psi(x')| \leqslant L[\rho(x', x'')]^{\alpha}$$

Q.E.D.

<u>Lemma 2</u>. There exists a positive constant A, depending

only on s, L, n, such that for sufficiently small ε

$$H_\varepsilon\left(F^{\rho, n}_{\varkappa, L, c}\right) \geqslant A\rho^n \left(\frac{1}{\varepsilon}\right)^{\frac{n}{\varkappa}}$$

Proof. We choose some positive number $k > 1$ such that when $\delta = \left[\frac{k\varepsilon}{A(s, L, n)}\right]^{\frac{1}{s}}$, $\frac{\rho}{\delta}$ is an integer.

We choose two different functions of the type $\varphi^{A, \delta}_{\eta_1, \eta_2, \ldots, \eta_h}(x)$ and $\varphi^{A, \delta}_{\tau_1, \tau_2, \ldots, \tau_h}$ $(A = A(s, L, n)\delta^s$ and $A(s, L, n)$ is taken so small that both functions belong to the family $F^{\rho, n}_{s, L, c}$. Since the functions we have chosen are assumed to be different, for some $i \tau_i \neq \eta_i$. And therefore

$$\left|\varphi^{A, \delta}_{\eta_1, \eta_2, \ldots, \eta_h}(C_i) - \varphi^{A, \delta}_{\tau_1, \tau_2, \ldots, \tau_h}(C_i)\right| = $$
$$= 2A = 2A(s, L, n)\delta^s = 2k\varepsilon > 2\varepsilon$$

Hence, by Lemma 3 § 5

$$H_\varepsilon\left(F^{\rho, n}_{s, L, c}\right) \geqslant \log 2^h = \frac{\rho}{\delta^n} = \left(\frac{A(s, L, n)}{k}\right)^{\frac{n}{\varkappa}} \rho^n \left(\frac{1}{\varepsilon}\right)^{\frac{n}{s}}$$

Q.E.D.

Lemma 3. There exists a constant $B > 0$ such that for sufficiently small $\varepsilon > 0$

$$H_\varepsilon\left(F^{\rho, n}_{s, L, c}\right) \leqslant B\rho^n \left(\frac{1}{\varepsilon}\right)^{\frac{n}{\varkappa}}$$

Proof. Let us choose some $\delta > 0$ such that the ratio $\frac{\rho}{\delta}$ is an integer. In the cube J^ρ_n consider the uniform lattice with step δ, consisting of the points $d_i\left(i = 1, 2, \ldots, h;\ h = \left(\frac{\rho}{\delta} + 1\right)^n\right)$.

We shall assume the corners of the lattice to be numbered so that the point d_i coincides with the origin of co-ordinates, and for any i

$$\rho_{E_n}(d_{i-1}, d_i) = \delta$$

We now choose some function $f(x)$ of the family $F^{\rho, n}_{s, L, c}$ and we shall show a method of constructing a table for this function the volume of which is less than $B\rho^n\left(\frac{1}{\varepsilon}\right)^{\frac{n}{s}}$.

Let h_0 denote the number of different kinds of partial derivative (of all orders up to and including the pth) of a function of n variables. It is not difficult to verify that $h_0 \leqslant (p+1)^n$. Let $\{\tau_1^{j,k}\}$ $(\tau_1^{j,k} = 0,1)$ be the coefficients of the binary representation (see § 1) of the numbers

$$\frac{\partial^{k_1+k_2+\ldots+k_n} f(d_1)}{\partial x_1^{k_1}, \partial x_2^{k_2}, \ldots, \partial x_n^{k_n}} \qquad (k_1+k_2+\ldots+k_n \leqslant p)$$

written in some order. Then the numbers

$$\left\{\frac{\partial^{k_1+k_2+\ldots+k_n} f(d_1)}{\partial x_1^{k_1} \partial x_2^{k_2} \ldots \partial x_n^{k_n}}\right\} \qquad (k_1+k_2+\ldots+k_n = k)$$

are represented in the table to an accuracy of δ^{s-k}, i.e.

$$h_1^k \leqslant \left(\left[\log \frac{c}{\delta^{s-k}}\right]+1\right)(k+1)^n$$

(see Lemma 3 § 6) binary digits $\tau_1^{j,k}$ $(j = 1, 2, \ldots, h_1^k)$ are sufficient to represent them in binary. Thus, to represent all partial derivatives of $f(x)$ at the point $x = d_1$ in binary we need

$$h_1 = \sum_{k=0}^{p} h_1^k \leqslant (p+1)^{n+1}\left(1+\log \frac{c}{\delta^s}\right)$$

binary digits

$$\tau_1^{j,k} \; (j = 1, 2, \ldots, h_1^k; \quad k = 0, 1, \ldots, p)$$

Let us assume now that we have found a method for selecting the digits $\{\tau_i^{j,k}\}$ $(i = 1, 2, \ldots, q-1)$, together with a rule for calculating from these digits the values of the numbers

$$\left\{\frac{\partial^{k_1+k_2+\ldots+k_n} f(d_i)}{\partial x_1^{k_1} \partial x_2^{k_2} \ldots \partial x_n^{k_n}}\right\} \qquad (k_1+k_2+\ldots+k_n = k)$$

$(i = 1, 2, \ldots, q-1)$ to an accuracy of δ^{s-k} $(k = 0, 1, \ldots, p)$. We examine the subsequent procedure for constructing the table for $f(x)$. Let $g_k(x)$ be one of the kth order partial derivatives of $f(x)$. According to the induction hypothesis, the values of all partial derivatives of order $m \leqslant p-k$ of $g_k(x)$ at the point $x = d_{q-1}$ can be calculated to an accuracy of δ^{s-k-m} $(m = 0, 1, 2, \ldots, p-k)$ from that part of the table already constructed. From Lagrange's formula, the value of $g_k(d_q)$ is found sufficiently accurately from the approximate values of the derivatives of $g(x)$ at d_{q-1}. Therefore, to represent the numbers $g_k(d_q)$ to an accuracy of δ^{s-k} we need only a small number of binary digits. Since $\rho_{E_n}(d_{q-1}, d_q) = \delta$, all the corresponding co-ordinates (except one) of the points d_{q-1}, d_q are equal. For definiteness, we shall suppose that

$$x_1(d_q) = x_1(d_{q-1}) + \delta \text{ and } x_i(d_q) = x_i(d_{q-1})$$

for $i = 2, 3, \ldots, n$. Then

$$g_k(d_q) = \sum_{m=0}^{p-k-1} \frac{\partial^m g_k(d_{q-1})}{\partial x_1^m} \frac{\delta^m}{m!} +$$

$$+ \frac{1}{(p-k)!} \frac{\partial^{p-k} g_k(d_{q-1} + \theta\delta)}{\partial x_1^{p-k}} \delta^{p-k} =$$

$$= \sum_{m=0}^{p-k} \frac{\partial^m g_k(d_{q-1})}{\partial x_1^m} \frac{\delta^m}{m!} + \frac{L}{(p-k)!} \Theta \delta^{s-k}$$

where $0 \leqslant \theta \leqslant 1$ and $-1 \leqslant \Theta' \leqslant 1$. But since $\frac{\partial^m g_k(d_{q-1})}{\partial x_1^m}$ is given by the table only to an accuracy of δ^{s-k-m} $(m = 0$ $1, \ldots, p-k)$ $g_k(d_q)$ is determined by the constructed part of the table only to an accuracy of

$$\sum_{m=0}^{p-k} \delta^{s-k-m} \frac{\delta^m}{m!} + \frac{L\delta^{s-k}}{(p-k)!} =$$

$$= \delta^{s-k} \left(\sum_{m=0}^{p-k} \frac{1}{m!} + \frac{L}{(p-k)!} \right) \leqslant e(L+1)\delta^{s-k}$$

Therefore, in order to represent the value of $g_k(d_q)$ in the table to an accuracy of δ^{s-k}, it is sufficient to put another $h_q^{j,k} = [\log\{(L+1)e\}]+1$ binary digits in the table. Hence, to determine the values of all kth order partial derivatives of $f(x)$ it is sufficient to add $h_q^k \leqslant (k+1)^n h_q^{j,k}$ binary digits to the table $(k=0, 1, \ldots, p)$. Thus, the approximate representation of the values of all partial derivatives of the functions $f(x)$ at the point d_q will use only

$$h_q = \sum_{k=0}^{p} h_q^k \leqslant (p+1)^{n+1}\{1+\log[e(L+1)]\}$$

binary digits.

The volume of the table T which we have constructed is equal to

$$P(T) = \sum_{q=1}^{h} h_q \leqslant (p+1)^{n+1}\left(1+\log\frac{c}{\delta^s}\right)+ \\ +(h-1)(p+1)^{n+1}\{1+\log[e(L+1)]\}$$

We shall now describe the rule we use to enable us to compute the value of $f(x)$ at any point of the cube J_n^ρ from the parameters of the table. To do this, we divide the cube J_n^ρ in some way into sets ω_q $(\omega_q \ni d_q)$ the diameter of each set not exceeding $\delta\sqrt{n}$, and such that $\sum_{q=1}^{h}\omega_q = J_n^\rho$. The approximate value of the function $f(x)$ is calculated using the parameters $\tau_q^{j,k}$ of T in the following way.

Let $x \in \omega_q$. Then, for the approximate value of $f(x)$ we take

$$f^*(x) = \sum_{k_1+k_2+\ldots+k_n \leqslant p} a_{k_1, k_2, \ldots, k_n} \prod_{i=1}^{n} \frac{[x_i - x_i(d_q)]^{k_i}}{k_i!}$$

where $a_{k_1, k_2, \ldots, k_n}$ is the approximate value (to an accuracy of δ^{s-k} $k=\sum_{i=1}^{n} k_i$) of the k_ith derivative with respect to the variable x_i $(i=1, 2, \ldots, n)$ of $f(x)$. Since $f(x) \in F_{s, L, c}^{\rho; n}$

$\|f(x)-f^*(x)\| \leqslant \delta^s[(p+1)^m+L+1]=B(s, L, n)\delta^s=\varepsilon'$. Therefore, from Theorem 2 § 4

$$H_{\varepsilon'}\left(F^{\rho, n}_{s, L, c}\right) \leqslant (p+1)^{n+1}\left(1+\log\frac{c}{\delta^s}\right)+ \\ +(h-1)(p+1)^{n+1}\{1+\log[e(L+1)]\}$$

We now define δ in the form

$$\delta=\left(\frac{k\varepsilon}{B(s, L, n)}\right)^{\frac{1}{s}}$$

We choose $k<1$ so that the ratio $\frac{\rho}{\delta}$ is an integer. Then

$$H_{\varepsilon}\left(F^{\rho, n}_{s, L, c}\right) \leqslant H_{\varepsilon'}\left(F^{\rho, n}_{s, L, c}\right) \leqslant (p+1)^{n+1}\left(1+\log\frac{c}{\delta^s}\right)+ \\ +(h-1)(p+1)^{n+1}\{1+\log[e(L+1)]\}$$

i.e. for sufficiently small ε

$H_{\varepsilon}\left(F^{\rho, n}_{s, L, c}\right) \leqslant B\rho^n\left(\frac{1}{\varepsilon}\right)^{\frac{n}{s}}$, where $B>0$ is a constant which can be taken to depend on s, L, n only.

Q.E.D.

<u>Theorem 1</u>. (A.N. Kolmogorov). For any $s>0, L>0$, $c>0$ and $n\geqslant 1$ we can find positive constants $A(s, n)$ and $B(s, n)$ such that for sufficiently small ε

$$A(s, n)\rho^n\left(\frac{L}{\varepsilon}\right)^{\frac{n}{s}} \leqslant H_{\varepsilon}\left(F^{\rho, n}_{s, L, c}\right) \leqslant B(s, n)\rho^n\left(\frac{L}{\varepsilon}\right)^{\frac{n}{s}}$$

<u>Proof</u>. First let $L=1$. Then from Lemmas 2 and 3 we have

$$A\rho^n\left(\frac{1}{\varepsilon}\right)^{\frac{n}{s}} \leqslant H_{\varepsilon}\left(F^{\rho, n}_{s, 1, c}\right) \leqslant B\rho^n\left(\frac{1}{\varepsilon}\right)^{\frac{n}{s}}$$

where A and B are positive constants, depending only on s and n, since in this case $L=1$. But since

$$H_{\frac{\varepsilon}{L}}\left(F^{\rho, n}_{s, 1, \frac{c}{L}}\right)=H_{\varepsilon}\left(F^{\rho, n}_{s, L, c}\right)$$

for sufficiently small ε

$$A(s, n)\rho^n\left(\frac{L}{\varepsilon}\right)^{\frac{n}{s}} \leqslant H_{\varepsilon}\left(F^{\rho, n}_{s, L, c}\right) \leqslant B(s, n)\rho^n\left(\frac{L}{\varepsilon}\right)^{\frac{n}{s}}$$

Q.E.D.

§ 17. The Entropy of the Space of Continuous Functions

$F^G_{\omega(\delta),c}$ is the space of all real functions $f(x)$, given on a compact metrical space G , with modulus of continuity $\omega(\delta)$ *, and such that $|f(x_0)| \leqslant c$, where x_0 is some point of G , constant for all functions of the family. We shall assume further that $\omega(\delta)$ is continuous at $\delta = 0$ and $\omega(0) = 0$.

Theorem 1. If F is some subset of the space $F^G_{\omega(\delta),c} = \Phi$, then for any $\varepsilon > 0$

$$H_\varepsilon(F) = H^\Phi_\varepsilon(F)$$

The proof is easily obtained from Lemma 1 § 3.

We shall say that the modulus of continuity $\omega(\delta)$ is regular if $\omega(\delta)$, considered only on the semi-axis $\delta \geqslant 0$, is a continuous function of δ at the point $\delta = 0\ (\omega(0) = 0)$ and such that (as a function of δ) it has itself modulus of continuity $\omega(\delta)$, i.e. for any $\delta \geqslant 0$ and $\alpha > 0$

$$0 < \omega(\delta + \alpha) - \omega(\delta) \leqslant \omega(\alpha)$$

It is not difficult to see that a regular modulus of continuity is a continuous, strictly monotonic increasing function everywhere on $(\delta \geqslant 0)$.

Lemma 1. If the modulus of continuity $\omega(\delta)$ is regular, then for any $\varepsilon < \frac{c}{18}$

$$H_\varepsilon(F^G_{\omega(\delta),c}) \geqslant 2^{h_{2\delta(4\varepsilon)}(G)} + \log \frac{c}{6\varepsilon}$$

where $\delta(\varepsilon)$ is the inverse of $\omega(\delta)$ at the point $\omega = \varepsilon$.

Proof. From Theorem 1 § 5 we can select $n = n_j(G) = n_{2\delta(4\varepsilon)}(G)$ points $x_1, x_2, \ldots, x_n$ in G , which are strictly further apart from one another than $2j = 4\delta(4\varepsilon)$. Put $x = \bigcup_{i=1}^{n} x_i$ and $\beta = \frac{3}{2}\delta(\varepsilon)$.

---

* We say that the function $f(x)$ has modulus of continuity $\omega(\delta)$ if, given any $\delta > 0$ for any pair of points x and y of G such that $\rho_G(x, y) \leqslant \delta$

$$|f(x) - f(y)| \leqslant \omega(\delta)$$

Let $f_i^A(x)$ be a function of the point $x\,(x \in G)$, defined in the following way:

$$f_i^A(x) = \begin{cases} \omega[\beta - \rho_G(x_i, x)] + A & \text{when } \rho_G(x_i, x) \leqslant \beta \\ A & \text{when } \rho_G(x_i, x) \geqslant \beta. \end{cases}$$

We prove that, for any $i \leqslant n$ and for real A, the function $f_i^A(x)$ defined in this way has modulus of continuity $\omega(\delta)$ For, if x and y are such that $\rho_G(x_i, y) \leqslant \beta$ and $\rho(x_i, x) \leqslant \beta$

$$|f_i^A(x) - f_i^A(y)| = |\omega[\beta - \rho_G(x_i, x)] - \omega[\beta - \rho_G(x_i, y)]| \leqslant$$

$$\leqslant \omega[\rho_G(x_i, x) - \rho_G(x_i, y)] \leqslant \omega[\rho_G(x, y)]$$

from the regularity of the modulus of continuity and the triangular axioms. If $\rho_G(x_i, x) \geqslant \beta$ and $\rho_G(x_i, y) \geqslant \beta$ then

$$|f_i^A(x) - f_i^A(y)| = 0 \leqslant \omega[\rho_G(x, y)]$$

Further, if, say, $\rho_G(x_i, x) \leqslant \beta$ while $\rho_G(x_i, y) \geqslant \beta$, then

$$|f_i^A(x) - f_i^A(y)| = |f_i^A(x) - A| \leqslant \omega[\rho_G(x, y)]$$

again from the regularity of the modulus of continuity and the triangular axioms. Thus, we have proved that the modulus of continuity of the functions $f_i^A(x)$ does not exceed $\omega(\delta)$.

Now let $f^k_{\alpha_1, \alpha_2, \ldots, \alpha_n}(x)$ be a function defined by

$$f^k_{\alpha_1, \alpha_2, \ldots, \alpha_n}(x) = c - 6(k+1)\varepsilon + \sum_{i=1}^{n} \alpha_i f_i^0(x)$$

$$\left(\alpha_i = \pm 1;\ i = 1, 2, \ldots, n;\ k = 1, 2, \ldots, \left[\frac{c}{3\varepsilon}\right] - 2\right)$$

Let σ_i be the set given by the inequality

$$f_i^0(x) > 0$$

Since

$$\beta = \frac{3}{2}\delta(\varepsilon) \leqslant \frac{3}{2}\delta(4\varepsilon) \text{ and } \rho_G(x_i, y_j) > 4\delta(4\varepsilon)$$

then $\rho_G(\sigma_i, \sigma_j) > \delta(4\varepsilon)$. But since

$$\max_G f_i^0(x) = f_i^0(x_i) = \omega(\beta) = \omega\left[\frac{3}{2}\delta(\varepsilon)\right] < 2\varepsilon$$

for any pair of points $x \in \sigma_i$, $y \in \sigma_j$

$$|f^k_{\alpha_1, \alpha_2, \ldots, \alpha_n}(x) - f^k_{\alpha_1, \alpha_2, \ldots, \alpha_n}(y)| \leqslant |f_i^0(x)| + |f_j^0(y)| \leqslant$$
$$\leqslant 4\varepsilon = \omega(\delta(4\varepsilon)) \leqslant \omega(\rho_G(x, y))$$

If $x \in \sigma_i$ and $y \in \sigma_i$ then

$$|f^k_{\alpha_1, \alpha_2, \ldots, \alpha_n}(x) - f^k_{\alpha_1, \alpha_2, \ldots, \alpha_n}(y)| =$$
$$= |f_i^0(x) - f_i^0(y)| \leqslant \omega[\rho_G(x, y)]$$

since $f_i^0(x)$ has modulus of continuity $\omega(\delta)$.

Further, if $x \in \sigma_i$, and $y \in G - \sum_{i=1}^{n} \sigma_i$, then

$$|f^k_{\alpha_1, \alpha_2, \ldots, \alpha_n}(x) - f^k_{\alpha_1, \alpha_2, \ldots, \alpha_n}(y)| = f_i^0(x) + 0 \leqslant \omega[\rho_G(x, y)].$$

We have thus proved that the functions $\{f^k_{\alpha_1, \alpha_2, \ldots, \alpha_n}(x)\}$ have modulus of continuity $\omega(\delta)$.

Since $\max f_i^0(x) \leqslant 2\varepsilon$ and $0 < k \leqslant \left[\frac{c}{3\varepsilon}\right] - 2$

$$\max_G f^k_{\alpha_1, \alpha_2, \ldots, \alpha_n}(x) \leqslant k + \max_G f_i^0(x) \leqslant c$$

Therefore the functions $f^k_{\alpha_1, \alpha_2, \ldots, \alpha_n}(x)$ belong to the family $F^G_{\omega(\delta), c}$.

If $k_1 \neq k_2$, at any point $x \in G - \sum_{i=1}^{n} \sigma_i$

$$|f^{k_1}_{\alpha_1, \alpha_2, \ldots, \alpha_n}(x) - f^{k_2}_{\alpha_1, \alpha_2, \ldots, \alpha_n}(x)| = 6\varepsilon|k_1 - k_2| \geqslant 6\varepsilon$$

If $f^k_{\alpha_1, \alpha_2, \ldots, \alpha_n}(x)$ and $f^k_{\beta_1, \beta_2, \ldots, \beta_n}(x)$ are such that for some i $\alpha_i \neq \beta_i$ then

$$|f^k_{\alpha_1, \alpha_2, \ldots, \alpha_n}(x_i) - f^k_{\beta_1, \beta_2, \ldots, \beta_n}(x_i)| =$$

$$= 2f_i^0(x_i) = 2\omega\left[\frac{3}{2}\delta(\varepsilon)\right] > 2\varepsilon$$

i.e. the difference between the functions $\{f^k_{\alpha_1, \alpha_j, \dots, \alpha_n}(x)\}$ is strictly more than 2ε.

But there are

$$\left(\left[\frac{c}{3\varepsilon}\right] - 2\right)2^n$$

such functions. Hence, from Lemma 3 § 5

$$H_\varepsilon(F^G_{\omega(\delta), c}) \geqslant \log\left\{\left(\left[\frac{c}{3\varepsilon}\right] - 2\right)2^n\right\} =$$
$$= n_{2\delta(4\varepsilon)} + \log\left(\left[\frac{c}{3\varepsilon}\right] - 2\right) \geqslant 2^{h_{2\delta(4\varepsilon)}(G)} + \log\left(\frac{c}{3\varepsilon} - 3\right) \geqslant$$
$$\geqslant 2^{h_{2\delta(4\varepsilon)}(G)} + \log\left(\frac{c}{6\varepsilon}\right),$$

since $\varepsilon \leqslant \frac{c}{18}$. Q.E.D.

<u>Lemma 2</u>. If the space G is connected, then for any $\varepsilon \leqslant \frac{c}{2}$

$$H_\varepsilon(F^G_{\omega(\delta), c}) \leqslant 2^{H_{\frac{1}{2}\delta\left(\frac{\varepsilon}{2}\right)}(G)} + \log\left(\frac{3c}{\varepsilon}\right)$$

<u>Proof</u>. We choose a δ-covering $\left(\delta = \delta\left(\frac{1}{2}\varepsilon\right)\right)$ of G by sets $\{\sigma_i\}$, $i = 1, 2, \dots, n$; $n = N_{\frac{1}{2}\delta\left(\frac{1}{2}\varepsilon\right)}(G)$ (see § 4). Since the diameter of a set does not increase on closure, we can obviously assume the sets σ_i to be closed (in G). We shall assume the sets σ_i to be numbered in such a way that the point x_0 (see the definition of the space $F^G_{\omega(\delta), c}$) proves to belong to the set σ_1, that σ_2 is one of the sets which has points in common with σ_1, and so on, that σ_q is a set which has at least one common point with the set $\omega_{q-1} = \sum_{i=1}^{q-1} \sigma_i$. It is possible to number them in this way, since otherwise we could divide G into two non-empty, closed and non-intersecting sets ω_{q-1} and $\omega_n - \omega_{q-1}$ which contradicts the condition that G is connected.

Let x_q be some point of the set $\omega_q \cap \sigma_{q+1}$ $(q = 1, 2, \dots, n)$. We now select a function $f(x)$ of the family $F^{G}_{\omega(\delta),c}$, and describe a method for constructing the table $T^{\Phi}_{\varepsilon}(f)$, which will give $f(x)$ to an accuracy of ε. We shall here take Φ to be the space of all bounded real functions, defined on the set G (the norm being the upper bound of the values of the functions on G).

We take the first n_0 parameters of the table $T^{\Phi}_{\varepsilon}(f)$ to be the coefficients $\alpha_1, \alpha_2, \ldots, \alpha_{n_0}$ in the binary representation of the value of $f(x_1)$ to an accuracy of $\frac{\varepsilon}{2}$. Since the diameter $D(\sigma_1) \leqslant \delta\left(\frac{\varepsilon}{2}\right)$ and $|f(x_0)| \leqslant c$

$$|f(x_1)| \leqslant |f(x_0)| + \frac{\varepsilon}{2} \leqslant c + \frac{\varepsilon}{2}$$

Therefore, from Lemma 3 § 6

$$\log\left(1 + \left[\frac{c + \frac{\varepsilon}{2}}{\frac{\varepsilon}{2}}\right]\right) \leqslant \log\left(2 + \frac{2c}{\varepsilon}\right) \leqslant \log\left(\frac{3c}{\varepsilon}\right) \quad \left(\varepsilon \leqslant \frac{c}{2}\right)$$

binary digits are sufficient to represent $f(x_1)$ (to an accuracy of $\frac{\varepsilon}{2}$), i.e. we can take

$$n_0 \leqslant \log\left(\frac{3c}{\varepsilon}\right)$$

All the remaining parameters of the table will also be binary numbers:

$$\beta_2, \beta_3, \ldots, \beta_n \qquad (\beta_i = \pm 1,\ i = 2, \ldots, n)$$

Suppose that a method for calculating the numbers $\beta_i\ (i = 2, \ldots, q-1)$ (for the values of $\{f(x_i)\}$) has already been described, and that it is such that we can calculate the values of $f(x_{q-1})$ to an accuracy of $\frac{\varepsilon}{2}$ with the numbers $\alpha_1, \alpha_2, \ldots, \alpha_{n_0}; \beta_2, \beta_3, \ldots, \beta_{q-1}$, i.e. we can find the number $f^*(x_{q-1})$ such that

$$|f(x_{q-1}) - f^*(x_{q-1})| \leqslant \frac{\varepsilon}{2}$$

Then we select the values of $\beta_q = \pm 1$ such that the number

$$f^*(x_q) = f^*(x_{q-1}) + \beta_q \frac{\varepsilon}{2}$$

differs from $f(x_q)$ by not more than $\frac{\varepsilon}{2}$, i.e. such that

$$|f^*(x_q) - f(x_q)| \leqslant \frac{\varepsilon}{2}.$$

This is possible, since $D(\sigma_q) \leqslant \delta\left(\frac{\varepsilon}{2}\right)$ $(x_{q-1} \in \sigma_q \; x_q \in \sigma_q)$, and since, by the induction hypothesis

$$f^*(x_{q-1}) - f(x_{q-1})| \leqslant \frac{\varepsilon}{2}$$

and hence

$$|f(x_q) - f(x_{q-1})| \leqslant \omega[D(\sigma_q)] \leqslant \frac{\varepsilon}{2}$$

In this way the parameters $\beta_2, \beta_3, \ldots, \beta_n (n = N_{\frac{1}{2}\delta\left(\frac{1}{2}\varepsilon\right)}(G))$ are determined. The values of $\{f(x_q)\}$ can be found to an accuracy of $\frac{\varepsilon}{2}$ with the parameters $\alpha_1, \alpha_2, \ldots, \alpha_{n_0}; \beta_1, \beta_2, \ldots, \beta_n$. We determine the function $f^*(x) \in \Phi$ approximating to $f(x)$ everywhere on G to an accuracy of ε, in the following way: if $x \in \sigma_q - \omega_{q-1}$, then

$$f^*(x) = f^*(x_q) \qquad (q = 1, 2, \ldots, n)$$

Since $D(\sigma_q) \leqslant \delta\left(\frac{\varepsilon}{2}\right)$ and

$$|f(x_q) - f^*(x_q)| \leqslant \frac{\varepsilon}{2} \qquad (q = 1, 2, \ldots, n)$$

we have

$$\|f(x) - f^*(x)\| \leqslant \omega\left[\delta\left(\frac{1}{2}\varepsilon\right)\right] + \frac{\varepsilon}{2} \leqslant \varepsilon$$

Therefore

$$H_\varepsilon\left(F^G_{\omega(\delta), c}\right) \leqslant H^\Phi_\varepsilon\left(F^G_{\omega(\delta), c}\right) \leqslant \log(2^{n_0+n}) = n_0 + n \leqslant$$
$$\leqslant \log\left(\frac{3c}{\varepsilon}\right) + N_{\frac{1}{2}\delta\left(\frac{\varepsilon}{2}\right)}(G) \leqslant \log\left(\frac{3c}{\varepsilon}\right) + 2^{H_{\frac{1}{2}\delta\left(\frac{\varepsilon}{2}\right)}(G)}$$

Q.E.D.

Theorem 2. If G is a connected compact metrical space, and the modulus of continuity $\omega(\delta)$ of the functions of the family $F^{G}_{\omega(\delta),c}$ is regular, then for $0 < \varepsilon < \frac{c}{18}$

$$N_{4\delta}(4\varepsilon)(G) + \log\left(\frac{c}{6\varepsilon}\right) \leqslant H_{\varepsilon}(F^{G}_{\omega(\delta),c}) \leqslant$$
$$\leqslant N_{\frac{1}{2}\delta}\left(\tfrac{1}{2}\varepsilon\right)(G) + \log\left(\frac{3c}{\varepsilon}\right)$$

i.e.

$$2^{H_{4\delta}(4\varepsilon)(G)} + \log\left(\frac{c}{6\varepsilon}\right) \leqslant H_{\varepsilon}(F^{G}_{\omega(\delta),c}) \leqslant 2^{H_{\frac{1}{2}\delta}\left(\frac{\varepsilon}{2}\right)(G)} + \log\left(\frac{3c}{\varepsilon}\right)$$

The proof of the theorem follows from Lemmas 1, 2 and Theorem 1 § 5.

CHAPTER IV

THE VARIATIONS OF A SET

Let E_n be an n-dimensional Euclidean space; $\boldsymbol{x}=(\boldsymbol{x}_1, \boldsymbol{x}_2, \ldots, \boldsymbol{x}_n)$ an orthonormalized base of this space; $x_1, x_2, \ldots, x_n$ the co-ordinates of an arbitrary point in E_n with respect to this base; τ_i^k a k-dimensional co-ordinate plane in E_n, i.e. a plane which stretches along some k co-ordinate axes ($i=1, 2, \ldots, C_n^k$; the numbering of the planes by the suffix i is arbitrary); $\beta_i^{n-k}(q)$ an $(n-k)$-dimensional plane in E_n which contains the point $q\in\tau_i^k$ and is orthogonal to τ_i^k; J_n an n-dimensional closed regular cube in E_n (a cube is said to be regular if its edges are parallel to fixed co-ordinate axes in E_n); J_n^* the boundary of the cube J_n; $v_0^{J_n}(e\cap\beta)$ the number of elements of the set $e\cap\beta\subset E_n$ which lie strictly inside the cube $J_n\subset E_n$ (i.e. not intersecting its boundary); and $\Psi_\tau(E)$ the transformation which projects the set $E\subset E_n$ orthogonally on the plane $\tau\subset E_n$.

§ 18. The Multiplicity Function and its Measurability for Closed Sets

We define the variation of a set as the integral of a certain function, the multiplicity function.

Definition. The ith multiplicity function of order k of the set $e\subset E_n$ (with respect to the cube J_n) is the function $v_0^{J_n}[e\cap\beta_i^{n-k}(q)]$ defined on the plane τ_i^k and equal to the number of elements of the set $e\cap\beta_i^{n-k}(q)$ lying strictly inside the cube J_n $(i=1, 2, \ldots, C_n^k;\ k=0, 1, 2, \ldots, n)$.

We will restrict ourselves to closed sets $e \subset E_n$. This is done fundamentally because the measurability of a wider class of sets has not been proved, even for sets of the type F_σ and G_δ.

Lemma 1. Given any closed subset e in the space E_n, the arbitrary numbers k and l and the regular cube $J_n \subset E_n$, the function $v_0^{J_n}[e \cap \beta_i^{n-k}(q)]$ is Lebesgue measurable, as a function of the point $q \in \tau_i^k$.

Proof. We choose an enumerable set $A \subset e$, which is dense everywhere (in e), and denote by σ_j^ε some finite set of spheres, open in E_n, with rational diameters not greater than $\varepsilon > 0$ in magnitude, and such that their theoretic-set sum Σ_j^ε covers the set $e \cap J_n$. We assume this set to be enumerated, with j as the suffix of the system. Enumeration is possible, since there is only an enumerable number of different systems of this type. It is clear, furthermore, that the multiplicity function $v_0^{J_n}[\Sigma_j^\varepsilon \cap \beta_i^{n-k}(q)]$ of the set Σ_j^ε takes only a finite number of values, and can change its value only when its argument (the point q) goes to a point q_0 which is such that the plane $\beta_i^{n-k}(q_0)$ touches either some sphere of the system σ_j^ε or the common part of some pair of spheres of that system, or finally, when $\beta_i^{n-k}(q_0)$ touches one of the $(n-1)$-dimensional boundaries of the cube J_n. This means that the multiplicity function is almost everywhere continuous (and, therefore, Lebesgue measurable), since it is obvious that the set of points of discontinuity (points where the multiplicity function changes its value) is made up of a finite number of $(k-1)$-dimensional surfaces, the boundaries of ellipsoids together with that of the cube, i.e. it has zero measure.

We shall now show that

$$v_0^{J_n}[e \cap \beta_i^{n-k}(q)] = \liminf_{\substack{\varepsilon \to 0 \\ j}} v_0^{J_n}[\Sigma_j^\varepsilon \cap \beta_i^{n-k}(q)]$$

The inequality

$$v_0^{J_n}[e \cap \beta_i^{n-k}(q)] \leqslant \liminf_{\substack{\varepsilon \to 0 \\ j}} v_0^{J_n}[\Sigma_j^\varepsilon \cap \beta_i^{n-k}(q)]$$

is true, since any two elements of the set $e \cap \beta_i^{n-k}(q)$ lie, for some sufficiently small ε (which is different for each given pair of elements), in different elements of any set $\Sigma_j^{\varepsilon} \cap \beta_i^{n-k}(q)$ (because the set is closed). To prove the inequality

$$v_0^{J_n}[e \cap \beta_i^{n-k}(q)] \geqslant \liminf_{\varepsilon \to 0} \inf_j v_0^{J_n}[\Sigma_j^{J_n} \cap \beta_i^{n-k}(q)]$$

we must make the following construction. We select a finite group of spheres $s_1, s_2, \ldots, s_e$, open (in E_n), and belonging to some group σ_j^{ε}, each of which contains points of $e \cap \beta_i^{n-k}(q)$ and such that their theoretic-set sum σ_1, covers the set $e \cap \beta_i^{n-k}(q)$. Since the set $(e \cap J_n) - \sigma_1$ is closed and has no common points with the plane $\beta_i^{n-k}(q)$, the group of spheres $s_1, s_2, \ldots, s_e$ can be made up to a group of the type σ_j^{ε} by spheres $s_{l+1}, s_{l+2}, \ldots, s_m$ whose diameter is so small that $\sigma_2 = \bigcup_{j=l+1}^{m} s_j$ does not intersect the plane $\beta_i^{n-k}(q)$. This means that for any $\varepsilon > 0$ we have found a group σ_j^{ε} for which

$$v_0^{J_n}[e \cap \beta_i^{n-k}(q)] \geqslant v_0^{J_n}[(\sigma_1 \cup \sigma_2) \cap \beta_i^{n-k}(q)]$$

i.e. for any ε

$$\inf_j v_0^{J_n}[\Sigma_j^{\varepsilon} \cap \beta_i^{n-k}(q)] \leqslant v_0^{J_n}[e \cap \beta_i^{n-k}(q)]$$

Hence

$$v_0^{J_n}[e \cap \beta_i^{n-k}(q)] \geqslant \liminf_{\varepsilon \to 0} \inf_j v_0^{J_n}[\Sigma_j^{\varepsilon} \cap \beta_i^{n-k}(q)]$$

Thus we have proved that

$$v_0^{J_n}[e \cap \beta_i^{n-k}(q)] = \liminf_{\varepsilon \to 0} \inf_j v_0^{J_n}[\Sigma_j^{\varepsilon} \cap \beta_i^{n-k}(q)]$$

But since the functions $\{v_0^{J_n}[\Sigma_j^{\varepsilon} \cap \beta_i^{n-k}(q)]\}$ are continuous almost everywhere (on τ_i^k) $v_0^{J_n}[e \cap \beta_i^{n-k}(q)]$ is Lebesgue measurable. Q.E.D.

We note that the condition made in the lemma that the cube shall be regular can easily be omitted. Moreover, the lemma is almost as easy to prove if we take J_n to be an arbitrary convex region, or, say, a field with a sufficiently smooth boundary (namely, such that there are k continuous derivatives on it).

§ 19. The Definition of the Variations of a Set

Definition. The variation of order k of the set $e \subset E_n$ inside the cube J_n is the number

$$v_k^{J_n}(e) = \frac{1}{C_n^k} \sum_{i=1}^{C_n^k} \int_{\tau_i^k} v_0^{J_n}\left[e \cap \beta_i^{n-k}(q)\right] dq = \frac{1}{C_n^k} \sum_{i=1}^{C_n^k} v_{\substack{k \\ \tau_i^k}}^{J_n}(e)$$

The number

$$v_{\substack{k \\ \tau_i^k}}^{J_n}(e) = \int_{\tau_i^k} v_0^{J_n}\left[e \cap \beta_i^{n-k}(q)\right] dq$$

is said to be the variation of order k of the set e (inside the cube J_n) with respect to the plane τ_i^k $(0 \leqslant k \leqslant n; n = 1, 2, \ldots)$.

When $k = 0$ the plane $\tau_i^k = \tau_1^0$ degenerates to a point and $\beta_i^{n-k}(q) = \beta_1^n$ becomes coincident with the whole space E_n, i.e. the zero order variation of the set e inside the cube J_n is equal to the number of elements of e which lie strictly inside J_n.

When $k = n$ $\tau_i^k = \tau_1^n = E_n$ and the plane $\beta_i^{n-k}(q) = \beta_1^0(q) = q$ then degenerates to a point; inside the cube J_n the multiplicity function of order n coincides with the characteristic function of the set e, i.e.

$$v_0^{J_n}\left[e \cap \beta_1^0(q)\right] = \begin{cases} 1, & \text{if } q \in e \cap J_n, \\ 0, & \text{if } q \overline{\in} e \cap J_n. \end{cases}$$

Thus

$$v_n^{J_n}(e) = \int_{J_n} v_0^{J_n}\left[e \cap \beta_1^0(q)\right] dq = \text{mes}_n(e)$$

is equal to the n-dimensional Lebesgue measure of that part of e which lies inside J_n.

From the lemma of the previous section, it follows that for a closed set $e \in E_n$ the corresponding multiplicity functions $\{v_0^{J_n}[e \cap \beta_i^{n-k}(q)]\}$ are measurable, and therefore the definition of a variation which we gave above is meaningful for closed sets.

The following theorem gives essentially another (inductive) definition of the variation of a set.

Theorem 1. To compute the variation $v_k^{J_n}(e)$ of order k of a closed set e from the variation of the section of this set $v_l^{J_n \cap \beta_i^{n-k+l}(q)}[e \cap \beta_i^{n-k+l}(q)]$ of order l, we have the following formula:

$$v_k^{J_n}(e) = \frac{1}{C_n^{k-l}} \sum_{i=1}^{C_n^{k-l}} \int_{\tau_i^{k-l}} v_l^{J_n \cap \beta_i^{n-k+l}(q)}[e \cap \beta_i^{n-k+l}(q)]\, dq =$$

$$= \frac{1}{C_n^{k-l}} \sum_{i=1}^{C_n^{k-l}} v^{J_n}_{k, \tau_i^{k-l}}(e),$$

where

$$v^{J_n}_{k, \tau_i^{k-l}}(e) = \int_{\tau_i^{k-l}} v_0^{J_n \cap \beta_i^{n-k+l}(q)}[e \cap \beta_i^{n-k+l}(q)]\, dq$$

is the kth order variation of e inside J_n with respect to the $(k-l)$-dimensional plane τ_i^{k-l} $(l = 0, 1, \ldots, k-1)$.

Proof. The proof of this theorem follows at once from Fubini's theorem and Lemma 1, § 18. For

$$v_k^{J_n}(e) = \frac{1}{C_n^k} \sum_{i=1}^{C_n^k} \int_{\tau_i^k} v_0^{J_n}[e \cap \beta_i^{n-k}(q)]\,(dm)^k =$$

$$= \frac{1}{C_n^k C_k^l} \sum_{i=1}^{C_n^k} C_k^l \int_{\tau_i^k} v_0^{J_n} [e \cap \beta_i^{n-k}(q)] (dm)^k =$$

$$= \frac{1}{C_n^k C_k^l} \sum_{i=1}^{C_n^k} \sum_{j=1}^{C_k^{k-l}} \int_{\tau_j^{k-l} \subset \tau_i^k} C_{n-k+l}^l v_l^{J_n \cap \beta_i^{n-k+l}(q)} [e \cap \beta_i^{n-k+l}(q)] (dm)^{k-l} =$$

$$= \frac{C_{n-k+l}^l}{C_n^k C_k^l} \sum_{i=1}^{C_n^{k-l}} \int_{\tau_i^{k-l}} v_l^{J_n \cap \beta_i^{n-k+l}(q)} [e \cap \beta^{n-k+l}(q)] (dm)^{k-l} =$$

$$= \frac{1}{C_n^{k-l}} \sum_{i=1}^{C_n^{k-l}} v^{J_n}_{k, \tau_i^{k-l}}(e).$$

Q.E.D.

Definition. The number $v^{J_n}(e) = \sum_{k=0}^{n} v_k^{J_n}(e)$ is the variation of the set $e \subset E_n$ inside the cube J_n.

It may not seem very natural to combine the variations into one characteristic in this way, but it will simplify the form of some of our calculations.

Corollary 1. Given any closed set $e \subset E_n$ the inequality

$$v_k^{J_n}(e) = \frac{1}{n} \sum_{i=1}^{n} \int_{\tau_i^1} v_{k-1}^{J_n \cap \beta_i^{n-1}(q)}(e)\, dq = \frac{1}{n} \sum_{i=1}^{n} v^{J_n}_{k, \tau_i^1}(e)$$

holds for any k $(1 \leqslant k \leqslant n)$, where

$$v^{J_n}_{k, \tau_i^1}(e) = \int_{\tau_i^1} v_{k-1}^{J_n \cap \beta_i^{n-1}(q)}(e)\, dq$$

is the kth order variation of e with respect to the straight line τ_i^1.

This is easily obtained from Theorem 1 by putting $l = k-1$.

Corollary 2. To calculate the variation $v^{J_n}(e)$ of the set

$e \subset E_n$ we can use the formula

$$v^{J_n}(e) = v_0^{J_n}(e) + \frac{1}{n} \sum_{i=1}^{n} \int_{\tau_i^1} v^{J_n \cap \beta_i^{n-1}(q)}(e)\, dq =$$

$$= v_0^{J_n}(e) + \frac{1}{n} \sum_{i=1}^{n} v_{\tau_i^1}^{J_n}(e)$$

where

$$v_{\tau_i^1}^{J_n}(e) = \int_{\tau_i^1} v^{J_n \cap \beta_i^{n-1}(q)}(e)\, dq$$

is (by definition) the variation of the set e inside the cube J_n with respect to the straight line τ_i^1, i.e. the variation of a set is equal to the arithmetic mean of the variations of the same set with respect to all co-ordinate axes plus its zero variation.

This follows at once from Theorem 1, by putting $l = k - 1$ and summing the variations of different dimensions over k.

This formula gives an inductive definition of the variation of a set.

§ 20. The Simplest Properties of the Variations of a Set

The variation $v_k^{J_n}(e)$ of the set e possesses the following properties as a function of the set*:

1. $v^{J_n}(e)$ is always non-negative, and is equal to zero when and only when the set e contains no internal points of the cube J_n. The function $v_k^{J_n}(e)$ is also non-negative for any set e, and is equal to zero when and only when the set e contains no internal points of the cube J_n (with the convention that $v_{k+1}^{J_n}(e) = 0$).

2. The variation $v_k^{J_n}(e)$ is a semi-additive function of the set e, i.e.

$$v_k^{J_n}\left(\bigcup_{i=1}^{\infty} e_i\right) \leqslant \sum_{i=1}^{\infty} v_k^{J_n}(e_i)$$

---

* We shall assume that all the multiplicity functions mentioned are measurable.

and therefore

$$v^{J_n}\left(\bigcup_{i=1}^{\infty} e_i\right) \leqslant \sum_{i=1}^{\infty} v^{J_n}(e_i)$$

3. If the sets $\{e_i\}$ are a positive distance apart, then

$$v_k^{J_n}\left(\bigcup_{i=1}^{\infty} e_i\right) = \sum_{i=1}^{\infty} v_k^{J_n}(e_i)$$

and therefore

$$v^{J_n}\left(\bigcup_{i=1}^{\infty} e_i\right) = \sum_{i=1}^{\infty} v^{J_n}(e_i)$$

4. If the regular cubes $\{J_n^i\}$ are all contained in the regular cube J_n, and no pair has any common points, then

$$v_k^{J_n}(e) \geqslant \sum_{i=1}^{\infty} v_k^{J_n^i}(e)$$

and therefore

$$v^{J_n}(e) \geqslant \sum_{i=1}^{\infty} v^{J_n^i}(e)$$

5. If Φ is the transformation which makes a parallel displacement, then

$$v_k^{\Phi(J_n)}[\Phi(e)] = v_k^{J_n}(e)$$

and therefore

$$v^{\Phi(J_n)}[\Phi(e)] = v^{J_n}(e)$$

6. If Ψ is the tranformation which multiplies uniformly in E_n (with multiplication coefficient $l > 0$), then

$$v_k^{\Psi(J_n)}[\Psi(e)] = l^k v_k^{J_n}(e)$$

7. If e is a polyhedron of dimension k then

$$A_n v_k^{J_n}(e) \leqslant \operatorname{mes}_k[e \cap (J_n - J_n^*)] \leqslant B_n v_k^{J_n}(e)$$

where J_n^* is the boundary of the cube J_n, and $A_n > 0$ and $B_n > 0$

are parameters depending only on n.

8. If the kth order Hausdorf measure $h^k(e)$ of the set e is equal to zero, then $v_k^{J_n}(e)=0$. In particular, if e is a continuously differentiable image of k-dimensional Euclidean space, then $v_{k+l}^{J_n}(e)=0$ for all $l>0$.

9. $v_0^{J_n}(e)$ is defined for any set $e\subset E_n$ and is equal to the number of elements of the set e which lie strictly inside J_n.

10. $v_n^{J_n}(e)$ is defined for any set e which is Lebesgue measurable, and for any such set

$$v_n^{J_n}(e)=\text{mes}_n(e\cap J_n)$$

11. If, given any positive $l\leqslant n-p$

$$v_{p+l}^{J_n}(e)=0$$

then the set e is projected on every $(p+1)$-dimensional coordinate plane into a set of zero $(p+1)$-dimensional measure.

12. The variations of a set, $v_k^{J_n}(e)$, of different orders are independent in the sense that given any non-negative numbers A_k ($k=0, 1, 2, \ldots, n$; A_0 an integer, and $A_n\leqslant \text{mes}_n(J_n)$), some of which may be infinite, we can construct a closed set $e\subset J_n$ such that $v_k^{J_n}(e)=A_k$ $(k=0, 1, 2, \ldots, n)$.

Properties 1-11 are easily obtained either immediately from the definition or from Theorem 1 (by induction on n). The proof of point 12, being the only one to present any difficulty, will be given below.

§ 21. A Basic Lemma Concerning the Variations of a Set

Definition. Given a set $e\subset E_n$ and a cube $J_n\subset E_n$ the upper bound (on the set $e\cap J_n$) of the distance from a point of $e\cap J_n$) to the boundary of J_n is called the "depth of embedding" of e in J_n and is denoted by $\Gamma(e, J_n)$.

The basic working result concerning the variation of a

set is the theorem formulated by A.S. Kronrod [5] which says that, given any set e and cube J_n we can find $k\,(0 \leqslant k \leqslant n)$ such that

$$v_k^{J_n}(e) \geqslant A(n, k)\,[\Gamma(e, J_n)]^k$$

where $A(n, k) > 0$ is some constant, dependent upon k and n. It is important to know the exact expression for the constant $A(n, k)$ when applying this theorem. We shall calculate a value of $A(n, k)$ here which is already known.

Lemma 1. Let e be a closed set in E_n, for which there exists some non-negative integer $p \leqslant n$ such that given any positive integer $l \leqslant n-p$ the corresponding variation $v_{p+l}^{J_n}(e) = 0$. Then we can find numbers $m_k \geqslant 0$ $(k = 0, 1, \ldots, p$, m_0 an integer), such that

$$\sum_{k=0}^{p} m_k \geqslant 1$$

and for any $k \leqslant p$

$$v_k^{J_n}(e) \geqslant \frac{m_k}{C_n^k}\,[\Gamma(e, J_n)]^k$$

Proof. If $m_0 \neq 0$, the lemma is obvious, so we shall assume that $m_0 = 0$. Since the set e is closed we can find a point $q_n^* \subset J_n \cap e$ whose distance from the boundary J_n^* of the cube J_n is $\Gamma(e, J_n) = A$. Let J_n' be a regular cube, side $2A$, with centre at q_n' Since, from property 4 § 20,

$$v_k^{J_n'}(e) \leqslant v_k^{J_n}(e)$$

we shall assume that $J_n' = J_n$ in order to simplify our notation, and without loss of generality, i.e. we assume henceforth that the centre of the cube J_n belongs to the set e and that the side of $J_n = 2A$. Remembering the property 5 of § 20 we can also assume in what follows that the centre $q_n' = 0$ of J_n coincides with the origin of co-ordinates.

Let Ψ_i^k denote the transformation which projects the space E_n orthogonally on the k-dimensional co-ordinate plane τ_i^k and put $\Phi_i^k = (\Psi_i^k)^{-1}$. Further, let Y_i^k be the mapping of the cube $J_n \cap \tau_i^k$ into the cube $\omega_i^{k'}$ which makes the point $y(q_i^k)$ with co-ordinates $y_j(q_i^k) = |x_j(q_i^k)|$ $(j = 1, 2, \ldots, n)$ correspond to the point $q_i^k \in J_n \cap \tau_i^k$ with co-ordinates $\{x_j(q_i^k)\}$. The cube ω_i^k plays a purely auxiliary role, and therefore we can assume it to lie in an n-dimensional Euclidean space E_n^* different from E_n. The inverse image of any point $y \in \omega_i^k$ distinct from the co-ordinate origin consists of 2^k points, symmetrically placed (with respect to $x = 0 = q_n'$), each of whose co-ordinates is constant in modulus for all 2^k points.

If f is some set of τ_i^k, let f^* denote the set $Y^{-1}[Y(f)]$. Put

$$e_i^k = \Psi_i^k(e)$$

and let $e_i^{k,+}$ be the Lebesgue set

$$\{v_0^{J_n}[e \cap \beta_i^{n-k}(q)] \geqslant 1\}$$

i.e. the set of all points $q \in \tau_i^k \cap J_n$ for which the corresponding set $e \cap \beta_i^{n-k}(q)$ has at least one element which does not reach the boundary of the cube $J_n \cap \beta_i^{n-k}(q)$; and similarly, let $e_i^{k,0}$ be the set

$$\{v_0^{J_n}[e \cap \beta_i^{n-k}(q)] = 0\}$$

We shall make an upper estimate of the quantity

$$\mu_k = \sum_{i=1}^{C_n^k} \mathrm{mes}_k(e_i^k)$$

To do this, we introduce the auxiliary set

$$f_k = J_n - \bigcup_{l=1}^{k-1} \bigcup_{i_l=1}^{C_n^l} \Phi_{i_l}^l\left(e_{i_l}^{l,+,*}\right)$$

From Lemma 1 § 18, it follows that f_k is Lebesgue measurable. Putting the number $\mathrm{mes}_l(e_i^{l,+,*}) = m_i^l(2A)^l$ $(0 \leqslant m_i^l \leqslant 1)$ it is not difficult to see that

$$\operatorname{mes}_n(f_k) \geqslant \operatorname{mes}_n(J_n) - \sum_{l=1}^{k-1} \sum_{i_l=1}^{C_n^l} (2A)^{n-l} m_{i_l}^l (2A)^l =$$

$$= (2A)^n \left(1 - \sum_{l=1}^{k-1} m_l\right),$$

where $m_l = \sum_{i_l=1}^{C_n^l} m_{i_l}^l$. We shall now show that the set f_k can be represented in the form $f_k = \bigcup_{i=1}^{C_n^k} f_{i,k}$ so that for any i the set $\Psi_i^k(f_{i,k})$ is contained in e_i^k. To do this we select an arbitrary point $q \in f_k$ and put $q_i^l = \Psi_i^l(q)$. The pairs of planes $\Phi_i^1(q_i^{1,*})$ $(i = 1, 2, \ldots, n)$ cut out a parallelepiped $\omega(q)$ from J_n. The centre of this parallelepiped coincides with the origin of co-ordinates, and the set of its vertices coincides with the set $q^* \subset f_k$. But, (in particular), since the origin of co-ordinates belongs to the set e, the element of e containing the origin of co-ordinates (the centre of the parallelepiped $\omega(q)$) must reach the boundary of the cube J_n and, therefore, must intersect one of the $(n-1)$-dimensional boundaries of the parallepiped $\omega(q)$. For definiteness, suppose this boundary lies in the plane $\beta_1^{n-1}(q_1^1) = \Psi_1^1(q_1^1)$. Since, by definition of the set f_k, q_1^1 belongs to the set $e_1^1 - e_1^{1,+,*}$, i.e. belongs to $e_1^{1,0}$, and also because $\omega(q) \cap \beta_1^{n-1}(q_1^1)$ is, as we have already seen, intersected by the set $\dot{e}$ at some point α_1, the element of the set $e \cap \beta_1^{n-1}(q_1^1)$ containing a_1 must go outside the boundary of the cube $J_n \cap \beta_i^{n-1}(q_1^1)$ and, therefore, must intersect some $(n-2)$-dimensional boundary of the parallelepipeds $\omega(q)$ and $\omega(q) \cap \beta_1^{n-1}(q_1^1)$. Continuing to reason in this way, we find that e is intersected by some $(n-k)$-dimensional boundary of the parallelepiped $\omega(q)$ in some point a_k. This $(n-k)$-dimensional boundary lies in some $(n-k)$-dimensional plane $\beta_j^{n-k}(q') = \Phi_j^k(q')$ $(q' \in q_j^{k,*})$ which is orthogonal to the co-ordinate plane τ_j^k. In such a case we include in $f_{j,k}$ the point q chosen previously, and the whole set $q^* \subset f_k$, and take this as a definition of the sets $\{f_{i,k}\}$.

Thus, any point $q \in f_k$ together with q^* must belong to at least one of the sets $\{f_{i,k}\}$. Put $f_i^k = \Psi_i^k(f_{i,k})$. Since, in the transformation Ψ_j^k, which projects the set $q^* \subset f_{i,k}$ at least one point $q\,(q \in q^*)$ goes to the point $q'\,(q' \in e_j^k)$, $\Psi_j^k(q^*) \subset e_j^{k,*}$ and therefore

$$f_j^k \subset e_j^{k,*} \qquad (j = 1, 2, \ldots, C_n^k)$$

But then, from Fubini's theorem and the fact that

$$\text{mes}_n(f_k) \geqslant (2A)^n\left(1 - \sum_{l\ 0}^{k-1} m_l\right)$$

we have

$$\sum_{i=1}^{C_n^k} \text{mes}_k(e_i^{k,*}) \geqslant \sum_{i=1}^{C_n^k} \text{mes}_k(f_i^k) \geqslant \sum_{i=1}^{C_n^k} \frac{\text{mes}_n(f_{i,k})}{(2A)^{n-k}} \geqslant$$
$$\geqslant \frac{1}{(2A)^{n-k}}\,\text{mes}_n(f_n) \geqslant (2A)^k\left(1 - \sum_{l=0}^{k-1} m_l\right)$$

i.e.

$$\sum_{i=1}^{C_n^k} \text{mes}_k(e_i^{k,*}) \geqslant (2A)^k\left(1 - \sum_{l=0}^{k-1} m_l\right)$$

But since $\text{mes}_k(e_i^k) \geqslant \frac{1}{2^k}\,\text{mes}_k\, e_i^{k,*})$ for any i, we have

$$\sum_{i=1}^{C_n^k} \text{mes}_k(e_i^k) \geqslant A^k\left(1 - \sum_{l=0}^{k=1} m_l\right)$$

This inequality holds for all $k \leqslant n$.

Since, given any $l > 0$ $(l \leqslant n - p)$ the corresponding variation $v_{p+l}^{J_n}(e) = 0$ (see the lemma), either

$$\text{mes}_p(e_i^{p,+}) = \sum_{i=1}^{C_n^p} \text{mes}_p(e_i^p) = \text{mes}_n(e_1^n) = m_p A^p, \text{ when } p = n$$

i.e.

$$A^p m_p \geqslant A^p\left(1 - \sum_{l=0}^{p-1} m_l\right)$$

or

$$\sum_{i=1}^{C_n^{p+1}} \mathrm{mes}_{p+1}(e_i^{p+1}) = 0 \text{ when } p < n$$

(this is easily proved by induction on n), i.e.

$$0 \geqslant A^{p+1}\left(1 - \sum_{l=0}^{p} m_l\right)$$

In both cases we have

$$\sum_{k=0}^{p} m_k \geqslant 1$$

From the definition of a variation we have

$$v_k^{J_n}(e) \geqslant \frac{1}{C_n^k} \sum_{i=1}^{C_n^k} \mathrm{mes}_k(e_i^{k,+}) = \frac{m_k}{C_n^k} A^k$$

where $\sum_{k=0}^{p} m_k \geqslant 1$. Q.E.D.

In the next section we shall show that the value given in Lemma 1 can be attained. We give at once some simple corollaries to Lemma 1.

Lemma 2. If the set e satisfies the conditions of Lemma 1, then there exists k $(0 \leqslant k \leqslant p \leqslant n)$ such that

$$v_k^{J_n}(e) \geqslant \frac{[\Gamma(e, J_n)]^k}{pC_n^k} \text{ when } p \neq 0$$

and

$$v_k^{J_n}(e) \geqslant 1 \text{ when } p = 0$$

Lemma 3. If the set e satisfies the conditions of Lemma 1 and $\Gamma(e, J_n) \leqslant 1$ then

$$v^{J_n}(e) \geqslant \frac{[\Gamma(e, J_n)]^p}{2^n}$$

Lemma 4. If the set e satisfies the conditions of Lemma 1, then there exists k $(0 \leqslant k \leqslant p \leqslant n)$ such that

$$v_k^{J_n}(e) \geqslant \frac{[\Gamma(e, J_n)]^k}{2^k C_n^k}$$

Lemmas 2 to 4 are easily obtained from Lemma 1.

§ 22. The Independence of the Variations of a Set

We shall show, firstly, that it is not possible to improve the estimate of the variations of the set e in the cube J_n using the depth of embedding of this set in J_n which was given by Lemma 1, § 21.

To do this we choose an arbitrary collection of non-negative numbers m_k $(k = 0, 1, \ldots, p;\ p \leqslant n)$ such that $\sum_{k=0}^{p} m_k \geqslant 1$ (m_0 is an integer) and A $\left(0 < A \leqslant \frac{1}{2}\rho,\ \rho\right.$ the side of $\left.J_n\right)$ and we construct in the cube J_n a closed set $e = e(m_0, m_1, \ldots, m_p)$ embedded in J_n to a depth $\Gamma(e, J_n) = A$, for which

$$v_k^{J_n}(e) = \frac{m_k}{C_n^k} A^k \qquad (k = 0, 1, \ldots, p),$$

$$v_{p+1}^{J_n}(e) = 0 \qquad (l = 1, 2, \ldots, n - p + 1)$$

Lemma 1. We are given the numbers $A > 0$, $m_k \geqslant 0$ $(k = 0, 1, \ldots, p;\ p \leqslant n;\ m_0$ an integer$)$ such that $\sum_{k=0}^{p} m_k = 1$. Then there exists a closed set e , lying in the n-dimensional closed cube J_n^{2A} of side $2A$ and containing its centre, such that

$$v_k^{J_n^{2A}}(e) = \frac{m_k A^k}{C_n^k} \qquad (k = 0, 1, \ldots, p),$$

$$v_{p+l}^{J_n^{2A}}(e) = 0 \qquad (l = 1, 2, \ldots, n - p)$$

Proof. For J_n^{2A} let us take the regular cube of E_n given by

$$-A \leqslant x_i \leqslant A \qquad (i = 1, 2, \ldots, n)$$

Put

$$\mu_i = \frac{1 - \sum_{k=0}^{i} m_k}{1 - \sum_{k=0}^{i-1} m_k}$$

and let $e = e\,(m_0, m_1, \ldots, m_p)$ be the set $e = \bigcup_{k=0}^{p} \omega_k$, where for $k = 0$ ω_k is the centre of the cube ω and, generally, ω_k is the k-dimensional parallelepiped defined by the relations

$$\begin{aligned} &A \geqslant x_i \geqslant \mu_i A && (i = 1, 2, \ldots, k-1), \\ &A \geqslant x_k \geqslant 0, && \\ &x_i = 0 && (i = k+1, k+2, \ldots, n) \end{aligned}$$

It is easy to verify that

$$\begin{aligned} &v_k^{J_n^{2A}}(e) = \frac{m_k A^k}{C_n^k} && (0 \leqslant k \leqslant p), \\ &v_k^{J_n^{2A}}(e) = \frac{1-\mu_k}{C_n^k} A^k \prod_{i=0}^{k-1} \mu_i && (k \geqslant 2), \\ &v_{p+l}^{J_n^{2A}}(e) = 0 && (l > 0). \end{aligned}$$

Q.E.D.

<u>Lemma 2.</u> We are given the numbers $A\left(0 < A < \frac{\rho}{2}\right)$ and $m_k \geqslant 0$ $(k = 0, 1, \ldots, n)$ such that m_0 is an integer $\sum_{k=0}^{n} m_k \geqslant 1$ and $m_n = 0$. Then, the closed set e can be put into any regular cube of side ρ in such a way that

$$\Gamma(e, J_n^\rho) = A, \; v_k^{J_n^\rho}(e) = \frac{m_k\left[\Gamma\left(e, J_n^\rho\right)\right]^k}{C_n^k} \quad (k = 0, 1, 2, \ldots, n)$$

<u>Proof.</u> Since $\sum_{k=0}^{n} m_k \geqslant 1$, we can choose a set of non-negative numbers $\{m'_k\}$ such that m'_0 is an integer $\sum_{k=0}^{n} m'_k = 1$ and $m'_k \leqslant m_k$ $(k = 0, 1, 2, \ldots, n)$. Let J_n^{2A} be a regular cube of side $2A$ lying in the cube J_n^ρ and having a vertex in common with it.

It follows from the previous lemma that we can place the closed set e' so that

$$\Gamma(e', J_n^\rho) = \Gamma(e, J_n^{2A}) = A,$$

$$v_k^{J_n^\rho}(e') = v_k^{J_n^{2A}}(e') = \frac{m_k' A^k}{C_n^k} \qquad (k=0,\ 1,\ 2,\ \dots,\ n)$$

To do this we need only orientate the set constructed in the proof of Lemma 1 in the cube J_n^{2A} in such a way that all the boundaries (of various dimensions) of the cube J_n^{2A} having a non-empty intersection with the set e', contain one vertex a_0 of J_n^ρ (common to all such boundaries), or we can turn the cube J_n^{2A} in a corresponding way.

Let J_n^A be a regular cube of side A lying in J_n^ρ and having the vertex a_0^*, symmetrical (with respect to the centre of J_n^ρ) to the vertex a_0, in common with J_n^ρ J_n^A cannot have more than one point in common with e'. This point can only be the centre of J_n^ρ if $\rho = 2A$. We put the set e in the form $e = e' + \bigcup_{k=0}^{n-1} e_k$. e' has already been defined.

For definiteness, we shall also assume that the cube J_n^ρ lies in the space E_n in such a way that its vertex a_0^* coincides with the origin and the one-dimensional edges lie on the positive portions of the co-ordinate axes. Put

$$m_k'' = m_k - m_k', \quad n_0 = m_0'', \quad n_k = 2\,[2^k m_k'' + 1]$$

$$\rho_k = \sqrt[k]{\frac{m_k'' A^k}{n_k}} \qquad (k=1,\ 2,\ \dots,\ n-1).$$

It is not difficult to verify that $\rho_k \leqslant \frac{A}{2}$.

Let $\omega_{i_k}^k$ be the k-dimensional cube given by the relations

$$0 \leqslant x_i \leqslant \rho_k \qquad (i=1,\ 2,\ \dots,\ k),$$

$$x_j = \frac{A}{2} \qquad (j=k+1,\ \dots,\ n-1),$$

$$x_n = \left(i_k + \sum_{l=0}^{k-1} n_l\right)^{-1} A$$

$$(i_k = 1,\ 2,\ \dots,\ n_k,\ \ k=0,\ 1,\ \dots,\ n-1)$$

Since m_0 and m_0' are integers, and $m_0' \leqslant m_0$, $m_0'' = m_0 - m_0'$ is a negative integer. Put

$$e_k = \bigcup_{i_k=1}^{n_k} \omega_{i_k}^k \qquad (k = 0, 1, \ldots, n-1)$$

$$e = e' + \bigcup_{k=0}^{n-1} e_k.$$

We now calculate the variations of the set e. By definition, each of the sets $\omega_{i_0}^0$ consists of one internal point of J_n^A and these points are different for different i_0, i.e.

$$v_0^{J_n^A}(e_0) = n_0 = m_0''$$

Since

$$v_0^{J_n^A}(e_0) = m_0'',$$

$$v_0^{J_n^{2A}}(e') = m_0'$$

therefore

$$v_0^{J_n^\rho}(e' + e_0) = m_0' + m_0'' = m_0$$

But since each of the cubes $\{\omega_{i_k}^k\}$ $(k > 0)$ has a common point with the boundary of the cube J_n^ρ,

$$v_0^{J_n^\rho}\left(\bigcup_{k=1}^{n-1} e_k\right) = 0$$

and therefore

$$v_0^{J_n^\rho}(e) = v_0^{J_n^\rho}(e' + e_0) + v_0^{J_n^\rho}\left(\bigcup_{k=1}^{n-1} e_k\right) = v_0^{J_n^\rho}(e' + e_0) = m_0$$

Since

$$x_n(\omega_{i_k}^k) = \left(i_k + \sum_{l=0}^{k-1} n_l\right)^{-1} A = \text{const}$$

and for different $\{k, i_k\}$ the co-ordinate $x_n(\omega^k_{i_k})$ takes different values, from point 3 of § 20 we have

$$v_k^{J^\rho_n}(e) = \sum_{l=0}^{n-1} \sum_{i_l=1}^{n_l} v_l^{J^\rho_n}(\omega^l_{i_l})$$

Since the sides of $\omega^k_{i_k}$ are parallel to the co-ordinate axes $x_1, x_2, \ldots, x_k$ and each of the co-ordinates $x_{k+1}, \ldots, x_n$ is constant on $\omega^k_{i_k}$, the set $\omega^k_{i_k}$ projected on to the co-ordinate plane τ^k_1 along the vectors $x_1, x_2, \ldots, x_k$ becomes a k-dimensional cube, of side ρ, and on each co-ordinate plane τ^k_i containing at least one of the vectors x_j $(j > k)$ the cube $\omega^k_{i_k}$ is projected into a set lying in a $(k-1)$-dimensional plane $(x_j = \text{const})$ i.e. into a set whose k-dimensional measure is equal to zero. Hence

$$v_k^{J^\rho_n}(\omega^k_{i_k}) = \frac{1}{C^k_n} \sum_{i=1}^{C^k_n} v_{\tau^k_i}^{J^\rho_n}(\omega^k_{i_k}) = \frac{1}{C^k_n} v_{\tau^k_1}^{J^\rho_n}(\omega^k_{i_k}) =$$

$$= \frac{1}{C^k_n}(\rho_k)^k = \frac{m''_k A^k}{C^k_n n_k}.$$

Since $\omega^k_{i_k}$ is projected into a set of zero measure (m^{k+l}) on each $(k+l)$-dimensional $(l > 0)$ co-ordinate plane, we have

$$v_{k+l}^{J^\rho_n}(\omega^k_{i_k}) = 0 \qquad (l > 0)$$

We now select some $(k-l)$-dimensional co-ordinate plane τ^{k-l}_i $(0 < l \leqslant k)$. If τ^{k-l}_i contains at least one of the vectors $x_{k+1}, \ldots, x_n$, x_{k+1} say, then $\Psi^{k-l}_i(\omega^k_{i_k})$ will belong to the $(k-l-1)$-dimensional plane $x_{k+1} = \text{const}$., i.e. in this case

$$v_{\tau^{k-1}_i}^{J^\rho_n}(\omega^k_{i_k}) = 0$$

But if τ^k_i does not contain any of the vectors $x_{k+1}, \ldots, x_n$, then the plane $\beta^{n-k+l}_i(q)$ corresponding to each point $q \in \tau^{k-l}_i$

either does not intersect the set $\omega^k_{i_k}$ at all or this intersection $\omega^k_{i_k} \cap \beta_i^{n-k+l}(q)$ is an l-dimensional cube, which has points in common with the boundary of the cube J^ρ_n, i.e. in this case too $v^{J^\rho_n}_{\tau_i^{k-l}}(\omega^k_{i_k}) = 0$.

Thus, for any $l > 0$ and for all i

$$v^{J^\rho_n}_{\tau_i^{k-l}}(\omega^k_{i_k}) = 0$$

and hence

$$v^{J^\rho_n}_{k-1}(\omega^k_{i_k}) = \frac{1}{C_n^{k-l}} \sum_{i=1}^{C_n^{k-l}} v^{J^\rho_n}_{\tau_i^{k-l}}(\omega^k_{i_k}) = 0$$

i.e. for all $m \neq k$

$$v^{J^\rho_n}_m(\omega^k_{i_k}) = 0,$$

$$v^{J^\rho_n}_k(\omega^k_{i_k}) = \frac{m''_k A^k}{C^k_n n_k}$$

But since the sets in each pair e', $\{\omega^k_{i_k}\}$ are a positive distance from one another

$$v^{J^\rho_n}_k = v^{J^\rho_n}_k(e') + \sum_{k=0}^{n-1} \sum_{i_k=1}^{n_k} v^{J^\rho_n}_k(\omega^k_{i_k}) =$$

$$= v^{J^\rho_n}_k(e') + \sum_{i_n=1}^{n_k} v^{J^\rho_n}_k(\omega^k_{i_k}) = \frac{m'_k A^k}{C^k_n} + \frac{m_k m''_k A^k}{C^k_n n_k} =$$

$$= \frac{(m'_k + m''_k) A^k}{C^k_n} = \frac{m_k A^k}{C^k_n}.$$

Since the sets e' and $\{\omega^k_{i_k}\}$ are closed, their sum is also closed and from the fact that $\{\omega^k_{i_k} \subset J^A_n\}$ and $\Gamma(e', J^\rho_n) = A$ we have

$$\Gamma(e, J^\rho_n) = A$$

Q.E.D.

Lemmas 1 and 2 prove that the estimate given in Lemma 1 § 21

$$\sum_{k=0}^{n} m_k \geqslant 1$$

is the best possible one.

Theorem 1. The variations of different orders of a set are independent, in the sense that, given any numbers $\rho > 0$ and $0 \leqslant A_k \leqslant +\infty$ $(k = 0, 1, 2, \ldots, n,$ where A_0 is an integer and $A_n < \rho^n)$ we can construct a closed set e lying inside the cube J_n^ρ, such that

$$v_k^{J_n^\rho}(e) = A_k \qquad (k = 0, 1, \ldots, n)$$

Proof. Let J_n^r be the regular cube, concentric with J_n^ρ, of side

$$r = \sqrt[n]{\rho^n - A_n} > 0$$

We define e in the form

$$e = \bigcup_{m=0}^{\infty} e_m$$

We take e_0 to be the closure of the set $J_n^\rho - J_n^r$.

We now select a sequence of regular cubes $J_n^{r_m}$ $(m = 1, 2, \ldots)$ possessing the following properties:

1. All the numbers $\{r_m\}$ are positive and

$$\sum_{m=1}^{\infty} r_m \leqslant r$$

2. One $(n-1)$-dimensional boundary of each of the cubes $J_n^{r_m} \subset J_n^r$ adjoins the boundary of J_n^r.

3. The cubes $\{J_n^{r_m}\}$ do not intersect one another.

We choose a system of non-negative numbers

$$A_k^m \; (k = 0, 1, 2, \ldots, n-1; \; m = 1, 2, \ldots)$$

such that

a) $A_k^1 = \begin{cases} A_k, & \text{if } A_k < +\infty, \\ 1, & \text{if } A_k = +\infty; \end{cases}$

b) for $m > 1$ $A_k^m = \begin{cases} 0, & \text{if } A_k < \infty, \\ 1, & \text{if } A_k = +\infty, \end{cases}$

c) $A_n^m = 0 \quad (m = 1, 2, \ldots).$

We put

$$m_k^m = \frac{A_k^m C_n^k}{\left(\frac{r_m}{2}\right)^k}$$

As in Lemma 2, we can construct a closed set e_m, lying in $J_n^{r_m}$, and having common points with only those of its boundaries which belong to the boundary of J_n^r, and are such that

$$v_k^{J_n^r}(e_m) = v_k^{J_n^{r_m}}(e) = \frac{m_k^m \left(\frac{r_m}{2}\right)^k}{C_n^k} = A_k^m \qquad (k = 0, 1, \ldots, n)$$

Put $e = \bigcup_{m=0}^{\infty} e_m$. Since the sets e_m $(m = 1, 2, \ldots)$ are closed, from conditions 1 and 2 the set e must also be closed, since all the limit points of the set $\bigcup_{m=1}^{\infty} e_m$ not belonging to this set belong to the boundary of the cube J_n^r, and therefore to the set e_0.

It is easy to see that for $k < n$

$$v_k^{J_n^\rho}(e) = v^{J_n^r}(e),$$

$$v_n^{J_n^\rho}(e) = v_n^{J_n^r}(e) + (\rho^n - r^n) = (\rho^n - r^n) = A_n$$

Since we have assumed that e_m has points in common with only those boundaries of $J_n^{r_m}$ which belong to the boundary of J_n^r it follows that

$$v_k^{J_n^r}(e_m) = v_k^{J_n^{r_m}}(e_m) \quad (k = 0, 1, 2, \ldots, n;\ m = 1, 2, \ldots)$$

Therefore, from point 3 of § 20, when

$$v_k^{J_n^\rho}(e) = v_k^{J_n^r}(e) = \sum_{m=1}^{\infty} v_k^{J_n^{r_m}}(e_m) =$$

$$= \sum_{m=1}^{\infty} \frac{m_k^m \left(\frac{r_m}{2}\right)^k}{C_n^k} = \sum_{m=1}^{\infty} A_k^m = A_k$$

(see conditions (a) and (b)). Q.E.D.

§ 23. The Metrical Law of Duality

Unlike other metrical characteristics, variations of sets possess the remarkable property that we can use them to find the metrical characteristics of the complement of the set. To be more precise, given a set which approximates to another with an accuracy ε, its variations must be quite large compared to the ε-entropy of the set to which it approximates. We give concrete estimates expressing this relation.

We restrict ourselves to subsets of Euclidean spaces. We define the metric in the space E_n as the maximum modulus of the co-ordinate difference of points, i.e. we take the distance $\rho_{E_n}(x', x'')$ between the points x' and x'' of E_n to be $\max_i |x_i' - x_i''|$. To distinguish a space of this kind from Euclidean space with the usual metric $\left(\rho_{E_n}(x', x'') = \sqrt{\sum_{i=1}^{n} (x_i' - x_i'')^2}\right)$ we denote it by E_n^C. This way of determining the distance between points is called the metric C. When we wish to consider the distance between points lying in any co-ordinate plane of E_n^C, we shall again mean the metric C. As our measure in E_n^C we take the usual Lebesgue measure $\mathrm{mes}_n(e) = m^n(e)$ and by the sign $\int_e$ we understand the usual Lebesgue integral.

Lemma 1. Let f be an arbitrary subset of the cube $J_n \subset E_n^C$ which is not nearer the boundary of this cube than $2\varepsilon > 0$, and let e be a closed set of E_n^C such that

$$v_{p+l}^{J_n}(e) = 0 \qquad (l = 1, 2, \ldots, n - p;\ p \leqslant n)$$

and suppose that for any $k\,(0 \leqslant k \leqslant p)$ and $q \in \tau_i^k$ (see the notation at the beginning of the chapter),

$$v_0^{J_n}\left[e \cap \beta_i^{n-k}(q)\right] \leqslant v$$

Then, if the set e approximates* to f to an accuracy of ε then there exists a k for which the inequality

$$v \geqslant \frac{1}{(p+1)^2\, 6^k C_n^k} \frac{n_{2\varepsilon}(f)}{n_\varepsilon^k(f)} \geqslant \frac{12^{-n}}{(p+1)^2} \frac{n_{2\varepsilon}(f)}{n_\varepsilon^k(f)}$$

is true, $(0 \leqslant k \leqslant p \leqslant n)$; $n_{2\varepsilon}(f)$ see § 5) where $n_\varepsilon^k(f)$ is the maximum of the number $N_\varepsilon[\Psi_i^k(f)]$ (with respect to i) (Ψ_i^k is the transformation which projects orthogonally on the plane τ_i^k or on the corresponding boundary of the cube J_n.

Proof. Let us select in f a maximal system of points $S_{2\varepsilon}(f)$ which are further than 4ε apart. By definition, the set $S_{2\varepsilon}(f)$ consists of $N_{2\varepsilon}(f)$ points (see § 5). ω_l and ω_l^* denote regular closed cubes in E_n^C, of sides 4ε and 2ε respectively, having a common centre at the point $a_l \in S_{2\varepsilon}(f)$. Since the set e approximates with an accuracy of ε to f, each of the cubes $\{\omega_l^*\}$ must contain points of e, i.e. the set e is embedded in each of the cubes $\{\omega_l\}$ to a depth of not less than ε. Then, since the cubes $\{\omega_l\}$ have no points in common with one another (the distance between their centres in the metric C being strictly greater than the length of their sides) and since all the cubes $\{\omega_l\}$ lie inside J_n (f being not nearer the boundary of J_n than 2ε) it follows (see Lemma 1, § 21) that there exists a k such that for some $\frac{n_{2\varepsilon}(f)}{p+1}$ cubes among $\{\omega_l\}$ the inequality

$$v_k^{\omega_l}(e) \geqslant \frac{[\Gamma(e, \omega_l)]^k}{(p+1)\, C_n^k} \geqslant \frac{\varepsilon^k}{(p+1)\, C_n^k}$$

---

* This means that any regular closed cube of side 2ε and centre on the set f contains at least one point of the set e.

holds.

Let ω denote the theoretic-set sum of the cubes among $\{\omega_l\}$ for which this inequality is true. Combining the previous inequalities we have

$$v_k^{\omega}(e) \geqslant \frac{\varepsilon^k}{(p+1)\,C_n^k}\,\frac{n_{2\varepsilon}(f)}{p+1} = \frac{\varepsilon^k n_{2\varepsilon}(f)}{(p+1)^2\,C_n^k}$$

Let $\gamma_{i,\varepsilon}^k$ be the set of all those points of the plane τ_i^k which are not further than 2ε from the set $\Psi_i^k(f)$ in the metric C). It is clear that $\Psi_i^k(\omega) \subset \gamma_{i,\varepsilon}^k$ and, therefore

$$\text{mes}_k\left[\Psi_i^k(\omega)\right] \leqslant \text{mes}_k\left(\gamma_{i,\varepsilon}^k\right)$$

We select the most economic 2ε-covering of the set $\Psi_i^k(f)$ by its subsets $\{\sigma_{i,m}^k\}$ $(m = 1, 2, \ldots, N_\varepsilon[\Psi_i^k(f)])$. Since the diameter of the set $\sigma_{i,m}^k$ is, by definition, not greater than 2ε (in the metric C), there exists a k-dimensional closed cube $\omega_{i,m}^k \subset \tau_i^k$ of side not greater than 2ε such that $\sigma_{i,m}^k \subset \omega_{i,m}^k$. Let $\omega_{i,m}^{k,*}$ be a k-dimensional closed cube of τ_i^k concentric with the cube $\omega_{i,m}^k$ and of side equal to 6ε. Since any point x of the set $\gamma_{i,\varepsilon}^k$ (by definition) is not further than 2ε from the set $\Psi_i^k(f)$ one of the cubes $\{\omega_{i,m}^k\}$ is not further than 2ε from the point x, and therefore the corresponding cube $\omega_{i,m}^{k,*}$ must contain the point x, i.e.

$$\gamma_{i,\varepsilon}^k \subset \bigcup_m \omega_{i,m}^{k,*}$$

Therefore

$$\text{mes}_k\left(\gamma_i^k\right) \leqslant \sum_m m_k\left(\omega_{i,m}^{k,*}\right) = 6\,(\varepsilon)^k N_\varepsilon\left[\Psi_i^k(f)\right] \leqslant (6\varepsilon)^k\, n_\varepsilon^k(f)$$

But since

$$v_k^{\omega}(e) \leqslant \frac{v}{C_n^k} \sum_{i=1}^{C_n^k} \text{mes}_k\left(\gamma_i^k\right) \leqslant v\,(6\varepsilon)^k\, n_\varepsilon^k(f)$$

from the inequality

$$v_k^{\omega}(e) \geqslant \frac{\varepsilon^k n_{2\varepsilon}(f)}{(p+1)^2\,C_n^k}$$

which was proved above, we have

$$v\,(6\varepsilon)^k\, n_\varepsilon^k\,(f) \geqslant \frac{\varepsilon^k n_2\,(f)}{(p+1)^2\, C_n^k}$$

i.e.

$$v \geqslant \frac{1}{6^k\,(p+1)^2\, C_n^k}\,\frac{n_{2\varepsilon}\,(f)}{n_\varepsilon^k\,(f)} \geqslant \frac{12^{-n}}{(p+1)^2}\,\frac{n_{2\varepsilon}\,(f)}{n_\varepsilon^k\,(f)}$$

Q.E.D.

Lemma 2. Let f be an arbitrary subset of the cube J_n, not further than 2ε from its boundary, and let e be a closed subset of E_n^C $(E_n^C \supset J_n)$ for which

$$v_{p+l}^{J_n}\,(e) = 0$$

$(l = 1,\,2,\,\ldots,\,n-p\ (p \leqslant n))$ and, given any k $(0 \leqslant k \leqslant p)$ and $q \in \tau_i^k$

$$v_0^{J_n}\left[e \cap \beta_i^{n-k}\,(q)\right] \leqslant v$$

Then, if the set e approximates to f to an accuracy of ε there exists $k \leqslant p$ such that

$$v \geqslant \frac{\varepsilon^k}{(p+1)^2\, C_n^k}\,\frac{n_{2\varepsilon}\,(f)}{\rho^k}$$

where ρ is the length of the side of the cube J_n.

Proof. As in the proof of Lemma 1, it is easy to prove that there exists a k such that

$$v_k^{\omega}\,(e) \geqslant \frac{\varepsilon^k}{(p+1)\, C_n^k}\,\frac{n_{2\varepsilon}(f)}{p+1}$$

But since $v_k^{\omega}\,(e) \leqslant v_k^{J_n}\,(e) \leqslant v\rho^k$ (see point 4, § 20),

$$v \geqslant \frac{\varepsilon^k}{(p+1)^2\, C_n^k}\,\frac{n_{2\varepsilon}(f)}{\rho^k}$$

Lemma 3. Let f be an arbitrary subset of the cube $J_n \subset E_n^C$, not less than 2ε from its boundary, and let e be a closed subset of the space E_n^C such that

$$v_{p+l}^{J_n}(e)=0 \qquad (l=1,\ 2,\ \dots,\ n-p;\ p\leqslant n)$$

Then, if the set e approximates to f to an accuracy of ε $(0<\varepsilon\leqslant 1)$

$$v^{J_n}(e)\geqslant\frac{\varepsilon^p}{2^n}n_{2\varepsilon}(f)$$

Proof. With the same notation as in the proof of Lemma 1, we have

$$v^{\omega_l}(e)=\sum_{k=0}^{n}v_k^{\omega_l}(e)=\sum_{k=0}^{p}v_k^{\omega_l}(e)=\sum_{k=0}^{p}\frac{m_k^l[\Gamma(e,\ \omega_l)]^k}{C_n^k}$$

where

$$m_k^l=\frac{v_k^{\omega_l}(e)\,C_n^k}{[\Gamma(e,\ \omega_l)]^k}$$

From Lemma 1, § 21 $\sum_{k=0}^{p}m_k^l\geqslant 1$. Therefore, using point 4 of § 20, we have

$$v^{J_n}(e)\geqslant\sum_{l=1}^{n_{2\varepsilon}(f)}v^{\omega_l}(e)=\sum_{l=1}^{n_{2\varepsilon}(f)}\sum_{k=0}^{p}\frac{m_k^l[\Gamma(e,\ \omega_l)]^k}{C_n^k}\geqslant$$

$$\geqslant\sum_{l=1}^{n_{2\varepsilon}(f)}\sum_{k=0}^{p}\frac{m_k^l\varepsilon^k}{2^n}\geqslant\frac{\varepsilon^p}{2^n}\sum_{l=1}^{n_{2\varepsilon}(f)}\sum_{k=0}^{p}m_k^l\geqslant\frac{\varepsilon^p}{2^n}n_{2\varepsilon}(f)$$

Q.E.D.

Theorem 1. Let J_n^ρ be a regular cube of side $\rho\leqslant 1$, and let e be a closed subset of this cube such that $v_{p+l}^{J_n^\rho}(e)=0$ $(l=1,2,\dots,n-p;\ p<n)$.

Then we can inscribe in J_n^ρ a regular n-dimensional closed cube J_n^d of side

$$d\geqslant\frac{\rho^{\frac{n}{n-p}}}{3+\sqrt[n-p]{6^n v^{J_n^\rho}(e)}}$$

Theorem 2. Suppose we are given the closed set $e \subset E_n^C$ such that

$$v_{p+l}^{J_n^\rho}(e) = 0 \qquad (l = 1, 2, \ldots, n-p;\ p \leqslant n)$$

and, for any i, k and $q \in \tau_i^k$

$$v_0^{J_n^\rho}[e \cap \beta_i^{n-k}(q)] \leqslant v \qquad (v > 0)$$

Then we can inscribe in $J_n^\rho - e$ a regular n-dimensional closed cube J_n^d of side

$$d \geqslant \frac{\rho}{3 + \sqrt[n-p]{6^n (p+1)^2 v}}$$

where ρ is the side of the cube J_n^ρ.

We could obtain Theorems 1 and 2 from Lemmas 1 to 3, giving a rougher estimate for d. We give here the proof of one of these theorems. The second is proved similarly.

Proof of Theorem 1. We divide the cube J_n^ρ into m^n congruent cubes $\{\omega_i\}$ by hyperplanes, parallel to the co-ordinate hyperplanes. We denote by ω_i' the cube of side $d = \frac{\rho'}{3m}$ concentric with the cube ω_i. If we assume that each of the cubes $\{\omega_i'\}$ contains points of the set e, then, from Lemma 3 § 21 we have

$$v^{J_n^\rho}(e) \geqslant \sum_{i=1}^{m^n} v^{\omega_i}(e) \geqslant \frac{m^n}{2^n}\left(\frac{\rho}{3m}\right)^p$$

i.e. m must satisfy the inequality

$$m \leqslant \sqrt[n-p]{3^p 2^n \rho^{-p} v^{J_n^\rho}(e)}$$

Fixing now

$$m = 1 + \left[\sqrt[n-p]{3^p 2^n \rho^{-p} v^{J_n^\rho}(e)}\right] > \sqrt[n-p]{3^p 2^n \rho^{-n} v^{J_n^\rho}(e)}$$

we find that at least one of the cubes ω_i' contains no points of the set e. But the side of such a cube will be equal to

$$d = \frac{\rho}{3m} \geqslant \frac{\rho\rho^{\frac{p}{n-p}}}{3\rho^{\frac{p}{n-p}} + \sqrt[n-p]{3^{n-p}3^{p}2^{n}v^{J_n^{\rho}(e)}}} \geqslant \frac{\cdot\,\rho^{\frac{n}{n-p}}}{3 + \sqrt[n-p]{6^{n}v^{J_n^{\rho}(e)}}}.$$

Q.E.D.

CHAPTER V

ESTIMATES OF THE VARIATIONS OF SOME CONCRETE SETS

In this chapter we shall give estimates of multiplicity functions for sets obtained from Euclidean spaces by transformations given by rational functions. It is easy to reduce estimates of this kind to estimates of Betti numbers for algebraic surfaces.

§ 24. Level-curves of a Polynomial

All the estimates of the multiplicity function which we shall give below are based on the following lemma.

Lemma 1. (O.A. Oleinik). The number of bounded elements of the set of points on a level-curve of a polynomial $P_n^k(x)$ in n variables $x_1, x_2, \ldots, x_n$ of degree k (in each of the variables) does not exceed $(k-1)^n$ for $k \geqslant 1$ and is equal to zero for $k=0$ $(n \geqslant 2)$ * .

For a proof of this lemma, see [7].

Lemma 2. Any set of points of a level-curve of the polynomial $P_n^k(x)$ in the n variables $x_1, x_2, \ldots, x_n$ $(x \in E_n)$ of degree k divides any n-dimensional closed sphere $\sigma \subset E_n$ into not more than $(k+1)^n$ parts $(n \geqslant 1,\ k \geqslant 0)$.

Proof. Let r be the radius of the sphere σ, and $\{x_i^0\}$ the co-ordinates of the centre of this sphere; let e_t^0 be the intersection of the set e_t of the t-level of the polynomial $P_n^k(x)$ $(x \in e_t$, if $P_n^k(x)=t)$ with the sphere σ; and

---

* For $n=1$ the number of elements (points) of a level-curve of the polynomial $P_n^k(x)$ will obviously not exceed the number of roots of the equation $P_n^k(x)-t=0$, i.e will not exceed k .

Let $\alpha_1, \alpha_2, \ldots, \alpha_l$ be some elements of $\sigma - e_t^0 = \sigma - e_t$.

We shall prove that l cannot exceed $(k+1)^n$. For $n=1$ this is obvious, since the number of elements of the set $\sigma - e_t^0$ cannot then exceed the number of roots of the equation $\frac{d}{dx_1} P_1^k(x_1) = 0$ by more than unity, i.e. cannot exceed $k+1$. Therefore, we shall take n to be $\geqslant 2$.

We put

$$P_n^{k+2}(x) = [P_n^k(x) - t]\left[r^2 - \sum_{i=1}^{n}(x_i - x_i^0)^2\right]$$

The polynomial $P_n^{k+2}(x)$ is of degree $k+2$, the set of points on its zero level-curve

$$e_0 = e_t + \sigma^*$$

Let β_i denote the element of the set $\sigma - l_0$ contained in α_i $(i = 1, 2, \ldots, l)$.

It is clear that in each of the regions $\{\beta_i\}$ there is at least one internal point at which the gradient of the polynomial $P_n^{k+2}(x)$ $\text{grad}\, P_n^{k+2}(x) = 0$ (such points are extremal points, i.e. points of a maximum or minimum of the polynomial $P_n^{k+2}(x)$). It is clear also that any other polynomial which approximates sufficiently well to $P_n^{k+2}(x)$ on σ will possess this property.

It is proved in [8] that by as small a change in its coefficients as we please, any polynomial $P_n^m(x)$ can be reduced to a real polynomial $P_{n,*}^m(x)$ which is such that the zero level-curve of its gradient consists of not more than $(m-1)^n$ different points. But a quite small change (in comparison to $r + \max_i x_i^0$)) in the coefficients of $P_n^{k+2}(x)$ transforms it into a new polynomial $P_{n,*}^{k+2}(x)$ which is quite a good first approximation on the sphere σ, and is such that the number of roots of the equation

$$\text{grad}\,[P_{n,*}^{k+2}(x)] = 0$$

does not exceed $(k+1)^n$. Therefore, from the above, $l \leqslant (k+1)^n$.

Q.E.D.

Lemma 3. (O.A. Oleinik). If the set of points of a level-curve of the polynomial $P_n^k(x)$ in n variables of degree k contains no points at which $\operatorname{grad} P_n^k(x) = 0$ then the number of bounded elements of this set does not exceed $\frac{1}{2}(k-1)^n$ $(n > 1,\ k \geqslant 1)$.

For the proof see [7].

Lemma 4. The number of elements of the polynomial $P_n^k(x)$ in n variables of degree k, considered only on the n-dimensiona closed sphere σ, does not exceed $(k+1)^n$ $(n \geqslant 1,\ k \geqslant 0)$.

Proof. Suppose the lemma is false. Then the number $v_0(e_t \cap \sigma$ of elements of some t-level set of the polynomial P_n^k, considered only on σ, will exceed $(k+1)^n$. Therefore we can choose an ε as small as we please (positive or negative) such that, firstly, at no point of the set $e_{t+\varepsilon}$ of the $t+\varepsilon$-level curve of the polynomial $P_n^k(x)$ will the gradient of this polynomial become zero, and, secondly $v_0(e_{t+\varepsilon} \cap \sigma)$ will be strictly greater than $\frac{1}{2}(k+1)^n$.

Let us choose such an ε. For definiteness we suppose that $\varepsilon > 0$. Then we can find $\delta > 0$ (its sign being determine by that of ε) such that the set f_δ of points of the δ-level curve of the polynomial

$$P_n^{k+2}(x) = [P_n^k(x) - t]\left[r^2 - \sum_{i=1}^{n} (x_i - x_i^0)^2\right]$$

will not contain points at which the gradient of this polynomial $P_n^{k+2}(x)$ is zero while the number of bounded elements of this set will be greater than $\frac{1}{2}(k+1)^n$, since any element of the $t+\varepsilon$-level curve of the polynomial $P_n^k(x)$ generates an element of the set of points of the δ-level curve of the polynomial $P_n^{k+2}(x)$ lying near to it, but necessarily not outside the boundary of the sphere σ. This contradicts

Lemma 3. Q.E.D.

Lemma 5. If the set of points of a level-curve of the polynomial $P_n^k(x)$ contains no points of the set of the zero level-curve of the gradient of this polynomial, then it splits up any n-dimensional closed sphere into not more than $\frac{1}{2}(k+1)^n$ parts.

Lemma 6. If the set of points of a level-curve of the polynomial $P_n^k(x)$ contains no points of the set of the zero level-curve of the gradient of this polynomial, then it is intersected by any n-dimensional closed sphere σ in not more than $\frac{1}{2}(k+1)^n$ elements.

The proof of these two lemmas is practically given in that of Lemmas 2 and 4.

Lemma 7. The set of points of a level-curve of the polynomial $P_n^k(x)$ $(x \in E_n)$ splits up the space E_n into not more than $(k+1)^n$ regions $(n \geqslant 1,\ k \geqslant 0)$.

Lemma 8. The number of elements (bounded and unbounded) of any set of points of a level-curve of the polynomial $P_n^k(x)$ does not exceed $(k+1)^n$ $(n \geqslant 1,\ k \geqslant 0)$.

These two lemmas are easily obtained from Lemmas 2 and 4 by taking σ to be a sufficiently large sphere with centre at the co-ordinate origin.

§ 25. The Level-curves of Rational Functions

We shall call the ratio of two polynomials of degree not higher than k a rational function of degree k in n variables.

Lemma 1. Let

$$R_n^k(x) = \frac{P_n^k(x)}{Q_n^k(x)} \qquad (x \in E_n)$$

be a rational function, being the ratio of the polynomials $P_n^k(x)$ and $Q_n^k(x) \neq 0$ of degree k.

Then any set of points of a level-curve of the function $R_n^k(x)$ divides any n-dimensional closed sphere $\sigma \subset E_n$ (and therefore also the whole space E_n) into not more than $(k+1)^n$ parts $(n \geqslant 1,\ k \geqslant 0)$.

Lemma 2. If the function $R_n^k(x)$ satisfies the conditions of Lemma 1, then the number of elements of the intersection of any set of points of a level-curve of this function with an arbitrary n-dimensional closed sphere σ (and therefore also with the whole space E_n) will not exceed $(k+1)^n\ (n \geqslant 1,\ k \geqslant 0)$.

Lemmas 1 and 2 are easily obtained from Lemmas 2 and 4 of § 24. To do this it is sufficient merely to see that the set of points of the t-level curve of the function $R_n^k(x)$ is the same as the set of points of the zero level-curve of the polynomial $P_n^k(x) - tQ_n^k(x)$, the degree of which is clearly not greater than k.

We now estimate the possible number of elements of the set of points of a level-curve of the rational function $R_n^k(x) = \frac{P_n^k(x)}{Q_n^k(x)}$ for the case when the function $Q_n^k(x)$ can take zero values.

Put $R_n^k(x) = \frac{P_n^k(x)}{Q_n^k(x)}$ where $P_n^k(x)$ and $Q_n^k(x)$ are polynomials in n variables of degree k, and let $\sigma_\varepsilon(Q_n^k)$ denote the set of all points of the n-dimensional closed sphere $\sigma\ (\sigma \subset E_n)$ for which $|Q_n^k(x)| \geqslant \varepsilon$.

Lemma 3. For any $\varepsilon > 0$ the number of elements of the intersection of the set $\sigma_\varepsilon(Q_n^k)$ with an arbitrary set of points of a level-curve of the rational function

$$R_n^k(x) = \frac{P_n^k(x)}{Q_n^k(x)} \qquad (k \geqslant 0,\ n \geqslant 1)$$

does not exceed

$$(4k+1)^n + (k+1)^n \leqslant (5k+2)^n$$

Proof. Since on the set $\sigma_\varepsilon(Q_n^k)$ $Q_n^k(x) \neq 0$ (by definition), then on this set the equation

$$R_n^k(x) = t$$

is equivalent to the equation

$$\frac{P_n^k(x) - tQ_n^k(x)}{Q_n^k(x)} = 0$$

i.e. inside $\sigma_\varepsilon(Q_n^k)$ the sets given by these equations coincide. Therefore, to prove the lemma it is sufficient to evaluate the number of elements of the intersection $e_t^0 \cap \sigma_\varepsilon(Q_n^k)$ of the set e_t^0 of points of the zero level-curve of the function $\frac{P_n^k(x) - tQ_n^k(x)}{Q_n^k(x)}$ with the set $\sigma_\varepsilon(Q_n^k)$.

Let e_t^1 denote the theoretic-set sum of all elements of the set $e_t^0 \cap \sigma_\varepsilon(Q_n^k)$ having points in common with the set $\{|Q_n^k(x)| = \varepsilon\}$ and e_t^2 the theoretic-set sum of all other elements of this set $e_t^0 \cap \sigma_\varepsilon(Q_n^k)$. Since $e_t^0 \cap \sigma_\varepsilon(Q_n^k) = e_t^1 \cup e_t^2$ it is obvious that

$$v_0[e_t^0 \cap \sigma_\varepsilon(Q_n^k)] \leqslant v_0(e_t^1) + v_0(e_t^2)$$

Since each element α of the set e_t^1 gives not less than one element (belonging to the set $\alpha \cap \{|Q_n^k(x)| = \varepsilon\}$) in the set $e_t^1 \cap \{|Q_n^k(x)| = \varepsilon\}$ the number of elements of the set e_t^1 cannot exceed the number of elements of the set $e_t^1 \cap \{|Q_n^k(x)| = \varepsilon\}$. But on σ this set coincides with the zero-level-curve of the polynomial

$$P_\varepsilon(x) = [(Q_n^k(x))^2 - \varepsilon^2]^2 + [P_n^k(x) + tQ_n^k(x)]^2$$

of degree not greater than $4k$. Therefore, from Lemma 4 § 24 the number of elements of the set $e_t^1 \cap \{|Q_n^k(x)| = \varepsilon\}$ does not exceed $(4k+1)^n$ and therefore also

$$v_0(e_t^1) \leqslant (4k+1)^n$$

From the same Lemma 4 § 24

$$v_0(e_t^2) \leqslant v_0(e_t^0 \cap \sigma) \leqslant (k+1)^n$$

since the set $\left\{ \frac{P_n^k(x) - tQ_n^k(x)}{Q_n^k(x)} = 0 \right\}$ coincides with the set $\{P_n^k(x) - tQ_n^k(x) = 0\}$ inside $o_\varepsilon(Q_n^k)$. Thus

$$v_0[e_t^0 \cap \sigma_\varepsilon(Q_n^k)] \leqslant v_0(e_t^1) + v_0(e_t^2) \leqslant$$
$$\leqslant (4k+1)^n + (k+1)^n \leqslant (5k+2)^n$$

Q.E.D.

Lemma 4. The number of elements of the intersection of the set $\sigma \cap \{Q_n^k(x) \neq 0\}$ (and therefore also the set $\{Q_n^k(x) \neq 0\}$) *) with an arbitrary set of points of a level-curve of the rational function

$$R_n^k(x) = \frac{P_n^k(x)}{Q_n^k(x)}$$

cannot exceed the number

$$(5k+2)^n \qquad (k \geqslant 0;\ n \geqslant 1)$$

Proof. We select a sequence of positive numbers $\varepsilon_m = \frac{1}{m}$ $(m = 1, 2, \ldots)$ and let e_t^m be that part of the set of points of the t-level for the rational function $R_n^k(x)$ which belongs to the set $\sigma_{\varepsilon_m}(Q_n^k)$, and let e_t^∞ be the intersection of the set $\sigma \cap \{Q_n^k(x) \neq 0\}$ with the set of points of the t-level curve of the function $R_n^k(x)$. From Lemma 3

$$v_0(e_t^m) \leqslant (5k+2)^n \qquad (m = 1, 2, \ldots)$$

Since, for any

$$m > 1 \quad \sigma_{\varepsilon_m}(Q_n^k) \subset \sigma_{\varepsilon_{m-1}}(Q_n^k)$$
and
$$e_t^m \supset e_t^{m-1} \qquad (m = 2, 3, \ldots)$$

and therefore

$$v_0(e_t^\infty) \leqslant \sup_m v_0(e_t^m) \leqslant (5k+2)^n$$

Q.E.D.

---

* Because the sphere σ is arbitrary.

Lemma 5. Any set of points of a level-curve of the rational function

$$R_n^k(x) = \frac{P_n^k(x)}{Q_n^k(x)}$$

divides the set

$$\sigma \cap \{Q_n^k(x) \neq 0\}$$

into not more than $(2k+1)^n$ parts ($k \geqslant 0$, $n \geqslant 1$).

Proof. Let e_t be the set of points of the t-level curve of the function $R_n^k(x)$ and f_t^0 the set of points of the zero level-curve of the polynomial $Q_n^k(x)[P_n^k(x) - tQ_n^k(x)]$. Then

$$\sigma \cap \{Q_n^k(x) \neq 0\} - e_t = \sigma - \{Q_n^k(x) = 0\} - e_t = \sigma - f_t^0$$

i.e. the set $\sigma \cap \{Q_n^k(x) \neq 0\} - e_t$ coincides with the complement of the sphere σ with respect to the zero level-curve of the polynomial $Q_n^k(x)[P_n^k(x) - tQ_n^k(x)]$ which is of degree not greater than $2k$. Therefore, from Lemma 2 § 24, the number of elements of this set does not exceed $(2k+1)^n$. Q.E.D.

§ 26. Piecewise-rational Functions

Definition. The function $r(x)$, defined on some subset Ω_n of the n-dimensional Euclidean space E_n, is said to be piecewise-rational, if it satisfies the following conditions:

(1) There exists a polynomial $P_n^q(x)$ such that on any element γ_i of the complement of the set of points of the zero level curve of this polynomial $r(x)$ can be put in the form of the ratio of two polynomials of degree k:

$$r(x) = r_{\gamma_i}(x) = \frac{P_{n,i}^k(x)}{Q_{n,i}^k(x)}$$

($i = 1, 2, \ldots, l$; $l \leqslant (q+1)^n$ is the number of elements of the complement of the set $\{P_n^q(x) = 0\}$);

(2) At any point $x \in \bar{\gamma}_i \cap \bar{\gamma}_j$ where $\bar{\gamma}_i$ is the closure of the region γ_i ($i \neq j$) the function $r(x)$, generally speaking, is not

single-valued; the number of values which it can take at any such point is equal to the number of sets $\gamma_i \ni x$ for which the corresponding polynomials $\{Q^k_{n,i}(x)\}$ at that point are not equal to zero.

We call the set $\{P^q_n(x)=0\}$ the barrier of the function $r(x)$ and the number q is the order of the barrier. The number k is called the degree of the function $r(x)$.

The set

$$\Omega_n = \bigcup_{i=1}^{l} [\bar{\gamma}_i - \{Q^k_{n,i}(x)=0\}] + \\ + \bigcup_{i=1}\bigcup_{j=1}^{l} [\bar{\gamma}_i \cap \bar{\gamma}_j - \{Q^k_{n,i}(x)=0\} - \{Q^k_{n,j}(x)=0\}]$$

is taken as the region of definition of the function $r(x)$.

The piecewise-rational function $r(x)$ is said to be continuous if, for any i, $Q^k_{n,i}(x) \neq 0$ everywhere on γ_i.

Lemma 1. We are given some natural number m and the continuous piecewise rational functions $r_i(x)$ $(i=1, 2, \ldots, m)$ in n variables of degree k with a common barrier $\{P^q_n(x)=0\}$ of order q.

Then the number of elements of the intersection of the set of all solutions of the system

$$r_i(x) = t_i \qquad (i=1, 2, \ldots, n)$$

(where $\{t_i\}$ are arbitrary real numbers) with an arbitrary n-dimensional closed sphere σ cannot exceed

$$\frac{1}{2}[(q+1)(2k+q+1)]^n \qquad (n \geqslant 1,\ k \geqslant 0,\ q \geqslant 0)$$

Proof. Let γ be an element of the set $\sigma - \sigma^* - \{P^q_n(x)=0\}$ (σ^* is the boundary of σ), and let γ^* be the boundary of this region. On the set $\gamma + \gamma^* = \bar{\gamma}$ each of the functions $r_i(x)$ can (by the definition of a continuous piecewise-rational function) be represented as the ratio of two polynomials of degree k:

$$r_i(x) = \frac{P^k_{i,\gamma}(x)}{Q^k_{i,\gamma}(x)}$$

Put

$$P_\gamma^{2k}(x)=\sum_{i=1}^{m}\left[P_{i,\gamma}^{k}(x)-t_iQ_{i,\gamma}^{k}(x)\right]^2,$$

$$P_\varepsilon^{2k+q+2}(x)=\left[\varepsilon-P_\gamma^{2k}(x)\right]\left[r^2-\sum_{j=1}^{n}(x_j-x_j^0)^2\right]P_n^q(x)\operatorname{sign}P_n^q(x)$$
$$x\in\gamma,$$

where $\varepsilon>0$ is some number, r is the radius of the sphere σ, and $\{x_j^0\}$ are the co-ordinates of the centre of this sphere. Given $\varepsilon>0$ we can find a neighbourhood for each element k_i of the set

$$e_0=\bar{\gamma}\cap\{P_\gamma^{2k}(x)=0\}$$

in which

$$P_\varepsilon^{2k+q+2}(x)>0$$

Let α_i be the maximum of these neighbourhoods for the element $k_i\in e_0$ $(l=1,2,\ldots,l)$. For sufficiently small ε the neighbourhoods $\{\alpha_i\}$ will have no internal points in common, and the equality

$$P_\varepsilon^{2k+q+2}(x)=0$$

will hold on their boundaries. Choose ε so that this is true. Then for sufficiently small $\delta>0$ the set e_ε^δ of points of the δ-level curve of the polynomial $P_\varepsilon^{2k+q+2}(x)$ will have at least one element in each of the regions $\{\alpha_i\}$ i.e. given any δ sufficiently small, the set e_ε^δ will have not less than l bounded slements. But since almost all the level-curves of the polynomial contain no points at which its gradient is zero, from Lemma 3 § 24 it follows that

$$l\leqslant\frac{1}{2}(2k+q+1)^n$$

It is not difficult to see that the set of all solutions (in $\bar{\gamma}_j=\bar{\gamma}$) of the given system coincides with the set

$$e_0=\bar{\gamma}_j\cap\{P_\gamma^{2k}(x)=0\}=e_0^j$$

And since $\sum_j e_0^j$ is the same as the set of all solutions of the given system which lie inside the sphere σ, from Lemma 4 § 24 it follows that the number of elements of the set of all solutions (on σ) of our system does not exceed

$$\sum_j v_0(e_0^j) \leqslant (q+1)^n \frac{1}{2}(2k+q+1)^n = \\ = \frac{1}{2}[(q+1)(2k+q+1)]^n.$$

Q.E.D.

Lemma 2. Let $m > 0$ be some natural number, and let $r_i(x)$ be a piecewise-rational function of degree $k \geqslant 0$ with barrier $\{P_n^q(x)=0\}$ of order $q \geqslant 0$, which can be represented on the element γ_i of the set $\sigma - \{P_n^q(x)=0\}$ in the form

$$r_i(x) = \frac{P^k_{i,\gamma_j}(x)}{Q^k_{i,\gamma_j}(x)} \qquad (i=1, 2, \ldots, m);$$

let l be the number of elements of the set $\sigma - \{P_n^q(x)=0\}$; $\bar{\gamma}_j$ the closure of the set γ_j;

$$\sigma_\varepsilon = \bigcup_{j=1}^{l} \left[\bar{\gamma}_j - \left\{ \left| \prod_{i=1}^{m} Q^k_{i,\gamma_j}(x) \right| < \varepsilon \right\}\right]$$

and e_t the set of all solutions of the system

$$r_i(x) = t_i$$

($i = 1, 2, \ldots, m$; $\{t_i\}$ are arbitrary real numbers).

Then for any ε

$$v_0(e_t \cap \sigma_\varepsilon) \leqslant \frac{1}{2}[(q+1)(2mk+2k+q+1)]^n$$

Proof. Since on the set

$$\bar{\gamma}_j - \left\{ \left| \prod_{i=1}^{m} Q^k_{i,\gamma_j}(x) \right| < \varepsilon \right\}$$

none of the polynomials $Q^k_{i,\gamma_j}(x)$ $(i=1, 2, \ldots, m)$ is zero

$$e_t \cap \left[\bar{\gamma}_j - \left\{ \left| \prod_{i=1}^{m} Q^k_{i,\gamma_j}(x) \right| < \varepsilon \right\}\right]$$

coincides with the set

$$f_t^j \cap \left[\bar{\gamma}_j - \left\{ \left| \prod_{i=1}^{m} Q_{i,\gamma_j}^k(x) \right| < \varepsilon \right\}\right]$$

where f_t^j is the set of all solutions of the system

$$P_{i,\gamma_j}^k(x) - t_i Q_{i,\gamma_j}^k(x) = 0 \qquad (i = 1, 2, \ldots, m)$$

Let us evaluate the number of elements of

$$f_t^j \cap \left[\bar{\gamma}_j - \left\{ \left| \prod_{i=1}^{m} Q_{i,\gamma_j}^k(x) \right| < \varepsilon \right\}\right]$$

To do this we put

$$P_{\gamma_j}^{2k}(x) = \sum_{i=1}^{m} [P_{i,\gamma_j}^k(x) - t_i Q_{i,\gamma_j}^k(x)]^2$$

and consider the polynomial

$$P_{\varepsilon,\delta}(x) = [\operatorname{sign} P_n^q(x)]\, P_n^q(x) \left[\left(\prod_{i=1}^{m} Q_{i,\gamma_j}^k(x)\right)^2 - \varepsilon^2\right] \times$$
$$\times \left[r^2 - \sum_{i=1}^{n} (x_i - x_i^0)^2\right] [\delta - P_{\gamma_j}^{2k}(x)]$$

where r is the radius of the sphere σ, $\{x_i^0\}$ are the coordinates of its centre, and $\varepsilon > 0$, $\delta > 0$.

Let us examine the behaviour of the polynomial $P_{\varepsilon,\delta}(x)$ on the set $\bar{\gamma}_j - \left\{ \left| \prod_{i=1}^{m} Q_{i,\gamma_j}^k(x) \right| > \varepsilon \right\}$. On the boundary of this set $P_{\varepsilon,\delta}(x)$ is equal to zero since this boundary consists of points of the set $\{P_n^q(x) = 0\}$ on which

$$P_n^q(x) = 0$$

together with points of the set

$$\left\{ \left| \prod_{i=1}^{m} Q_{i,\gamma_j}^k(x) \right| = \varepsilon \right\} \cap \bar{\gamma}_j$$

on which

$$\left(\prod_{i=1}^{m} Q_{i,\gamma_j}^k(x)\right)^2 - \varepsilon^2 = 0$$

If the point $x \in \{P^{2k}_{\gamma_j}(x) = \delta\}$ does not belong to the boundary of the set

$$\bar{\gamma}_j - \left\{ \left| \prod_{i=1}^{m} Q^k_{i,\gamma_j}(x) \right| < \varepsilon \right\}$$

then

$$P_{\varepsilon,\delta}(x) > 0$$

If it does belong to the boundary of this set, then $P_{\varepsilon,\delta}(x) = 0$ but at any point

$$x' \in \gamma_j - \left\{ \left| \prod_{i=1}^{m} Q^k_{i,\gamma_j}(x) \right| \leqslant \varepsilon \right\}$$

however near x

$$P_{\varepsilon,\delta}(x') > 0$$

If the point $x \in \gamma_j - \left\{ \left| \prod_{i=1}^{m} Q^k_{i,\gamma_j}(x) \right| \leqslant \varepsilon \right\}$ is sufficiently far from the set $\{P^{2k}_{\gamma_j}(x) = 0\}$ or, to be more precise, if it belongs to the set $\{P^{2k}_{\gamma_j}(x) > \delta\}$, then

$$P_{\varepsilon,\delta}(x) < 0$$

Since, from Lemma 4 § 24 the set $\{P^{2k}_{\gamma_j}(x) = 0\}$ consists of a finite number of elements $k_1, k_2, \ldots, k_s$ each of which is a closed set because of the continuity of $P^{2k}_{\gamma_j}(x)$, we can find $\delta > 0$ which is so small that any pair of elements of $\{k_i\}$ inside $\bar{\gamma}_j - \left\{ \left| \prod_{i=1}^{m} Q^k_{i,\gamma_j}(x) \right| < \varepsilon \right\}$ is divided by the set $\{P_{\varepsilon,\delta}(x) = 0\}$. Choose such a δ, i.e. choose δ so that the number of elements of the open set

$$\{P_{\varepsilon,\delta}(x) > 0\} \cap \left[\gamma_j - \left\{ \left| \prod_{i=1}^{m} Q^k_{i,\gamma_j}(x) \right| \leqslant \varepsilon \right\} \right]$$

will be not less than s, where s is the number of elements of the set

$$\{P^{2k}_{\gamma_j}(x)=0\}\cap\left[\bar{\gamma}_j-\left\{\left|\prod_{i=1}^{m}Q^k_{i,\gamma_j}(x)\right|<\varepsilon\right\}\right]$$

Then for any sufficiently small $\delta'>0$ at least one element of the set

$$\{P_{\varepsilon,\delta}(x)>0\}\cap\left[\gamma_j-\left\{\left|\prod_{i=1}^{m}Q^k_{i,\gamma_j}(x)\right|\leqslant\varepsilon\right\}\right]$$

will lie in each element of the set

$$\{P_{\varepsilon,\delta}(x)=\delta'\}\cap\left[\gamma_j-\left\{\left|\prod_{i=1}^{m}Q^k_{i,\gamma_j}(x)\right|\leqslant\varepsilon\right\}\right]$$

Since almost no level-curve of a polynomial contains points where its gradient takes a zero value, we can choose $\delta'>0$ so small that on the corresponding set $\{P_{\varepsilon,\delta}(x)=\delta'\}$ the gradient of $P_{\varepsilon,\delta}(x)$ is not zero. Therefore, from Lemma 3 § 24 the number of elements of the set

$$\{P_{\varepsilon,\delta}(x)=\delta'\}\cap\left[\gamma_j-\left\{\left|\prod_{i=1}^{m}Q^k_{i,\gamma_j}(x)\right|\leqslant\varepsilon\right\}\right]\leqslant$$
$$\leqslant\frac{1}{2}(2mk+2k+q+1)^n$$

since the degree of $P_{\varepsilon,\delta}(x)$ is not greater than $(2mk+2k+q+2)$. Hence

$$s\leqslant\frac{1}{2}(2mk+2k+q+1)^n$$

But since

$$\{P^{2k}_{\gamma_j}(x)=0\}\cap\left[\bar{\gamma}_j-\left\{\left|\prod_{i=1}^{m}Q^k_{i,\gamma_j}(x)\right|<\varepsilon\right\}\right]=$$
$$=f^j_t\cap\left[\bar{\gamma}_j-\left\{\left|\prod_{i=1}^{m}Q^k_{i,\gamma_j}(x)\right|<\varepsilon\right\}\right]$$

the number of elements of the set

$$f^j_t\cap\left[\bar{\gamma}_j-\left\{\left|\prod_{i=1}^{m}Q^k_{i,\gamma_j}(x)\right|<\varepsilon\right\}\right]$$

will not exceed $\frac{1}{2}(2mk+2k+q+1)^n$.

And, finally, since

$$e_t \cap \sigma_\varepsilon = \bigcup_{j=1}^{l} [\bar{\gamma}_j - \{|Q^k_{i,\gamma_j}(x)| < \varepsilon\}] \cap e_t =$$
$$= \bigcup_{j=1}^{l} f^j_t \cap \left[\bar{\gamma}_j - \left\{\left|Q^k_{i,\gamma_j}(x)\right| < \varepsilon\right\}\right]$$

and, from Lemma 4 § 24 since $l \leqslant (q+1)^n$ we have

$$v_0(e_t \cap \sigma_\varepsilon) \leqslant \sum_{j=1}^{l} v_0\left(f^j_t \cap \left[\bar{\gamma}_j - \left\{\left|Q^k_{i,\gamma_j}(x)\right| < \varepsilon\right\}\right]\right) \leqslant$$
$$\leqslant \frac{1}{2}[(q+1)(2mk+2k+q+1)]^n.$$

Q.E.D.

§ 27. Rational Surfaces and the Properties of their Complements

Suppose that we are given two Euclidean spaces E_p and E_m $(p \geqslant 1,\ m \geqslant 1)$. In the space E_p we choose an orthonormal base $Y = (Y_1, Y_2, \ldots, Y_p)$ and let $y_1, y_2, \ldots, y_p$ be the coordinates of an arbitrary point $y \in E_p$ with respect to this base; similarly, in the space E_m we choose the orthonormal base $T = (T_1, T_2, \ldots, T_m)$ and let $t_1, t_2, \ldots, t_m$ be the coordinates of an arbitrary point $t \in E_m$ in this system of coordinates.

Definition. A transformation of the space E_p into the space E_m is said to be piecewise-rational if it can be given by the equations

$$t_i = r^{k,q}_i(y) = r^{k,q}_i(y_1, y_2, \ldots, y_p) \qquad (i = 1, 2, \ldots, m)$$

where $\{r^{k,q}_i(y)\}$ are piecewise-rational functions of degree k with a common barrier of q.

The transformation R is said to be a continuous piecewise-rational transformation if all the $\{r^{k,q}_i(y)\}$ are continuous piecewise-rational functions.

The set $e \subset E_m$ is said to be a p-dimensional piecewise-rational surface of degree k and order q if this set is the image of the space E_p in E_m under a piecewise-rational transformation given by piecewise-rational functions of degree k with a barrier of order q.

$\bar{e}$ will denote the closure of e.

<u>Theorem 1</u>. Let J_m be an m-dimensional regular cube in E_m of side $\rho \leqslant 1$ and let $e \subset E_m$ be a continuous piecewise-rational surface of degree $k \geqslant 0$ and order $q \geqslant 0$.

Then we can inscribe an m-dimensional open regular cube of side

$$d \geqslant \frac{\rho}{3 + \sqrt[m-p]{6^m (p+1)^2 (q+1)^p (2k+q+1)^p}}.$$

in $J_m - \bar{e}$.

<u>Theorem 2</u>. Let J_m be an m-dimensional regular cube in E_m of side $\rho \leqslant 1$ and let $e \subset E_m$ be any piecewise-rational surface of degree k and order q.

Then we can inscribe an m-dimensional open regular cube of side

$$d \geqslant \frac{\rho}{3 + \sqrt[m-p]{6^m (p+1)^2 (q+1)^p (2mk+2k+q+1)^p}}.$$

in $J_m - \bar{e}$.

The proofs of these theorems are similar. We shall prove only one of them.

<u>Proof of Theorem 2</u>. Let σ_n denote the set in E_p which is the intersection of the p-dimensional closed sphere of radius n with centre at the origin, and the set

$$\bigcup_{j=1}^{l} \left[\bar{\gamma}_j - \left\{ \left| \prod_{i=1}^{m} Q^k_{i,\gamma_j}(y) \right| < \frac{1}{n} \right\} \right]$$

where $\gamma_1, \gamma_2, \ldots, \gamma_l$ are elements of the complement of the barrier of this sphere and $Q^k_{i,\gamma_j}(y)$ are the denominators of the rational functions which give the mapping on the region γ_j

$$r^{k,q}_{i,\gamma_j}(y)=\frac{P^k_{i,\gamma_j}(y)}{Q^k_{i,\gamma_j}(y)}$$

Put $e_n=R(\sigma_n)$. Let β be an $(m-s)$-dimensional plane, orthogonal to the s-dimensional co-ordinate plane τ^s_1 which stretches along the vectors $T_1, T_2, \ldots, T_s$ say, and passing through the point $(t_1, t_2, \ldots, t_s; \underbrace{0, 0, \ldots, 0}_{m-s})$. Let e^*_n denote the inverse image (for the transformation R) of the set $e_n \cap \beta$. It is easy to see that e^*_n is the aggregate of all solutions of the system

$$r^{k,q}_i(y)=t_i \qquad (i=1, 2, \ldots, s)$$

belonging to the set σ_n. Therefore, by Lemma 2 § 26

$$v_0(e^*_t)\leqslant\frac{1}{2}(q+1)^p(2s_k+2k+q+1)^p\leqslant$$
$$\leqslant(q+1)^p(2mk+2k+q+1)^p.$$

On the set σ_n, as we can easily verify, all the functions $\{r^{k,q}_i(y)\}$ are continuous, and σ_n itself is closed. But since a continuous transformation of a set does not increase the number of its elements,

$$v_0(e_n \cap \beta)\leqslant\frac{1}{2}(q+1)^p(2mk+2k+q+1)^p$$

We have thus shown that all the multiplicity functions (of various orders) of the set e_n are uniformly bounded by the constant

$$(q+1)^p(2mk+2k+q+1)^p$$

The set e_n is closed, since the set σ_n is closed and the transformation R (on σ_n) is continuous.

Thus we have proved the following lemma.

<u>Lemma 1</u>. If $e\subset E_m$ is a p-dimensional piecewise-rational surface of degree k and order q, then we can find in e a

denumerable sequence of closed subsets e_n $(n=1, 2, \ldots)$ such that all the multiplicity functions of each subset are uniformly bounded by the constant

$$(q+1)^p (2mk+2k+q+1)^p$$

and such that $\bigcup_{n=1}^{\infty} e_n = e$.

From Lemma 1 and Theorem 1 § 23 we find that a regular m-dimensional closed cube $J_{m,n}$ of side

$$d \geqslant \frac{\rho}{3+\sqrt[m-p]{6^m (p+1)^2 (q+1)^p (2mk+2k+q+1)^p}}$$

$(n=1, 2, \ldots)$ can be inscribed in $J_m \dot{-} e_n$. Let c_n be the centre of the cube $J_{m,n}$. The sequence of points c_n $(n=1, 2, \ldots)$ in the cube J_m has at least one limit point c_0. Let J'_m be the open regular cube whose centre is c_0 and side is

$$d = \frac{\rho}{3+\sqrt[m-p]{6^m (p+1)^2 (q+1)^p (2mk+2k+q+1)^p}}$$

Since $e = \bigcup_{n=1}^{\infty} e_n$ and, for all n

$$J_{m,n} \cap e_n = J_{m,n} \cap \left(\bigcup_{i=1}^{n} e_i \right) = 0$$

there is some internal point of the cube J'_m which cannot belong to the set e and hence to the set $\bar{e}$. It is obvious too that J'_m lies strictly inside J_m since each of the cubes $J_{m,n}$ $(n=1, 2, \ldots)$ does so. Q.E.D.

§ 28. Approximating to Sets By Means of Piecewise-Rational Surfaces

We shall formulate some theorems expressing the relation between the ε-entropy of a set and the parameters of the piecewise-rational surface which approximates to it.

Theorem 1. Let f be an arbitrary subset of the m-dimensional regular cube $J_m \subset E_m$ (see § 23) which is not nearer its boundary than 3ε, and let e be a p-dimensional piecewise rational surface of degree k and order q approximating to the set f with an accuracy ε (in the sense of the metric C).

Then the numbers p, k, q, m and ε must satisfy the inequality

$$[(q+1)(2mk+2k+q+1)]^p \geqslant \frac{n_{3\varepsilon}(f)}{12^m (p+1)^2 n^p_{3\varepsilon/2}(f)}$$

(see Lemma 1 § 23).

Proof. We choose an $\frac{\varepsilon}{2}$-net $S^f_{\varepsilon/2}(f)$ in the set f consisting of the points $f_1, f_2, \ldots, f_l$. Since e approximates to f with an accuracy of ε, we can find points $f^*_i \in e (i=1, 2, \ldots, l)$ such that

$$\rho_{E^C_m}(f_i, f^*_i) \leqslant \varepsilon$$

According to Lemma 1 of the last section we can find a closed set $e_n \subset e$ all of whose multiplicity functions are uniformly bounded by the constant

$$v = (q+1)^p (2mk+2k+q+1)^p$$

and such that $e_n \supset \bigcup_{i=1}^{l} f^*_i$ (for this it is only necessary to choose sufficiently large n). Since the set $\bigcup_{i=1}^{l} f_i$ forms an $\frac{\varepsilon}{2}$-net in f, and the set $\bigcup_{i=1}^{l} f^*_i$ approximates to the set $\bigcup_{i=1}^{l} f_i$ with an accuracy of ε, the set $e_n \supset \bigcup_{i=1}^{l} f^*_i$ approximates to f with an accuracy of $\frac{3\varepsilon}{2}$ (from the triangular axiom). Therefore, using Lemma 1 § 23

$$v \geqslant \frac{n_{3\varepsilon}(f)}{12^m (p+1)^2 n^p_{3\varepsilon/2}(f)}$$

i.e.

$$[(q+1)(2mk+2k+q+1)]^p \geqslant \frac{n_{3\varepsilon}(f)}{12^m (p+1)^2 n^p_{3\varepsilon/2}(f)}.$$

Q.E.D.

Theorem 2. Let f be an arbitrary subset of the regular cube $J^{\rho}_{m} \subset E^{C}_{m}$ (of side $\rho \leqslant 1$), whose distance from the boundary of J^{ρ}_{m} is not less than 3ε, and let e be a p-dimensional piecewise rational surface of degree k and order q which approximates to the set f with an accuracy of ε.

Then the numbers p, k, q, m, ε must satisfy the inequality

$$[(q+1)(2k+q+1)]^{p} \geqslant \frac{\varepsilon^{p} n_{3\varepsilon}(f)}{(p+1)^{2} 2^{m}}$$

Theorem 2 is obtained from Lemma § 23 and Lemma 1 § 27. The proof is similar to that of Theorem 1.

Lemma 1. Any continuous p-dimensional piecewise rational surface $e \subset E_m$ of degree k and order q can be put in the form of the sum of the sets e_n $(n = 1, 2, \ldots)$ closed in E_m, all of whose multiplicity functions (of different orders) are uniformly bounded by the constant

$$v = [(q+1)(2k+q+1)]^{p}$$

Proof. By definition $e = R(E_p)$ (see § 27) where R is the continuous mapping of the space E_p into the space E_m. Let σ_n denote the p-dimensional closed sphere in E_p of radius n and centre at the co-ordinate origin, and put $e_n = R(\sigma_n)$ $(n = 1, 2, \ldots)$. The sets e_n are closed, since the transformation R is continuous.

Let β be the $(m-s)$-dimensional plane orthogonal to the s-dimensional co-ordinate plane τ^{s}_{1} which stretches, for example, along the vectors $T_1, T_2, \ldots, T_s$ and passing through the point $(t_1, t_2, \ldots, t_s, \underbrace{0, 0, \ldots, 0}_{m-s})$. Let e^{*}_{n} denote the inverse image (in the transformation R) of the set $e_n \cap \beta$. It is not difficult to see that e^{*}_{n} is the aggregate of all the solutions of the system

$$r^{k,q}_{i}(y) = t_i \qquad (i = 1, 2, \ldots, s)$$

belonging to the set σ_n. Therefore, from Lemma 1 § 26

$$v_0(e^{*}_{t}) = (q+1)^{p}(2k+q+1)^{p}$$

Q.E.D.

Theorem 3. Let f be an arbitrary subset of the cube $J_m \subset E_m^C$ whose distance from the boundary of J_m is not less than 3ε, and let e be a continuous p-dimensional piecewise rational surface of degree k and order q which approximates to f with an accuracy of ε.

Then the numbers p, k, q, m and ε must satisfy the inequality

$$[(q+1)(2k+q+1)]^p \geqslant \frac{n_{3\varepsilon}(f)}{12^m (p+1)^2 n^p_{3\varepsilon/2}(f)}$$

Theorem 4. Let f be an arbitrary subset of the regular cube J^ρ_m (of side $\rho \leqslant 1$) whose distance from the boundary of J^ρ_m is not less than 3ε, and let e be a continuous p-dimensional piecewise rational surface of degree k and order q, which approximates to f with an accuracy of ε.

Then

$$[(q+1)(2k+q+1)]^p \geqslant \frac{\varepsilon^p n_{3\varepsilon}(f)}{(p+1)^2 2^m}$$

By using Lemma 1 these theorems can be obtained by repeating the proof of Theorem 1 almost word for word.

§ 29. Approximating to Sets by Algebraic Surfaces

Let E_p and E_m be two Euclidean spaces and P^k the transformation of the space E_p into E_m given by the equations $t_i = P_i^k(y)$ $(i = 1, 2, \ldots, m)$ (see § 27), where $\{P_i^k(y)\}$ are polynomials in the p variables $y_1, y_2, \ldots, y_p$ the degree of each variable being not higher than k.

Definition. Surfaces of the form $P^k(E_p)$ are called algebraic surfaces of degree k.

Theorem 1. Let f be some bounded subset of the space E_m^C, and $p \geqslant 0$, $k \geqslant 0$ natural numbers such that

$$p \log(1+k) \geqslant H_\varepsilon(f)$$

Then there exists a p-dimensional algebraic surface $e \subset E_m^C$ of degree k which approximates to the set f with an accuracy of ε.

Proof. Let us choose the most economic (2ε)-covering of the set f by its subsets $\sigma_1, \sigma_2, \ldots, \sigma_n$ ($n = N_\varepsilon(f) = 2^{H_\varepsilon(f)} < +\infty$ since f is bounded). Since the diameter of the set σ_i, by the definition of a 2ε-covering, is not greater than 2ε (in the sense of the metric of C), on each of the co-ordinate axes σ_i is projected into a set contained in a segment of length 2ε. Therefore we can find a regular cube ω_i of side 2ε such that $\sigma_i \subset \omega_i$.

Let c_i be the centre of the cube ω_i, and $t_1(c_i), t_2(c_i), \ldots, t_m(c_i)$ the co-ordinates of c_i. We select in the space E_p an integral lattice, consisting of $(k+1)^p$ points $a_l = a_{i_1, i_2, \ldots, i_p}$ ($i_q = 0, 1, 2, \ldots, k$; $q = 1, 2, \ldots, p$). We assume the points a_l to be numbered in some way $(l = 1, 2, \ldots, (k+1)^p)$. We complete the set $\{c_i\}$ with the arbitrary points $c_j \in E_m$, $j = n+1, \ldots, (k+1)^p$ (since, by hypothesis $p \log(k+1) \geqslant H_\varepsilon(f)$ we have $n \leqslant (k+1)^p$). Thus we have in E_m $(k+1)^p$ fixed points $c_1, c_2, \ldots, c_{(k+1)^p}$.

Put

$$P_i^k(y) = \sum_{l=1}^{(k+1)^p} t_i(c_l) \prod_{q=1}^{p} \prod_{i_q \neq y_q(a_l)} \frac{y_q - i_q}{y_q(a_l) - i_q};$$

$$(i_q = 0, 1, 2, \ldots, k; \; q = 1, 2, \ldots, p).$$

It is not difficult to verify that

$$P_i^k(a_l) = t_i(c_l) \qquad (i = 1, 2, \ldots, m; \; l = 1, 2, \ldots, (k+1)^p)$$

Every polynomial $P_i^k(y)$ $(i = 1, 2, \ldots, m)$ is of degree k in each of the variables.

We take e to be the surface in E_m given by the equations

$$t_i = P_i^k(y) \qquad (i = 1, 2, \ldots, m)$$

The degree of the algebraic surface e is equal to k. This surface passes through all the points $c_1, c_2, \ldots, c_n, c_{n+1}, c_{n+2}, \ldots, c_{(k+1)^p}$. But since the set $\bigcup_{l=1}^{n} c_l$ approximates to the set f with an accuracy of ε, $e \supset \bigcup_{l=1}^{n} c_l$ also approximates to f with an accuracy of ε. Q.E.D.

Theorem 2. Let f be some bounded subset of the space E_m^C, and p, k and q natural numbers such that

$$p \log[(q+1)(k+1)] \geqslant H_\varepsilon(f)$$

Then there exists a continuous piecewise rational surface $e \subset E_m^C$ of degree k and order q which approximates to f with an accuracy of ε.

The proof of this theorem is similar to that of Theorem 1, and so we shall only touch upon it.

We select in E_m^C a set of points $c_1, c_2, \ldots, c_n$ $\left(n = N_\varepsilon(f) = 2^{H_\varepsilon(f)}\right)$. Consider the polynomials

$$P^q(y) = P^q(y_1, y_2, \ldots, y_p) = \prod_{i=1}^{p} \prod_{l=0}^{q-1} (y_i - 2^{k+1} l)$$

The zero level-curve of this polynomial is the set-theoretic sum of the q^p hyperplanes of the space E_p $\{y_i = 2^{k+1} l\}$ dividing the space E_p into $(q+1)^p$ regions $\gamma_1, \gamma_2, \ldots, \gamma_{(q+1)^p}$. In the region γ_j we fix an arbitrary integral lattice with unit step, consisting of the points a_i^j $\left(i = 1, 2, \ldots, (k+1)^p\right)$. Since, by hypothesis,

$$p \log[(q+1)(k+1)] \geqslant H_\varepsilon(f)$$

we have

$$n = N_\varepsilon(f) \leqslant (q+1)^p (k+1)^p = n'$$

We select in E_m^C some set consisting of $n' - n$ points $c_{n+1}, c_{n+2}, \ldots, c_{n'}$ and we re-number all the points $c_1, c_2, \ldots, c_{n'}$ with the help of two suffixes

$$\bigcup_{j=1}^{(q+1)^p} \bigcup_{i=1}^{(k+1)^p} c_i^j = \bigcup_{i=1}^{n'} c_i$$

Let $\{P^k_{i,\gamma_j}(y)\}$ be polynomials in $y_1, y_2, \ldots, y_p$ of degree k in each of the variables such that

$$t_l(c^j_i) = P^k_{i,\gamma_j}(a^j_i)$$
$$(l=1, \ldots, m;\ i=1, \ldots, (k+1)^p;\ j=1, \ldots, (q+1)^p)$$

(see the proof of Theorem 1). Further, let $r^{k,q}_i(y)$ be a continuous piecewise-rational function of degree k and with a barrier $\{P^q(y)=0\}$ of order q such that

$$r^{k,q}_i(y) = P^k_{i,\gamma_j}(y) \text{ when } y \in \bar{\gamma}_j \quad (i=1, 2, \ldots, (q+1)^p)$$

and let $R^{k,q}_p$ be the transformation of the space E_p into the space E_m given by the equations

$$t_i = r^{k,q}_i(y) \qquad (i=1, 2, \ldots, m)$$

Put $e = R^{k,q}_p(e_p)$. The set e is a continuous piecewise rational surface of degree k and order q which passes through the points $c_1, c_2, \ldots, c_n$ and therefore approximates to the set f with an accuracy of ε. Q.E.D.

Theorems 1 and 2 are the converse of Theorems 3 and 4 of §28. However the estimates given by these theorems (direct and converse) are very different from one another. It is not possible to combine the results of these theorems for the general case (for arbitrary f). This is demonstrated by taking sets f with a small entropy some of which can be concentrated in a neighbourhood of relatively simple surfaces of small dimensions, while others can be dispersed quite widely in space. The first sets (concentrated about simple surfaces) are approximated to by these (quite simple) surfaces with the necessary accuracy; the second group of sets, i.e. those having the same entropy as the first, but which are quite widely dispersed in space, require comparatively complex surfaces as approximations. Thus, in order to combine the results of the direct and converse theorems in one formulation, we must introduce metrical characteristics of sets which are more refined than the concept of ε-entropy. But we shall be interested in another problem, that of the application of these theorems to concrete problems in the theory of tabulation.

CHAPTER VI

EASILY REPRESENTABLE FAMILIES OF FUNCTIONS

In this chapter we are concerned with estimates of the complexity of tables of analytic functions.

§ 30. Admissible Algorithms

Let G be a set and F an aggregate of complex (or real) functions defined on G. We define the distance between two elements f_1 and f_2 of F as

$$\rho_F(f_1, f_2) = \sup_{x \in G} |f_1(x) - f_2(x)|$$

Definition. The ε-representation of the family F is defined as any complex function $F_{\varepsilon, p}^{k, q}(x, y)$, defined on the set $G \times E_p$ (where E_p is a p-dimensional Euclidean space) $(x \in G, \ y \in E_p)$ possessing the following properties:

(1) Given any $x_0 \in G$ the real and imaginary parts of the function $F_{\varepsilon, p}^{k, q}(x_0, y)$ are piecewise-rational functions of the point $y = (y_1, y_2, \ldots, y_p)$ of degree not higher than k with barrier $\{P^{q, x_0}(y) = 0\}$ of order q; the barrier $\{P^{q, x_0}(y) = 0\}$ generally speaking is assumed to depend on x_0;

(2) For every function $f(x)$ of the family F we can find at least one point $y_0 = y[f(x)]$ such that given any $x \in G$

$$|f(x) - F_{\varepsilon, p}^{k, q}(x, y_0)| \leqslant \varepsilon$$

The ε-representation $F_{\varepsilon, p}^{k, q}(x, y)$ of the family F is said to be continuous if, given any $x \in G$ $F_{\varepsilon, p}^{k, q}(x, y)$ is a piecewise-rational function of the point $y \in E_p$, $F_{\varepsilon, p}^{k, q}(x, y)$ is said to be an algebraic ε-representation of the family F if, given any $x \in G$ $F^{k,q}_{\varepsilon,p}(x, y)$ is a polynomial in y. The set $\{P^{q,x}(y)=0\}$ is called the barrier of the function $F^{k,q}_{\varepsilon,p}(x, y)$, and the number q is its order.

Let us consider some examples of ε-representations.

I. Approximation to functions by algebraic polynomials. Let $f(x)$ be an analytic function of the family $F^{-1,1}_{\rho,c}$ (see § 7). Then we can find a polynomial $R^p(x)$ of degree $p=\left[\log_\rho\left(\frac{2c}{\varepsilon}\right)\right]+1$ which approximates to the function $f(x)$ with an accuracy of $\frac{2c}{\rho^p}\leqslant\varepsilon$ (see [1]). Therefore, if we take the coefficients of the polynomial $R^p(x)$ as parameters $y_1, y_2, \ldots, y_{p+1}$ the function

$$F^{1,0}_{\varepsilon,p+1}(x, y)=\sum_{n=1}^{p+1} y_n x^{n-1}$$

is an algebraic ε-representation of the family $F^{-1,1}_{\rho,c}$ $\left(k=1,\ q=0,\ p=\left[\log_\rho\left(\frac{2c}{\varepsilon}\right)\right]+1\right)$. For, condition (1) is satisfied, since the function $F^{1,0}_{\varepsilon,p+1}(x, y)$ is linear whatever the value of x; condition (2) is also satisfied, since in this case we can take $y[f(x)]$ as the point y of the space E_{p+1} whose co-ordinates $y_1, y_2, \ldots, y_{p+1}$ coincide with the coefficients of the polynomial $R^p(x)$.

II. Local interpolation for functions using polynomials.

Let $f(x)=f(x_1, x_2, \ldots, x_n)$ be an element of the space $F^{\rho,n}_{s,L,c}$ (see § 16). In the cube J^ρ_n which is the region of definition of the function $f(x)$ we select a uniformly spaced lattice with step $\delta=A(s, L, n)\varepsilon^{\frac{1}{s}}$ consisting of the points $a_i\ \left(i=1, 2, \ldots, \left(\frac{\rho}{\delta}\right)^n\right)$. We will choose the value of the constant $A(s, L, \rho)$ later, assuming meanwhile only that $\frac{\rho}{\delta}$ is an integer. We divide the cube J^ρ_n into $\left(\frac{\rho}{\delta}\right)^n$ sets $\{\omega_i\}$ in such a way that $\omega_i\supset a_i$ and the one-dimensional diameter

$$D(\omega_i)\leqslant\delta\sqrt{n}\qquad\left(i=1, 2, \ldots, \left(\frac{\rho}{\delta}\right)^n\right)$$

Put

$$y_i = y^j_{k_1, k_2, \ldots, k_n} = \frac{\partial^{k_1+k_2+\ldots+k_n} f(a_j)}{\partial x_1^{k_1} \partial x_2^{k_2} \ldots \partial x_n^{k_n}}$$

$$\Big(k_m = 0, 1, \ldots, [s];\ m = 1, 2, \ldots, n;$$

$$i = 1, 2, \ldots, p, \text{ где } p \leqslant ([s]+1)^n \left(\frac{\rho}{\delta}\right)^n\Big)$$

and

$$F^{1,0}_{\varepsilon, p}(x, y) = F^{1,0}_{\varepsilon, p}(x_1, \ldots, x_n;\ y_1, \ldots, y_p) =$$

$$= \sum\sum\ldots\sum_{k_1+k_2+\ldots+k_n \leqslant [s]} \frac{y^l_{k_1, k_2, \ldots, k_n}}{k_1!\, k_2! \ldots k_n!} \prod_{m=1}^{n} [x_m - x_m(a_l)]^{k_m}$$

$$(x \in \omega_l).$$

From Lagrange's theorem it follows that

$$\| f(x) - F^{1,0}_{\varepsilon, p}(x, y) \| \leqslant B(s, L, n)\, \delta^s =$$

$$= B(s, L, n)\, [A(s, L, n)]^s\, \varepsilon$$

We choose the constant $A(s, L, n)$ so that

$$B(s, L, n)\, [A(s, L, n)]^s \leqslant 1$$

Then the function $F^{1,0}_{\varepsilon, p}(x, y)$ is an algebraic (linear) representation of the family $F^{\rho}_{s, L, c}$.

III. The integral representation of functions. Let $f(x)$ be a function of the family $F^{\rho, n}_{s, L, c}$ (see § 15). Then this function can be represented in the form

$$f(x) \approx \sum_{k=0}^{s-1} \frac{a_k x^k}{k!} + \frac{1}{(s-1)!} \int_0^x (x-t)^{s-1} f^*(t)\, dt$$

with an accuracy of ε, where $f^*(t)$ is a function which is constant on each of the intervals $\{\delta_k\}$ $((k-1)\delta < t < k\delta)$ $\left(\delta = A\varepsilon^{\frac{1}{s}};\ k = 1, 2, \ldots, h;\ h = \left[\frac{\rho}{\delta}\right]\right)$ and on the interval δ_{h+1} $(h\delta < t < \rho)$. Therefore

$$f(x) \approx \sum_{k=0}^{s-1} \frac{a_k x^k}{k!} + \frac{1}{(s-1)!} \int_0^x (x-t)^{s-1} f^*(t)\, dt =$$

$$= \sum_{k=0}^{s-1} \frac{a_k x^k}{k!} + \frac{1}{s!} \sum_{k=1}^{h+1} f^*(\delta_k) [(x - k\delta + \delta)^s - (x - k\delta)^s]$$

If we take the numbers $a_0, a_1, \ldots, a_{s-1}, \ f^*(\delta_1), \ f^*(\delta_2), \ldots, f^*(\delta_{h+1})$ for the parameters $y_1, y_2, \ldots, y_p$ $\left(p = s + h + 1 = s + \left[\frac{\rho}{\delta}\right] + 1\right)$ then the function $F^{1,0}_{\varepsilon, p}(x, y) = \sum_{k=0}^{s-1} \frac{y_{k+1} x^k}{k!} + \frac{1}{s!} \sum_{k=1}^{h+1} y_{s+k} [(x - k\delta + \delta)^s - (x - k\delta)^s]$ is a linear ε-representation of the family $F^{\rho}_{s, L, c}$.

IV. The representation of a function in the form of a superposition.

Let $f(x) = f(x_1, x_2, x_3)$ be a function which can be represented on the three-dimensional closed cube $J_3 (0 \leqslant x_i \leqslant 1; i = 1, 2, 3)$ in the form

$$f(x_1, x_2, x_3) = \varphi(u, v)$$

where $u = u(x_1, x_2)$, $v = v(x_2, x_3)$ and $\varphi(u, v)$ are s-times continuously differentiable functions, all the partial derivatives of which, of all orders (up to and including the s th), are themselves also functions of u, v and φ, not exceeding unity in absolute magnitude. Put

$$\delta = A(s, 1, 2) \varepsilon^{\frac{1}{s}}, \quad \delta' = \left(\frac{\delta}{B(s, 1, 2)}\right)^{\frac{1}{s}}$$

(see II). Further, put

$$x_i^1 = \frac{\delta}{2} + i\delta'$$

$$\left(i = 0, \pm 1, \pm 2, \ldots, \pm p^1; \ p^1 = \left[\frac{1 - \frac{\delta}{2}}{\delta}\right] + 1\right);$$

$$x_i^2 = \frac{\delta'}{2} + i\delta'$$

$$\left(i = 0, \pm 1, \pm 2, \ldots, \pm p^2; \ p^2 = \left[\frac{1 - \frac{\delta}{2}}{\delta}\right] + 1\right);$$

$$y^{k_1, k_2, (1)}_{i_1, i_2} = \frac{\partial^{k_1 + k_2} \varphi\left(x^1_{i_1}, x^1_{i_2}\right)}{\partial u^{k_1} \partial v^{k_2}};$$

$$y^{k_1, k_2, (2)}_{i_1, i_2} = \frac{\partial^{k_1 + k_2} u\left(x^2_{i_1}, x^2_{i_2}\right)}{\partial x_1^{k_1} \partial x_2^{k_2}};$$

$$y_{i_1, i_2}^{k_1, k_2, (3)} = \frac{\partial^{k_1+k_2} v\left(x_{i_1}^2, x_{i_2}^2\right)}{\partial x_2^{k_1} \partial x_3^{k_2}};$$

$$(i_1 = 0, \pm 1, \pm 2, \ldots, \pm p^1; \ i_2 = 0, \pm 1, \pm 2, \ldots, \pm p^2, \\ k_1 + k_2 = 0, 1, 2, \ldots, s-1).$$

We now write the approximate value of the function $f(x)$ in terms of the parameters $\{y_{i_1, i_2}^{k_1, k_2, (l)}\}$:

$$f(x) \approx F_{\varepsilon, p}^{k, q}(x, y) = \sum_{k_1+k_2 \leqslant s-1} \sum \frac{y_{i_1, i_2}^{k_1, k_2, (1)}}{k_1! \, k_2!} \left(u_0 - x_{i_1}^1\right)^{k_1} \left(v_0 - x_{i_2}^1\right)^{k_2}$$

where

$$u_0 = \sum_{l_1+l_2 \leqslant s-1} \sum \frac{y_{j_1, j_2}^{l_1, l_2, (2)}}{l_1! \, l_2!} \left(x_1 - x_{j_1}^2\right)^{l_1} \left(x_2 - x_{j_2}^2\right)^{l_2},$$

$$v_0 = \sum_{m_1+m_2 \leqslant s-1} \sum \frac{y_{j_2, j_3}^{m_1, m_2, (3)}}{m_1! \, m_2!} \left(x_2 - x_{j_2}^2\right)^{m_1} \left(x_3 - x_{j_3}^2\right)^{m_2}$$

and the numbers j_1, j_2, j_3, i_1, i_2 which depend on the co-ordinates x_1, x_2, x_3 are selected so that

$$\left|x_i - x_{j_i}^2\right| \leqslant \frac{\delta'}{2} \qquad (i = 1, 2, 3),$$

$$\left|u_0 - x_{i_1}^1\right| \leqslant \frac{\delta}{2},$$

$$\left|v_0 - x_{i_1}^1\right| \leqslant \frac{\delta}{2}$$

(the suffices p, k, q will be determined below). We choose the values of δ and δ' so that

$$\left|f(x) - F_{\varepsilon, p}^{k, q}(x, y)\right| \leqslant \varepsilon$$

(see II). For any (fixed) values of x_1, x_2, x_3 the function $F_{\varepsilon, p}^{k, q}(x, y)$ is a continuous piecewise-rational function of degree $k = s - 1$ with barrier

$$\left\{P^{q, x}(y) = \prod_{i_1=-p_1}^{+p_1} \prod_{i_2=-p_1}^{+p_1} \left(u_0 - x_{i_1}^1\right)\left(v_0 - x_{i_2}^1\right) = 0\right\}$$

of order

$$q = (2p^2 + 1)^2 \, 2 \, (s - 1)$$

The number p, which is the number of variables $\{y_{i_1, i_2}^{k_1, k_2, (l)}\}$ of the function $F_{\varepsilon, p}^{k, q}(x, y)$ is

$$p \leqslant (s-1)(2p^2+1)^3 + (s-1)(2p^1+1)^2 \leqslant \frac{\alpha}{\delta^2}$$

where $\alpha > 0$ is some constant.

At any point y which does not belong to the cube $\{|y_{i_1, i_2}^{k_1, k_2, (l)}| \leqslant 1\}$ we put the function $F_{\varepsilon, p}^{k, q}(x, y)$ equal to zero. Thus, this function $F_{\varepsilon, p}^{k, q}(x, y)$ is a continuous ε-representation for the family of all functions of the form $\varphi(u, v)$.

§ 31. The Approximation to Functional Spaces by Finite Dimensional Spaces

Let F be the space of complex (or real) functions $f(x)$, defined on the set G (its norm being the upper bound of the values of the modulus of the function on the set G). We choose in G the set α, consisting of the points $x_1, x_2, \ldots, x_n$, and by Φ_m^α we denote the transformation of the space of all complex functions defined on the set G into the m-dimensional $(m = 2n)$ space E_m^C in which each function $f(x)$ corresponds to a point $t \in E_m^C$ with co-ordinates $t_i = \operatorname{Re} f(x_i)$ and $t_{i+n} = \operatorname{Im} f(x_i)$ $(i = 1, 2, \ldots, n)$. Let $\nu_\varepsilon^\delta(F)$ denote the number of elements of the minimal set $\alpha = \alpha_\varepsilon^\delta$ for which the corresponding set

$$f_\varepsilon^\delta = \Phi_m^\alpha(F) \subset E_m^C \qquad \left(m = 2\nu_\varepsilon^\delta(F)\right)$$

is such that

$$H_\varepsilon(f_\varepsilon^\delta) \geqslant H_\delta(F)$$

We recall once more that the distance between points in the space E_m^C is defined as the maximum of the modulus of the co-ordinate difference between these points.

Lemma 1. If G is a complete compact metrical space, and the space F is compact and consists only of continuous functions, then for any $\delta \geqslant \frac{3}{2}\varepsilon > 0$ the corresponding set $\alpha_\varepsilon^\delta$

consists of a finite number of points, i.e.

$$\nu_{\varepsilon}^{\delta}(F) < +\infty$$

Proof. We choose a set α which consists of a finite number n of points and is an ε'-net of the space G. It is possible to do this for any ε' since the space G is compact. The value of ε' will be chosen later. Let $S_{\varepsilon}(f)$ be the most economical (2ε)-covering of the set $f=\Phi_m^{\alpha}(F)(m=2n)$ by its subsets $\{S_i\}$ $(i=1, 2, \ldots, M_{\varepsilon}(f))$, and let S_i^{-1} denote the complete (in F) inverse image of the set S_i in the transformation Φ_m^{α}. Since

$$\bigcup_i S_i = f$$

we have

$$\bigcup_i S_i^{-1} = F$$

We choose two functions $f_1(x)$ and $f_2(x)$ of the set S_i^{-1}. Since

$$\rho_{E_m^C}\left\{\Phi_m^{\alpha}[f_1(x)],\ \Phi_m^{\alpha}[f_2(x)]\right\} \leqslant 2\varepsilon$$

at any point $x \in \alpha$

$$|f_1(x)-f_2(x)| = \sqrt{\{\mathrm{Re}\,[f_1(x)-f_2(x)]\}^2+\{\mathrm{Im}\,[f_1(x)-f_2(x)]\}^2} \leqslant$$
$$\leqslant \sqrt{(2\varepsilon)^2+(2\varepsilon)^2} = 2\varepsilon\sqrt{2},$$

i.e.

$$|f_1(x)-f_2(x)| \leqslant 2\varepsilon\sqrt{2} \qquad (x \in \alpha)$$

Since G is a complete compact space, and F consists of continuous functions and is also compact, according to Artsel's theorem, functions of the family F are uniformly continuous. Therefore, by choosing ε' sufficiently small, we can arrange that in every ε'-neighbourhood of an arbitrary point $x \in \alpha$ the oscillation of any function of the family F does not exceed

$$\delta' = \left(\frac{3}{2} - \sqrt{2}\right)\varepsilon > 0$$

Then at any point $x \in G$

$$|f_1(x) - f_2(x)| \leqslant 2\varepsilon\sqrt{2} + 2\delta' = 2\varepsilon\,\frac{3}{2} \leqslant 2\delta$$

Hence, the diameter of each of the sets S_i^{-1} $(i = 1, 2, \ldots, N_\varepsilon(f))$ does not exceed 2δ, i.e. the sets $\{S_i^{-1}\}$ form a (2δ)-covering of the space F. Therefore

$$H_\delta(F) \leqslant \log N_\varepsilon(f) = H_\varepsilon(f)$$

Thus, for sufficiently small ε' the corresponding set α consists of a finite number of points and

$$H_\varepsilon(f) \geqslant H_\delta(F)$$

§ 32. Basic Inequalities

Theorem 1. Let G be a complete compact metrical space, F some compact family of continuous complex (or real) functions defined on the space G, and $F^{k,\,q}_{\varepsilon,\,p}(x, y)$ some ε-representation of this family $\left(0 < \varepsilon \leqslant \frac{1}{2}\right)$. Then, for any $\delta \geqslant 9\varepsilon > 0$

$$m + p\log\left[\frac{(q+1)(k+1)}{\varepsilon}\right] + 16\rho p \log\left[(m+1)(q+2)(k+1)\right] \geqslant \\ \geqslant H_\delta(F),$$

where $\rho > 0$ is some constant which depends only on F, and $m = 2\nu^\delta_{6\varepsilon}(F)$.

Proof. By Artsel's theorem, the family F is uniformly bounded by some constant M. Therefore the corresponding set

$$f^\delta_{6\varepsilon} = \Phi_m^{\alpha^\delta_{6\varepsilon}}(F)$$

(see § 31) has a one-dimensional diameter not exceeding $2M$. But since $\varepsilon \leqslant \frac{1}{2}$ there exists an m-dimensional regular cube $J^\rho_m \subset E^{C^*}_m \left(m = 2\nu^\delta_{6\varepsilon}(F)\right)$ of side $\rho = 2M + 3$ such that $J^\rho_m \supset f^\delta_{6\varepsilon}$ and the boundary of the cube J^ρ_m is at a distance of not less than 3ε

from the set $f^{\delta}_{6\varepsilon}$.

Put

$$P^{(mq)}(y)=\prod_{i=1}^{m} P^{q,x_i}(y) \qquad (x_i \in \alpha^{\delta}_{\varepsilon})$$

Taking the set $\{P^{(mq)}(y)=0\}$ as the barrier of the surface $e^{\delta}_{6\varepsilon}=\Phi_m^{\alpha^{\delta}_{6\varepsilon}}[F^{k,q}_{\varepsilon,p}(x,y)]$ * we find that $e^{\delta}_{6\varepsilon}$ is a piecewise-rational surface of degree k with barrier of order mq. Since $e^{\delta}_{6\varepsilon}$ approximates to $f^{\delta}_{6\varepsilon}$ with an accuracy of ε, from Theorem 3 § 28 it follows that

$$[(mq+1)(2mk+2k+mq+1)]^p \geqslant \frac{\varepsilon^p n_{3\varepsilon}(f^{\delta}_{6\varepsilon})}{\rho^p (p+1)^2 2^m}$$

By taking the logarithm of this inequality, we have

$$m+p\log\left[\frac{\rho}{\varepsilon}(mq+1)(2mk+2k+mq+1)\right]+ \\ +2\log(1+p)\geqslant n_{3\varepsilon}(f^{\delta}_{6\varepsilon})\geqslant H_{6\varepsilon}(f^{\delta}_{6\varepsilon})\geqslant H_{\delta}(F)$$

(from the definition of the set $f^{\delta}_{6\varepsilon}$ and Lemma 1 § 31), i.e.

$$H_{\delta}(F)\leqslant m+p\log\left[\frac{\rho}{\varepsilon}(mq+1)(2mk+2k+mq+1)\right]+ \\ +2\log(1+p)\leqslant \\ \leqslant m+p\log\left[\frac{(q+1)(k+1)}{\varepsilon}\rho(m+1)^2(q+1)4\right]+2\log(1+p)\leqslant \\ \leqslant m+p\log\left[\frac{(q+1)(k+1)}{\varepsilon}\right]+16\rho p\log[(m+1)(q+2)(k+1)].$$

Thus

$$m+p\log\left[\frac{(q+1)(k+1)}{\varepsilon}\right]+ \\ +16\rho p\log[(m+1)(q+2)(k+1)]\geqslant H_{\delta}(F)$$

Q.E.D.

---

* Here $F^{k,q}_{\varepsilon,p}(x,y)$ is considered as a family of functions of x depending on the parameter y.

Theorem 2. Let F satisfy the conditions of Theorem 1, and let $F_{\varepsilon,p}^{k,q}(x, y)$ be a continuous ε-representation $\left(0<\varepsilon\leqslant\frac{1}{2}\right)$ of the family F with barrier of order q, not depending on x. Then for any $\delta\geqslant 9\varepsilon$

$$m+p\log\left[\frac{(q+1)(k+1)}{\varepsilon}\right]+4\rho p\log(q+2)\geqslant H_{\delta}(F)$$

where $m=2\nu_{6\varepsilon}^{\delta}(F)$ and $\rho>0$ is some constant depending only on F.

The proof is similar to that of Theorem 1.

Theorem 3. If F and $F_{\varepsilon,p}^{k,q}(x, y)$ satisfy the conditions of Theorem 1, then for any $\delta\geqslant 9\varepsilon$

$$m+p\log\left[\frac{(q+1)(k+q+1)}{\varepsilon}\right]+$$
$$+2p\log[2\rho(m+1)]+2\log(p+1)\geqslant H_{\delta}(F)$$

where $m=2\nu_{6\varepsilon}^{\delta}(F)$ and $\rho>0$ is a constant depending only on F.

Theorem 4. If F and $F_{\varepsilon,p}^{k,q}(x, y)$ satisfy the conditions of Theorem 2, then for any $\delta\geqslant 9\varepsilon$

$$m+p\log\left[\frac{(q+1)(k+q+1)}{\varepsilon}\right]+3p\log(2\rho)\geqslant H_{\delta}(F)$$

where $m=2\nu_{6\varepsilon}^{\delta}(F)$ and $\rho>0$ is a constant depending only on F.

The proofs of Theorems 3 and 4 are similar to that of Theorem 1.

§ 33. Easily Representable Families of Functions

Definition. The family F of functions defined on the set G is said to be easily representable if there exists a function $\delta=\delta(\varepsilon)\geqslant 2\varepsilon$ $(\varepsilon>0)$ which decreases monotonically to zero as $\varepsilon\to 0$ and is such that for any $B>0$ and for sufficiently small $\varepsilon>0$

$$\nu_{B\varepsilon}^{\delta(\varepsilon)}(F)<+\infty$$

(see § 31) and

$$\lim_{\varepsilon \to 0} \frac{\nu_{B\varepsilon}^{\delta(\varepsilon)}(F)}{H_{\delta(\varepsilon)}(F)} = 0$$

The function $\delta(\varepsilon)$ satisfying these conditions is called the representation characteristic of the family F.

As we shall see below, all the spaces of analytic functions which we met in Chapter II are easily representable families.

In a definite sense these functions $\delta(\varepsilon)$ characterize the difficulty of constructing the ε-representations of the family. The estimate of the complexity of the ε-representation of such families reduces to the search for the representation characteristics of the family which decrease to zero as fast as possible. This can be expressed more precisely by the following theorems:

<u>Theorem 1</u>. Let F be some easily representable compact space (its norm being the maximum of the modulus of the function on the set G) of continuous complex (or real) functions, defined on the complete compact metrical space G, such that for any positive $\varepsilon \geqslant \frac{1}{2}$

$$H_{\varepsilon}(F) \leqslant A\left(\log\frac{1}{\varepsilon}\right)^{n} \qquad (n > 0,\ A > 0)$$

Let $\delta = \delta(\varepsilon) \geqslant 9\varepsilon$ be some representation characteristic of the space F, and $F_{\varepsilon,p}^{k,q}(x, y)$ an arbitrary ε-representation of the family F. Then the numbers ε, p, k and q must satisfy the inequality

$$p\log\left[\frac{(q+1)(k+q+1)}{\varepsilon}\right] \geqslant H_{\delta}(F) - o\left[H_{\delta}(F)\right]$$

<u>Proof</u>. From Theorem 3 § 32 we have:

$$m + p\log\left[\frac{(q+1)(k+q+1)}{\varepsilon}\right] + \\ + 2p\log\left[2\rho(m+1)\right] + 2\log(p+1) \geqslant H_{\delta}(F)$$

since $\delta = \delta(\varepsilon) \geqslant 9\varepsilon$. Hence

$$m + p\log\left[\frac{(q+1)(k+q+1)}{\varepsilon}\right] + 8\rho p\log(m+2) \geqslant H_{\delta}(F)$$

If $p \geqslant \frac{H_\delta(F)}{\log\frac{1}{\varepsilon}}$, then

$$p \log\left[\frac{(q+1)(k+q+1)}{\varepsilon}\right] \geqslant H_\delta(F)$$

i.e. in this case the theorem is true.

Let $p \leqslant \frac{H_\delta(F)}{\log\frac{1}{\varepsilon}}$. Then

$$p \log\left[\frac{(q+1)(k+q+1)}{\varepsilon}\right] \geqslant H_\delta(F) - m - 8\rho p \log(m+2) \geqslant$$
$$\geqslant H_\delta(F) - m - 8\rho \frac{H_\delta(F)}{\log\frac{1}{\varepsilon}} \log(m+2).$$

Since, by the definition of an easily representable family, for any $B > 0$

$$\lim_{\varepsilon\to 0} \frac{\nu^\delta_{B\varepsilon}(F)}{H_\delta(F)} = 0$$

we have

$$\lim_{\varepsilon\to 0} \frac{m}{H_\delta(F)} = 2 \lim_{\varepsilon\to 0} \frac{\nu^\delta_{6\varepsilon}(F)}{H_\delta(F)} = 0$$

i.e.

$$m = o\,[H_\delta(F)] \leqslant A_0\left(\log\frac{1}{\delta}\right)^n \leqslant A_0\left(\log\frac{1}{\varepsilon}\right)^n$$

($A_0 > 0$ is some constant). Therefore

$$p \log\left[\frac{(q+1)(k+q+1)}{\varepsilon}\right] \geqslant$$
$$\geqslant H_\delta(F) - m - 8\rho \frac{H_\delta(F)}{\log\frac{1}{\varepsilon}} \log\left[A_0\left(\log\frac{1}{\varepsilon}\right)^n + 2\right] \geqslant$$
$$\geqslant H_\delta(F) - o\,[H_\delta(F)] - A_1 H_\delta(F) \frac{\log\log\frac{1}{\varepsilon}}{\log\frac{1}{\varepsilon}} \geqslant$$
$$\geqslant H_\delta(F) - o\,[H_\delta(F)]$$

($A_1 > 0$ is some constant). Q.E.D.

Theorem 2. Let F, $\delta = \delta(\varepsilon)$, $F_{\varepsilon, p}^{k, q}(x, y)$ satisfy the conditions of Theorem 1,

$$H_\varepsilon(F) = A\frac{\left(\log\frac{c}{\varepsilon}\right)^n}{\left(\log\log\frac{c}{\varepsilon}\right)^s} + o\left[\frac{\left(\log\frac{c}{\varepsilon}\right)^n}{\left(\log\log\frac{c}{\varepsilon}\right)^s}\right]$$

$$\left(A > 0,\ c > 0,\ n > 0,\ s \geqslant 0,\ 0 < \varepsilon \leqslant \frac{c}{4}\right)$$

and let $\delta(\varepsilon)$ satisfy the inequality

$$\delta(\varepsilon) \leqslant B\varepsilon\left(\log\frac{1}{\varepsilon}\right)^r \qquad (B > 0,\ r \geqslant 0)$$

when $\varepsilon \leqslant \frac{1}{2}$.

Then

$$p\log\left[\frac{(q+1)(k+q+1)}{\varepsilon}\right] \geqslant H_\varepsilon(F) - o\left[H_\varepsilon(F)\right]$$

Proof. From Theorem 1 we have

$$p\log\left[\frac{(q+1)(k+q+1)}{\varepsilon}\right] \geqslant H_\delta(F) - o\left[H_\delta(F)\right] =$$

$$= A\frac{\left(\log\frac{c}{\delta}\right)^n}{\left(\log\log\frac{c}{\delta}\right)^s} - o\left\{A\frac{\left(\log\frac{c}{\delta}\right)^n}{\left(\log\log\frac{c}{\delta}\right)^s} + o\left[\frac{\left(\log\frac{c}{\delta}\right)^n}{\left(\log\log\frac{c}{\delta}\right)^s}\right]\right\} =$$

$$= A\frac{\left(\log\frac{c}{\delta}\right)^n}{\left(\log\log\frac{c}{\delta}\right)^s} - o\left[\frac{\left(\log\frac{c}{\delta}\right)^n}{\left(\log\log\frac{c}{\delta}\right)^s}\right] =$$

$$= A\frac{\left(\log\frac{c}{\varepsilon}\right)^n}{\left(\log\log\frac{c}{\varepsilon}\right)^s} - o\left[\frac{\left(\log\frac{c}{\varepsilon}\right)^n}{\left(\log\log\frac{c}{\varepsilon}\right)^s}\right],$$

since

$$\frac{\left(\log\frac{c}{\varepsilon}\right)^n}{\left[\log\left(\log\frac{c}{\varepsilon} + \log\frac{\varepsilon}{\delta}\right)\right]^s} + o\left\{\frac{\left(\log\frac{c}{\varepsilon}\right)^n}{\left[\log\left(\log\frac{c}{\varepsilon} + \log\frac{\varepsilon}{\delta}\right)\right]^s}\right\} =$$

$$= \frac{\left(\log\frac{c}{\varepsilon}\right)^n}{\left(\log\log\frac{c}{\varepsilon}\right)^s} + \left[\frac{\left(\log\frac{c}{\varepsilon}\right)^n}{\left(\log\log\frac{c}{\varepsilon}\right)^s}\right] +$$

$$+o\left\{\frac{\left(\log\frac{c}{\varepsilon}\right)^n}{\left(\log\log\frac{c}{\varepsilon}\right)^s}+o\left[\frac{\left(\log\frac{c}{\varepsilon}\right)^n}{\left(\log\log\frac{c}{\varepsilon}\right)^s}\right]\right\}=$$

$$=\frac{\left(\log\frac{c}{\varepsilon}\right)^n}{\left(\log\log\frac{c}{\varepsilon}\right)^s}+o\left[\frac{\left(\log\frac{c}{\varepsilon}\right)^n}{\left(\log\log\frac{c}{\varepsilon}\right)^s}\right],$$

and since

$$H_\varepsilon(F)=A\frac{\left(\log\frac{c}{\varepsilon}\right)^n}{\left(\log\log\frac{c}{\varepsilon}\right)^s}+o\left[\frac{\left(\log\frac{c}{\varepsilon}\right)^n}{\left(\log\log\frac{c}{\varepsilon}\right)^s}\right]$$

we have

$$p\log\left[\frac{(q+1)(k+q+1)}{\varepsilon}\right]\geqslant$$

$$\geqslant A\frac{\left(\log\frac{c}{\varepsilon}\right)^n}{\left(\log\log\frac{c}{\varepsilon}\right)^s}-o\left[\frac{\left(\log\frac{c}{\varepsilon}\right)^n}{\left(\log\log\frac{c}{\varepsilon}\right)^s}\right]=H_\varepsilon(F)-o\,[H_\varepsilon(F)]$$

Q.E.D.

Theorem 3. Let F be some easily representable compact space of continuous complex (or real) functions, defined on the complete metrical space G, such that for any positive ε

$$H_\varepsilon(F)\leqslant A_0+\left(\frac{1}{\varepsilon}\right)^n \qquad (A_0>0,\ n>0)$$

Let $\delta=\delta(\varepsilon)\geqslant 9\varepsilon$ be some representation characteristic, and $F_{\varepsilon,\,p}^{k,\,q}(x,\,y)$ an arbitrary ε-representation of the space F.

Then there exists a constant $A(F)>0$ depending only on F, such that for sufficiently small $\varepsilon>0$

$$p\log\left[\frac{(q+1)(k+q+1)}{\varepsilon}\right]\geqslant A(F)\,H_\delta(F)$$

Proof. From Theorem 3 § 32 we have:

$$m+p\log\left[\frac{(q+1)(k+q+1)}{\varepsilon}\right]+$$
$$+2p\,[2\rho\,(m+1)+2\log(p+1)]\geqslant H_\delta(F)$$

Let A be some positive constant, to be chosen later. If

$$p \geqslant \frac{AH_\delta(F)}{\log \frac{1}{\varepsilon}}$$

then

$$p \log\left[\frac{(q+1)(k+q+1)}{\varepsilon}\right] \geqslant AH_\delta(F)$$

Further, suppose $p \leqslant \frac{AH_\delta(F)}{\log \frac{1}{\varepsilon}}$. Then

$$\begin{aligned} p \log\left[\frac{(q+1)(k+q+1)}{\varepsilon}\right] &\geqslant \\ &\geqslant H_\delta(F) - m - 2p\log[2\rho(m+1)] - 2\log(p+1) \geqslant \\ &\geqslant H_\delta(F) - m - 8\rho p \log(m+2) \geqslant \\ &\geqslant H_\delta(F) - m - 8\rho \frac{AH_\delta(F)}{\log \frac{1}{\varepsilon}} \log(m+2). \end{aligned}$$

But, from the definition of an easily representable family

$$m = o[H_\delta(F)]$$

and for sufficiently small ε

$$m \leqslant \left(\frac{1}{\varepsilon}\right)^n - 2$$

Hence, for sufficiently small ε we have:

$$\begin{aligned} p \log\left(\frac{(q+1)(k+q+1)}{\varepsilon}\right] &\geqslant \\ &\geqslant H_\delta(F) - m - 8\rho \frac{AH_\delta(F)}{\log \frac{1}{\varepsilon}} \log(m+2) \geqslant \\ &\geqslant H_\delta(F) - \frac{1}{2} H_\delta(F) - 8\rho \frac{AH_\delta(F)}{\log \frac{1}{\varepsilon}} \log\left(\frac{1}{\varepsilon}\right)^n = \\ &= \left(\frac{1}{2} - 8\rho A_n\right) H_\delta(F). \end{aligned}$$

Putting $A = \frac{1}{32} \frac{1}{\rho n}$ and $A(F) = \min\left\{\frac{1}{4};\, A\right\}$ we find that for sufficiently small ε

$$p \log\left[\frac{(q+1)(k+q+1)}{\varepsilon}\right] \geqslant A(F) H_\delta(F)$$

Q.E.D.

Theorem 4. Let F be some easily representable compact space of continuous complex (or real) functions, defined on the complete compact metrical space G, and let $\delta = \delta(\varepsilon) \geqslant 9\varepsilon$ be some representation characteristic of this family, and $F^{k;\,q}_{\varepsilon,\,p}(x;\ y)$ a continuous ε-representation of the family F with a barrier not depending on x (for example, an algebraic representation).

Then

$$p \log\left[\frac{(q+1)(k+q+1)}{\varepsilon}\right] \geqslant H_\delta(F) - o\,[H_\delta(F)]$$

Proof. From Theorem 4 § 32 we have

$$m + p \log\left[\frac{(q+1)(k+q+1)}{\varepsilon}\right] + 3p \log(2\rho) \geqslant H_\delta(F)$$

When $p \geqslant \dfrac{H_\delta(F)}{\log \frac{1}{\varepsilon}}$

$$p \log\left[\frac{(q+1)(k+q+1)}{\varepsilon}\right] \geqslant H_\delta(F)$$

When $p \leqslant \dfrac{H_\delta(F)}{\log \frac{1}{\varepsilon}}$

$$p \log\left[\frac{(q+1)(k+q+1)}{\varepsilon}\right] \geqslant H_\delta(F) - m - 3p \log(2\rho) \geqslant$$

$$\geqslant H_\delta(F) - m - 3\,\frac{H_\delta(F)}{\log \frac{1}{\varepsilon}} \log(2\rho) =$$

$$= H_\delta(F) - m - o\,[H_\delta(F)] = H_\delta(F) - o\,[H_\delta(F)]$$

(see the definition of an easily representable family of functions). Q.E.D.

Note. As we shall see later, the estimates obtained in Theorems 1 to 4 can be attained, i.e. there exist families of functions and representations of them for which the inequalities given become equalities (to an accuracy of a constant factor on the right-hand sides).

§ 34. Some Easily Representable Spaces of Analytic Functions

In this section we shall prove that all the spaces of

analytic functions which we met in Chapter II are easily representable families.

Let $\mathcal{E}_\rho^{l,k,z}$ denote the closed region of the complex plane (z_k), bounded by an ellipse with foci at the points $z-l$ and $z+l$, for which the ratio of the semi-major-axis to the number $l > 0$ is equal to $\rho > 1$, and put

$$\mathcal{E}_\rho^{l,z} = \mathcal{E}_\rho^{l,1,z_1} \times \mathcal{E}_\rho^{l,2,z_2} \times \ldots \times \mathcal{E}_\rho^{l,n,z_n}$$

where $z_1, z_2, \ldots, z_n$ are the co-ordinates of the point $z \in F_n^z$ (see § 9). Let J_n^{l,z_0} denote the n-dimensional closed cube

$$\{\mathrm{Re}\,[z_k(z_0) - l] \leqslant \mathrm{Re}\, z_k \leqslant \mathrm{Re}\,[z_k(z_0) + l],$$
$$\mathrm{Im}\, z_k = \mathrm{const} = \mathrm{Im}\, z_k(z_0)\} \qquad (k = 1, 2, \ldots, n)$$

<u>Lemma 1</u>. Given any positive $\varepsilon \leqslant \frac{1}{2}$ we can choose $\nu \leqslant A\left(\log\frac{1}{\varepsilon}\right)^n$ points $\{a_{i_1, i_2, \ldots, i_n}\}$ in the cube $J_n^{1,0}$ such that any function $f(x)$ analytic in $\mathcal{E}_\rho^{1,0}$ and bounded in this region by the constant c which takes values at the points $\{a_{i_1, i_2, \ldots, i_n}\}$ not exceeding ε in modulus, will be bounded (in modulus) everywhere in the region $\mathcal{E}_r^{1,0}$ $(r < \rho)$ by the quantity $B\varepsilon^{1-\omega}\left(\log\frac{1}{\varepsilon}\right)^{2n}$, where $\omega = n\dfrac{\log r}{\log\rho - \log r}$ and $A > 0$ and $B > 0$ are constants not dependent on ε or r.

<u>Proof</u>. We expand $f(z)$ (in series by Chebyshev polynomials

$$f(z) = \sum_{k_1=0}^{\infty}\sum_{k_2=0}^{\infty}\cdots\sum_{k_n=0}^{\infty} a_{k_1, k_2, \ldots, k_n} t_{k_1}(z_1) t_{k_2}(z_2) \ldots t_{k_n}(z_n)$$

(see § 7 and § 12) and put

$$P_k(z) = \sum_{k_1=0}^{k}\sum_{k_2=0}^{k}\cdots\sum_{k_n=0}^{k} a_{k_1, k_2, \ldots, k_n} t_{k_1}(z_1) t_{k_2}(z_2) \ldots t_{k_n}(z_n)$$

From the results given in Chapter II we know that for positive

$k_1, k_2, \ldots, k_n$

$$|a_{k_1, k_2, \ldots, k_n}| \leqslant \frac{A_1 k_1 k_2 \ldots k_n}{\rho^{k_1+k_2+\ldots+k_n}}$$

But since in the region $\partial_r^{1,0}$

$$|t_p(z_i)| \leqslant r^p$$

(see [6]), when $z \in \partial_r^{1,0}$

$$|f(z) - P_k(z)| \leqslant$$

$$\leqslant \sum_{k_1=k+1}^{\infty} \sum_{k_2=k+1}^{\infty} \cdots \sum_{k_n=k+1}^{\infty} |a_{k_1, k_2, \ldots, k_n}| \, |t_{k_1}(z_1)| \ldots |t_{k_n}(z_n)| \leqslant$$

$$\leqslant \sum_{k_1=k+1}^{\infty} \sum_{k_2=k+1}^{\infty} \cdots \sum_{k_n=k+1}^{\infty} \frac{A_1 k_1 k_2 \ldots k_n r^{k_1+k_2+\ldots+k_n}}{\rho^{k_1+k_2+\ldots+k_n}} \leqslant$$

$$\leqslant A_1 \sum_{p=k+1}^{\infty} (p+1)^n p^n \left(\frac{r}{\rho}\right)^p \leqslant A_0 \left(\frac{r}{\rho}\right)^k = \frac{A_0}{q^k}.$$

Choose k so that

$$\|f(z) - P_k(z)\| \leqslant \varepsilon, \quad z \in \partial_r^{1,0}$$

From the inequality obtained above it follows that k must satisfy the inequality

$$k \leqslant \log_q \frac{A_0}{\varepsilon}$$

Let $a^j_{i_j}$ $(i_j = 1, 2, \ldots, k+1)$ be the nodes of the Chebyshev segment $(-1 \leqslant \operatorname{Re} z_j \leqslant 1, \ \operatorname{Im} z_j = 0)$ (see [6]). As the point $a_{i_1, i_2, \ldots, i_n}$ we take the point of $J_n^{1,0}$ with co-ordinates $a^1_{i_1}, a^2_{i_2}, \ldots, a^n_{i_n}$ $(i_j = 1, 2, \ldots, k+1; \ j = 1, 2, \ldots, n)$.

The number of different points $\{a_{i_1, i_2, \ldots, i_n}\}$ is equal to

$$(k+1)^n \leqslant \left(1 + A_0 \log \frac{1}{\varepsilon}\right)^n \leqslant A \left(\log \frac{1}{\varepsilon}\right)^n$$

Since

$$\left|f\left(a_{i_1, i_2, \ldots, i_n}\right) - P_k\left(a_{i_1, i_2, \ldots, i_n}\right)\right| \leqslant \varepsilon$$

we have

$$|P_k(a_{i_1, i_2, \dots, i_n})| \leqslant 2\varepsilon$$

We put $P_k(z)$ in the form

$$P_k(z) = \sum_{i_1=1}^{k+1} \sum_{i_2=1}^{k+1} \dots \sum_{i_n=1}^{k+1} P_k(a_{i_1, i_2, \dots, i_n}) \prod_{j=1}^{n} \prod_{i \neq i_j} \frac{z_j - a_i^j}{a_{i_j}^j - a_i^j}$$

Since $|P_k(a_{i_1, i_2, \dots, i_n})| \leqslant 2\varepsilon$ for any j and for

$$z = (z_1, z_2, \dots, z_n) \in J_n^{1,0}$$

$$\sum_{i_j=1}^{k+1} \prod_{i \neq i_j} \frac{|z_j - a_i^j|}{|a_{i_j}^j - a_i^j|} = \lambda_k(z_j) \leqslant A_2 \log k$$

(see [6]), i.e.

$$\prod_{i \neq i_j} \frac{|z_j - a_i^j|}{|a_{i_j}^j - a_i^j|} \leqslant A_2 \log k$$

If, in addition $z_j \in \partial_r^{i, j, 0}$, then

$$\prod_{i \neq i_j} \frac{|z_j - a_i^j|}{|a_{i_j}^j - a_i^j|} \leqslant (A_2 \log k)\, r^k$$

(see [6]). Hence, when $z \in \partial_r^{1,0}$

$$|P_k(z)| \leqslant \sum_{i_1=1}^{k+1} \sum_{i_2=1}^{k+1} \dots \sum_{i_n=1}^{k+1} |P_k(a_{i_1, i_2, \dots, i_n})| \prod_{j=1}^{n} \prod_{i \neq i_j} \frac{|z_j - a_i^j|}{|a_{i_j}^j - a_i^j|} \leqslant$$
$$\leqslant (k+1)^n 2\varepsilon (A_2 r^k \log k)^n \leqslant A_3 k^{2n} r^{nk} 2\varepsilon \leqslant$$
$$\leqslant A_4 \varepsilon \left(\log \frac{1}{\varepsilon}\right)^{2n} \left(\frac{1}{\varepsilon}\right)^{n \frac{\log r}{\log q}} = A_4 \varepsilon^{1-\omega} \left(\log \frac{1}{\varepsilon}\right)^{2n}$$

where $\omega = n \dfrac{\log r}{\log \rho - \log r}$. But therefore, when $z \in \partial_r^{1,0}$

$$|f(z)| \leqslant |P_k(z)| + |f(z) - P_k(z)| \leqslant A_4 \varepsilon^{1-\omega} \left(\log \frac{1}{\varepsilon}\right)^{2n} + \varepsilon \leqslant$$
$$\leqslant B \varepsilon^{1-\omega} \left(\log \frac{1}{\varepsilon}\right)^{2n}$$

Q.E.D.

Lemma 2. Given any positive $\varepsilon \leqslant \frac{1}{2}$, $\nu \leqslant A\left(\log \frac{1}{\varepsilon}\right)^n$ points $\{a_{i_1, i_2, \ldots, i_n}\}$ can be fixed in the cube J_n^{l, z_0} such that any function $f(z)$ analytic in $\mathcal{Э}_\rho^{l, z_0}$ and bounded in this region by the constant c, which takes values not exceeding ε in modulus at the points $\{a_{i_1, i_2, \ldots, i_n}\}$, will be bounded (in modulus) everywhere in the region $\mathcal{Э}_r^{l, z_0}$ $(r < \rho)$ by the quantity $B\varepsilon^{1-\omega}\left(\log \frac{1}{\varepsilon}\right)^{2n}$ (where $\omega = n \frac{\log r}{\log \rho - \log r}$; $A > 0$ and $B > 0$ are constants independent of ε and r).

This lemma can easily be reduced to the previous one by a change in the variables.

Lemma 3. We are given the group of positive numbers

$$\rho' = (\rho_1', \rho_2', \ldots, \rho_n'), \quad \rho'' = (\rho_1'', \rho_2'', \ldots, \rho_n''),$$

$$r' = (r_1', r_2', \ldots, r_n'), \quad r'' = (r_1'', r_2'', \ldots, r_n''),$$

$$(0 \leqslant r_k'' < r_k' \leqslant \rho_k' < \rho_k'' \leqslant +\infty; \quad k = 1, 2, \ldots, n)$$

Then, for any positive $\varepsilon \leqslant \frac{1}{2}$ on the boundary $\widetilde{B}_{\rho'}^{r'}$ of the set

$$B_{\rho'}^{r'} = B_{\rho_1}^{r_1'} \times B_{\rho_2}^{r_2'} \times \ldots \times B_{\rho_n}^{r_n'} \subset E_n^z$$

(see § 9) we can select $\nu \leqslant A'\left(\log \frac{1}{\varepsilon}\right)^n$ points $\{a_{i_1, i_2, \ldots, i_n}\}$ such that any function $f(z)$ analytic in $B_{\rho''}^{r''}$ and bounded in this region by the constant c, which takes values not exceeding ε in modulus at the points $\{a_{i_1, i_2, \ldots, i_n}\}$, will be bounded (in modulus) everywhere in the region $B_{\rho'}^{r'}$ by the quantity $B'\varepsilon\left(\log \frac{1}{\varepsilon}\right)^{2n}$ (where $A' > 0$ and $B' > 0$ are constants which do not depend on ε or the function $f(z)$).

Proof. Consider the transformation $\Psi\{z_k = e^{iw_k}\}$ of the complex space E_n^w into the space E_n^z. The transformation Ψ sends the segment $J_1^{\pi, -\ln \rho_k'}$ of the complex plane of w into the circle $|z_k| = \rho_k'$. Since $f(z)$ is analytic in $B_{\rho''}^{r''} \supset B_{\rho'}^{r'}$, $f(e^{iw})$ is analytic in some neighbourhood of the segment $J_1^{\pi, -\ln \rho_k}$. For the same reason, $f(e^{i,w})$ is bounded in this neighbourhood by the constant c. Therefore, from Lemma 2, we can select $\nu_k \leqslant A_k \log \frac{1}{\varepsilon_k}$ points $b_{i_k}^k$ $(i_k = 1, 2, \ldots, \nu_k)$ on the segment $J_1^{\pi, -\ln \rho_k'}$ such that if

$$\left| f\left(e^{ib_{i_k}^k}\right)\right| \leqslant \varepsilon_k \qquad (i_k = 1, 2, \ldots, \nu_k)$$

then

$$|f(e^{iw})| \leqslant \varepsilon_k B \left(\log \frac{1}{\varepsilon_k}\right)^2 \leqslant \varepsilon_{k-1}$$

$$\left(\varepsilon_k = \varepsilon B^{k-1} 2^{k-1} (k-1)! \left(\log \frac{1}{\varepsilon}\right)^{2k-2} = \varepsilon B_{k-1} \left(\log \frac{1}{\varepsilon}\right)^{2k-2}\right)$$

everywhere on $J_1^{\pi, -\ln \rho_k'}$.

Put

$$a_{i_k}^{k, \rho_k'} = \Psi(b_{i_k}^k) = e^{ib_{i_k}^k}$$

We note that if

$$\left| f\left(z_1, z_2, \ldots, z_{k-1}, a_{i_k}^{k, \rho_k'}, z_{k+1}, \ldots, z_n\right)\right| \leqslant \varepsilon_k$$
$$(i_k = 1, 2, \ldots, \nu_k),$$

then

$$|f(z)| \leqslant \varepsilon_k B \left(\log \frac{1}{\varepsilon_k}\right)^2$$

everywhere on the circle $|z_k| = \rho_k'$.

Similarly, on the circle $|z_k| = r_k'$ we can select points

$a_{i_k}^{k, r'_k}$ $(i_k = 1, 2, \ldots, \nu_k)$ such that if

$$\left|f\left(z_1, z_2, \ldots, z_{k-1}, a_{i_k}^{k, r'_k}, z_{k+1}, \ldots, z_n\right)\right| \leqslant \varepsilon_k$$

then

$$|f(z_1, z_2, \ldots, z_n)| \leqslant \varepsilon_k B\left(\log \frac{1}{\varepsilon_k}\right)^2$$

everywhere on the circle $|z_k| = r'_k$.

We renumber the points of the set

$$\bigcup_{i_k=1}^{\nu_k} a_{i_k}^{k, \rho'_k} + \bigcup_{i_k=1}^{\nu_k} a_{i_k}^{k, r'_k}$$

putting them into one sequence, and we call them $\{a_{i_k}^k\}$ $(i_k = 1, 2, 3, \ldots, 2\nu_k)$. If

$$\left|f\left(z_1, z_2, \ldots, z_{k-1}, a_{i_k}^k, z_{k+1}, \ldots, z_n\right)\right| \leqslant \varepsilon_k$$

then, on the circles $|z_k| = \rho'_k$ and $|z_k| = r'_k$

$$|f(z)| \leqslant \varepsilon_{k+1}$$

and therefore, from the principle of the maximum for analytic functions

$$|f(z)| \leqslant \varepsilon_{k+1}$$

everywhere in the ring $B_{\rho'_k}^{r'_k}$.

As the point $a_{i_1, i_2, \ldots, i_n}$ we take the point of E_n^z with coordinates $a_{i_1}^1, a_{i_2}^2, \ldots, a_{i_n}^n$ $(i_k = 1, 2, \ldots, 2\nu_k;\ k = 1, 2, \ldots, n)$. The number of such points is equal to

$$\nu = \prod_{k=1}^{n} 2\nu_k \leqslant 2 \prod_{k=1}^{n} A_k \log \frac{1}{\varepsilon_k} \leqslant A' \left(\log \frac{1}{\varepsilon}\right)^n$$

Suppose now that at each of the points $\{a_{i_1, i_2, \ldots, i_n}\}$

$$|f(z)| \leqslant \varepsilon = \varepsilon_1 \leqslant \varepsilon_2 \leqslant \varepsilon_3 \leqslant \ldots \leqslant \varepsilon_n$$

For every possible $i_2, i_3, \ldots, i_n$ and when $z_1 \in B^{r_1^1}_{\rho_1^1}$

$$\left|f\left(z_1, a^2_{i_2}, \ldots, a^n_{i_n}\right)\right| \leqslant \varepsilon_1 B\left(\log\frac{1}{\varepsilon_1}\right)^2 \leqslant \varepsilon_2$$

and therefore for all $i_3, i_4, \ldots, i_n$ and $z_1 \in B^{r_1^1}_{\rho_1^1}$, $z_2 \in B^{r_2^1}_{\rho_2^1}$

$$\left|f\left(z_1, z_2, a^3_{i_3}, \ldots, a^n_{i_n}\right)\right| \leqslant \varepsilon_2 B\left(\log\frac{1}{\varepsilon_2}\right)^2 \leqslant \varepsilon_3$$

and so on. Doing this n times, we have for $z \in B^{r'}_{\rho'}$

$$|f(z_1, z_2, \ldots, z_n)| \leqslant \varepsilon_n B\left(\log\frac{1}{\varepsilon_n}\right)^2 \leqslant \varepsilon_{n+1} =$$
$$= \varepsilon B^n 2^n n!\left(\log\frac{1}{\varepsilon}\right)^{2n} = \varepsilon B'\left(\log\frac{1}{\varepsilon}\right)^{2n}$$

Q.E.D.

Theorem 1. Let F be one of the families $F^{r,n}_{\rho,c}$, $F^{\delta}_{d,c,2\pi}$, $F^{a,b}_{\rho,c}$, $F^{\sigma,c}_{s}$ (see Chapter II). Then F is an easily representable family and has representation characteristic

$$\delta = \delta(\varepsilon) = 9\varepsilon\left(\log\frac{1}{\varepsilon}\right)^{2n+1} \quad \left(\varepsilon \leqslant \frac{1}{2}\right)$$

We prove the different cases of this theorem from Lemmas 1 to 3 by the same method. Therefore we shall only consider the case when $F = F^{r,n}_{\rho,c}$.

Put

$$\delta = \delta(\varepsilon) = 9\varepsilon\left(\log\frac{1}{\varepsilon}\right)^{2n+1}$$

Let $B > 0$ be a constant. Let α be the set of points $\{a_{i_1, i_2, \ldots, i_n}\}$ (see Lemma 3, putting the number $\varepsilon' = 2B\varepsilon$) in place of the ε in the formulation of Lemma 3, and put

$$f = \Phi^{\alpha}_m(F) \subset E^c_m \text{ (cm. § 31) } \left(m = 2\nu^{\delta}_{B\varepsilon}(F) \leqslant 2A'\left(\log\frac{1}{\varepsilon'}\right)^n\right)$$

If f_1 and f_2 from $f \subset E^c_m$ are such that $\rho_{E^C_m}(f_1, f_2) \leqslant \varepsilon$ then, from

Lemma 3

$$\rho_F\left\{\left[\Phi_m^\alpha\right]^{-1}(f_1),\ \left[\Phi_m^\alpha\right]^{-1}(f_2)\right\} \leqslant \varepsilon' B'\left(\log\frac{1}{\varepsilon'}\right)^{2n}$$

i.e. for sufficiently small ε

$$\rho_F\left\{\left[\Phi_m^\alpha\right]^{-1}(f_1),\ \left[\Phi_m^\alpha\right](f_2)\right\} \leqslant 9\varepsilon\left(\log\frac{1}{\varepsilon}\right)^{2n+1} < 2\delta$$

This means that if the system of sets $\{\sigma_i \subset f\}$ forms a $2B\varepsilon$-covering of the set f_1, then the corresponding system of sets $\left\{\left[\Phi_m^\alpha\right]^{-1}(\sigma_i) \subset F\right\}$ forms a 2δ-covering of the space F, i.e. for sufficiently small ε

$$H_{B\varepsilon}(f) \geqslant H_\delta(F)$$

Then

$$m = 2\nu^\delta_{B\varepsilon}(F) \leqslant 2A'\left(\log\frac{1}{2B\varepsilon}\right)^n$$

And therefore

$$\lim_{\varepsilon\to 0}\frac{\nu^\delta_{B\varepsilon}(F)}{H_\delta(F)} \leqslant \lim_{\varepsilon\to 0}\frac{A'\left(\log\frac{1}{2B\varepsilon}\right)^n}{A\left(B^{r'}_{\rho'}, B^{r''}_{\rho''}\right)\left(\log\frac{1}{\delta}\right)^{n-1}} =$$

$$= \lim_{\varepsilon\to 0}\frac{A'\left(\log\frac{1}{2B\varepsilon}\right)^n}{A\left(B^{r'}_{\rho'}, B^{r''}_{\rho''}\right)\left[\log\frac{1}{9\varepsilon} - (2n+1)\log\log\frac{1}{\varepsilon}\right]^{n+1}} = 0$$

i.e. F is an easily representable family and $\delta(\varepsilon)$ is one of its representation characteristics.

§ 35. The Complexity of Tables for Analytic Functions

Theorem 1. Let F be one of the spaces $F^{r,n}_{\rho,c}$, $F^\delta_{\alpha,c,2\pi}$, $F^{a,b}_{\rho;c}$, $F^{\sigma,c}_s$ (see Chapter II), and $F^{k,q}_{\varepsilon,p}(x,y)$ an arbitrary representation of the space F.

Then

$$p\log\frac{(q+1)(k+q+1)}{\varepsilon} \geqslant H_\varepsilon(F) - o\left[H_\varepsilon(F)\right]$$

This theorem is easily obtained from Theorems 2 § 33, 1 § 34 and the corresponding estimates for $H_\varepsilon(F)$ (see Chapter II).

Theorem 2. Let F be the space of all complex functions analytic in the region $G_1 \subset E_n^z$, which have analytic continuations bounded in the finite region $G_2 \supset G_1$ by the constant c (the norm is the maximum of the modulus of the function on the closure of the region G_1) and let $F_{\varepsilon, p}^{k, q}(x, y)$ be an arbitrary ε-representation of the space F on the set G_1.

Then

$$p \log \frac{(q+1)(q+k+1)}{\varepsilon} \geqslant A(F) H_\varepsilon(F) \geqslant B(F)\left(\log \frac{c}{\varepsilon}\right)^n$$

where $A(F)$ and $B(F)$ are positive constants depending only on G_1, G_2 and c.

Proof. For definiteness we assume that the origin of coordinates $z = 0$ of the space E_n^z is an internal point of the region G_1. Then, choosing the numbers $\rho_1^1, \rho_2^1, \ldots, \rho_n^1$ sufficiently small, we have the result that the corresponding set

$$B^0_{\rho^1} = B^0_{\rho_1^1} \times B^0_{\rho_2^1} \times \ldots \times B^0_{\rho_n^1} \quad (\text{see § 9})$$

is wholly embedded in the region G_1. But since the region G_2 is assumed to be bounded, by selecting the numbers $\rho_1'', \rho_2'', \ldots, \rho_n''$ sufficiently large, we have

$$B^0_{\rho''} = B^0_{\rho_1''} \times B^0_{\rho_2''} \times \ldots \times B^0_{\rho_n''} \supset G_2$$

It is not difficult to verify that the space $F_{\rho, c}^{0, n}$ (see § 9) is a subset of the space F and for every pair of functions f_1 and f_2 of $F_{\rho, c}^{0, n}$

$$\rho_{F_{\rho, c}^{0, n}}(f_1, f_2) \leqslant \rho_F(f_1, f_2)$$

Therefore $F_{\varepsilon, p}^{k, q}(x, y)$ is an ε-representation for the space $F_{\rho, c}^{0, n}$

also. Then, from Theorem 1 we obtain the result that

$$p \log \frac{(q+1)(k+q+1)}{\varepsilon} \geqslant H_\varepsilon(F^{0,\,n}_{\rho,\,c}) - o\,[H_\varepsilon(F^{0,\,n}_{\rho,\,c})] =$$

$$= \frac{2}{(n+1)!} \prod_{l=1}^{n} \frac{1}{\log\left(\frac{\rho_l''}{\rho_l'}\right)} \left(\log \frac{c}{\varepsilon}\right)^{n+1} +$$

$$+ o\left[\left(\log \frac{c}{\varepsilon}\right)^{n+1}\right] \geqslant A(F)\, H_\varepsilon(F) \geqslant B(F) \left(\log \frac{c}{\varepsilon}\right)^{n+1}$$

(see Theorems 1 and 2 of § 9). Q.E.D.

Theorem 3. Let G_1 be a region of n-dimensional Euclidean space E_n, G_2 a bounded $2n$-dimensional region of the space $E_n^z \supset E_n$ containing G_1 as a subset, F the space of all real functions, analytic in G_1, and bounded by the constant c, $F^{k,\,q}_{\varepsilon,\,p}(x, y)$ an arbitrary ε-representation of the family F (on the set G_1). Then

$$p \log \frac{(q+1)(k+q+1)}{\varepsilon} \geqslant A(F)\, H_\varepsilon(F) \geqslant B(F) \left(\log \frac{c}{\varepsilon}\right)^{n+1}$$

where $A(F)$ and $B(F)$ are positive constants depending only on G_1, G_2 and c.

The proof is similar to that of Theorem 2.

The meaning of Theorems 1 to 3 consists in the fact that if we take the expression

$$\xi_\varepsilon = p \log \frac{(q+1)(k+q+1)}{\varepsilon}$$

for a measure of the complexity of a table for an analytic function $f \in F$ (where p, k and q are suffixes of the ε-representation $F^{k,\,q}_{\varepsilon,\,p}(x, y)$ of the space F, which corresponds to the method of constructing the table being considered), then

$$\xi_\varepsilon \geqslant A(F)\, H_\varepsilon(F)$$

i.e. for a whole group of classes of analytic functions the difficulty of constructing a table for the element $f \in F$ is basically determined by the ε-entropy of the corresponding space F.

For one concrete example we shall consider how exact the results of Theorems 1 to 3 are. For F we consider the space $F_{\rho, c}^{-1, 1}$ of all real functions analytic on the segment $(-1 \leqslant x \leqslant 1)$, whose analytic continuations in $\mathcal{E}_{\rho}^{-1, 1}$ are bounded by the constant c (see § 7).

As we showed in section 1 § 30, the method of approximation to a function by algebraic polynomials is an algebraic ε-representation of the family $F_{\rho, c}^{-1, 1}$ for which $q=0, k=1$ and

$$p=\left[\log_{\rho}\left(\frac{2c}{\varepsilon}\right)\right]+1$$

Hence, for the given method of constructing the table

$$\xi_{\varepsilon}=p \log \frac{(q+1)(k+q+1)}{\varepsilon}=\left[\left[\log_{\rho}\left(\frac{2c}{\varepsilon}\right)\right]+1\right] \log \frac{2}{\varepsilon}=$$
$$=\frac{1}{\log \rho}\left(\log \frac{c}{\varepsilon}\right)^{2}+o\left[\left(\log \frac{c}{\varepsilon}\right)^{2}\right]=2 H_{\varepsilon}(F)+o\left[H_{\varepsilon}(F)\right]$$

(see § 7), and the estimate of Theorem 1 is in this case

$$\xi_{\varepsilon} \geqslant H_{\varepsilon}(F)-o\left[H_{\varepsilon}(F)\right]$$

i.e. the method for finding the best algebraic approximations to the function (with an accuracy of 2) is the best method for constructing the table for analytic functions.

For the general case, the following theorem can be proved.

Theorem 4. For the family F to be easily representable by a family of functions it is necessary and sufficient that for any $\varepsilon>0$ we can find an ε-representation $F_{\varepsilon, p}^{k, q}(x, y)$ of this family such that

$$p \log \frac{(q+1)(k+q+1)}{\varepsilon} \leqslant c(F) H_{\varepsilon}(F)$$

where $c(F)>0$ is a constant depending only on F.

We omit the proof of this theorem.

CHAPTER VII

THE REPRESENTATION OF SOME CLASSES OF CONTINUOUS FUNCTIONS

In this chapter we consider the ε-representation of some classes of differentiable and continuous real functions.

§ 36. Spaces of the type C

Let G be a set, and F a compact family of real functions, defined on G (for the distance between functions we take the upper bound of the values of the absolute magnitude of their difference). Further, let $\alpha = (a_1, a_2, \ldots, a_m)$ be a set from G consisting of the points $a_1, a_2, \ldots, a_m$; let E_m^C be an m-dimensional space with metric C ; Φ_m^α the projective transformation of the space F into the space E_m^C which sets the function $f(x) \in F$ in correspondence with the point $t \in E_m^C$ with co-ordinates $t_i = f(a_i)$ $(i = 1, 2, \ldots, m)$; and let $f_\alpha = \Phi_m^\alpha(F)$ be the projection of the set F on the space E_m^C .

Definition. The family F is said to be a space of the type C if there exist two positive constants A and B such that for any sufficiently small $\varepsilon > 0$ in G we can find a set α consisting of

$$m = m_\varepsilon \geqslant AH_{B\varepsilon}(F)$$

points $a_1, a_2, \ldots, a_m$ and a function $f_\varepsilon(x) \in F$ possessing the property that for arbitrary given real numbers $\delta_1, \delta_2, \ldots, \delta_m$ $(|\delta_i| \leqslant \varepsilon, i = 1, 2, \ldots, m)$ we can find in F a function $f_{\delta_1, \delta_2, \ldots, \delta_m}(x)$ such that

$$f_{\delta_1, \delta_2, \ldots, \delta_m}(a_i) = f_\varepsilon(a_i) + \delta_i \quad (i = 1, 2, \ldots, m)$$

As we shall see below, any uniformly-bounded family of functions with a given modulus of continuity is a space of type C. All families of differentiable functions also belong to this class of space.

Lemma 1. If F is a space of type C, then for any $\delta > 0$ we can find in the set G a set α consisting of $m = m_\delta \geqslant AH_{B\delta}(F$ points $a_1, a_2, \ldots, a_m$ such that the corresponding set $f_\alpha = \Phi^\alpha_m(F) \in E^C_m$ will contain some m-dimensional regular closed cube $J^{2\delta}_m$ of side 2δ.

It is not difficult to verify that this lemma is only a reformulation of the definition of a space of type C.

Theorem 1. Let F be a space of type C, and $F^{k,q}_{\varepsilon,p}(x, y)$ a continuous ε-representation of the family F with a barrier not depending on x.

Then the numbers ε, p, k and q must satisfy the inequality

$$p \log[(q+1)(k+1)] \geqslant A(F) H_{B(F)\varepsilon}(F)$$

where $A(F)$ and $B(F)$ are positive constants not depending on ε, p, k, q.

Proof. Put $\delta = l\varepsilon$ (we fix the value of $l > 0$ below). Let $\alpha = (a_1, a_2, \ldots, a_m)$ be the set mentioned in Lemma 1. Then the corresponding set f_α contains the regular cube $J^{2\delta}_m$ of side 2δ. Let l_α denote the projection of the family of functions $\{F^{k,q}_{\varepsilon,p}(x, y) = F^{k,q}_{\varepsilon,p,y}(x)\}$ into the space $E^C_m \supset f_\alpha$, i.e. the image of this family in the transformation which sets the function $F^{k,q}_{\varepsilon,p,y}(x)$ in correspondence with the point $t \in E^C_m$ with coordinates $t_i = F^{k,q}_{\varepsilon,p,y}(a_i)\,(i = 1, 2, \ldots, m)$.

From the definition of $F^{k,q}_{\varepsilon,p}(x, y)$ it follows that e_α is a p-dimensional continuous piecewise-rational surface of degree k with a barrier of order q which does not depend on x. Then in the cube $J^{2\delta}_m$ we can inscribe a regular cube J^d_m of side

$$d = \frac{2\delta}{3 + \sqrt[m-p]{6^m (p+1)^2 (q+1)^p (2k+q+1)^p}}$$

(see Theorem 1 § 27) which does not contain points of the surface e_α. But since e_α, from the definition of an ε-representation, approximates to f_α with an accuracy of ε_1 and since $f_\alpha \supset J_m^{2\delta}$, we have

$$d \leqslant 3\varepsilon$$

Hence,

$$3\varepsilon \geqslant \frac{2\delta}{3 + \sqrt[m-p]{6^m (p+1)^2 (q+1)^p (2k+q+1)^p}}.$$

But since $\delta = l\varepsilon$, we have

$$6^m (p+1)^2 [(q+1)(2k+q+1)]^p \geqslant \left(\frac{2}{3} l - 3\right)^{m-p}$$

i.e.

$$\left(\frac{2}{3} l - 3\right)^{m-p} \leqslant 6^m (p+1)^2 [(q+1)(2k+q+1)]^p \leqslant$$
$$\leqslant 6^m 2^{2p+2} 2^p [(q+1)(k+q+1)]^p \leqslant$$
$$\leqslant 8^{m+3p+2} [(q+1)(k+q+1)]^p.$$

By taking logarithms, we obtain

$$p \log [(q+1)(k+q+1)] \geqslant$$
$$\geqslant (m-p) \log \left(\frac{2}{3} l - 3\right) - 3(m+3p+2)$$

Now put $l = 30$. Then

$$p \log [(q+1)(k+1)] \geqslant \frac{1}{2} p \log [(q+1)(k+q+1)]^p \geqslant$$
$$\geqslant \frac{1}{2} \left[(m-p) \log \left(\frac{2}{3} l - 3\right) - 3(m+3p+2)\right] \geqslant$$
$$\geqslant \frac{1}{2} [4(m-p) - 3(m+3p+2)] = \frac{m}{2} - \frac{13}{2} p - 3 \geqslant \frac{m}{2} - 10p$$

If $p \leqslant \frac{1}{40} m$ then

$$p \log [(q+1)(k+1)] \geqslant \frac{1}{2} m - 10p \geqslant \frac{1}{4} m \geqslant$$
$$\geqslant \frac{1}{4} AH_{B_\delta}(F) = \frac{1}{4} AH_{B_{l\varepsilon}}(F)$$

While if $p \geqslant \frac{1}{40} m$ and $\log[(q+1)(k+1)] \geqslant 1$ then

$$p \log[(q+1)(k+1)] \geqslant \frac{1}{40} m \geqslant \frac{1}{4} AH_{Bl\varepsilon}(F)$$

If $\log[(q+1)(k+1)] = 0$ then $q = k = 0$ i.e. in this case $F^{k,q}_{\varepsilon,p}(x, y)$ degenerates into a function depending only on x which, by the definition of $F^{k,q}_{\varepsilon,p}(x, y)$, approximates to any function of F with an accuracy of ε, i.e. in this case

$$H_{\varepsilon}(F) = 0 = p \log[(q+1)(k+1)]$$

Thus, taking $B(F)$ to be the maximum of the numbers 1 and Bl and putting $A(F) = \frac{1}{40} A$ we find that in all cases

$$p \log[(q+1)(k+1)] \geqslant A(F) H_{B(F)\varepsilon}(F)$$

Q.E.D.

In order to emphasize the relative accuracy of Theorem 1, we prove the following theorem:

Theorem 2. Let G be a compact metrical space, F a uniformly bounded uniformly continuous family of functions defined on the space G, and let the numbers $\varepsilon > 0$, $p \geqslant 0$, $k \geqslant 0$, $q \geqslant 0$ satisfy the inequality

$$p \log[(q+1)(k+1)] \geqslant H_{\frac{1}{2}\varepsilon}(F)$$

Then there exists a continuous ε-representation for F (with p parameters) of degree k with barrier of order q not depending on x.

Proof. Since the family F is uniformly continuous, we can find $\delta > 0$ such that on any set $\omega \subset G$ the diameter δ of the oscillation of a function from F will not be greater than $\frac{1}{2}\varepsilon$. We choose in G a finite number of sets $\omega_1, \omega_2, \ldots, \omega_m$, the one-dimensional diameter of each set not exceeding δ and such that $\bigcup_{i=1}^{m} \omega_i = G$. In each of the sets $\{\omega_i\}$ we select one point and denote the set of points $a_1, a_2, \ldots, a_m$ $(a_i \in \omega_i)$ chosen in this way by α.

Consider the corresponding sets

$$f_\alpha = \Phi_m^\alpha(F) \subset E_m^C$$

It is easy to verify that

$$H_{\frac{\varepsilon}{2}}(f_\alpha) \leqslant H_{\frac{\varepsilon}{2}}(F)$$

But since

$$p \log [(q+1)(k+1)] \geqslant H_{\frac{\varepsilon}{2}}(F)$$

then, even more

$$p \log [(q+1)(k+1)] \geqslant H_{\frac{\varepsilon}{2}}(f_\alpha)$$

Therefore, from Theorem 2 § 29 there exists a p-dimensional piecewise-rational surface e of degree k and order q, which approximates to f_α with an accuracy of $\frac{\varepsilon}{2}$.

By the definition of a piecewise-rational surface e is the image of a p-dimensional Euclidean space E_p in the transformation given by the equations

$$t_i = r_i(y) \quad (i = 1, 2, \ldots, m)$$

where $\{r_i(y)\}$ are continuous piecewise-rational functions of the p variables $(y_1, y_2, \ldots, y_p) = y$ of degree k with a barrier of order q not depending on the suffix i. Put

$$\gamma_i = \omega_i - \bigcup_{j=1}^{\varepsilon\, i-1} \omega_j$$

For $F_{\varepsilon, p}^{k, q}(x, y)$ we take the function which, as a function of y, is equal to

$$r_i(y) \qquad (i = 1, 2, \ldots, m)$$

for any i and at any point $x \in \gamma_i$.

Let $f(x) \in F$ and $f^* = \Phi_m^\alpha[f(x)]$. Since e approximates to f_α with an accuracy of $\frac{\varepsilon}{2}$, we can find a point $y_0 = (y_1, y_2, \ldots, y_p)$

such that

$$|t_i(f^*) - r_i(y_0)| \leqslant \frac{\varepsilon}{2} \qquad (i = 1, 2, \ldots, m)$$

i.e. such that

$$|f(a_i) - r_i(y_0)| \leqslant \frac{\varepsilon}{2} \qquad (i = 1, 2, \ldots, m)$$

But since, for any $x \in \gamma_i$ and for fixed y the function $F^{k,q}_{\varepsilon,p}(a_i, y)$ takes the one value $F^{k,q}_{\varepsilon,p}(x, y)$ and since the oscillation of the function $f(x)$ on the set ω_i and therefore also on the set γ_i, does not exceed $\frac{\varepsilon}{2}$ $(i = 1, 2, \ldots, m)$ then for any $x \in G$

$$|f(x) - F^{k,q}_{\varepsilon,p}(x, y_0)| \leqslant$$
$$\leqslant |f(a_i) - r_i(y_0)| + |f(x) - f(a_i)| \leqslant \frac{\varepsilon}{2} + \frac{\varepsilon}{2} = \varepsilon$$

Thus, we have proved that $F^{k,q}_{\varepsilon,p}(x, y)$ is the required ε-representation of the family F.
Q.E.D.

For arbitrary ε-representations of a space of type C, only the following theorem can be proved.

Theorem 3. Let F be a space of type C such that for any $\delta > 0$

$$H_\delta(F) \leqslant \left(\frac{1}{\varepsilon}\right)^s$$

and let $F^{k,q}_{\varepsilon,p}(x, y)$ be an arbitrary ε-representation $\left(\varepsilon \leqslant \frac{1}{2}\right)$ of it.

Then

$$p \log \frac{(q+1)(k+q+1)}{\varepsilon} \geqslant A(F)\, H_{B(F)\varepsilon}(F)$$

where $A(F) > 0$ and $B(F) > 0$ are constants not dependent upon ε, p, k and q.

Proof. Put $\delta = l\varepsilon$. Let $a_2, \ldots, a_m)$ be the set mentioned in Lemma 1. Then the corresponding set f_α contains a regular cube $J^{2\delta}_m$ of side 2δ. Let $f_1^*, f_2^*, \ldots, f_n^*$ $(n = 2^m)$ denote the vertices of the cube $J_m^{2\delta}$, and $f_1(x), f_2(x), \ldots, f_n(x)$ a group of functions of F such that

$$\Phi_m^{\alpha}[f_i(x)] = f_i^* \qquad (i = 1, 2, \ldots, n)$$

Since when $i \neq j$

$$\rho_{E_m^C}(f_i^*, f_j^*) = 2\delta$$

we have

$$\|f_i(x) - f_j(x)\| \geqslant 2\delta$$

Hence, from Theorem 1 § 5

$$H_{\frac{\delta}{2}}(F) \geqslant h_{\frac{\delta}{2}}(F) \geqslant \log n = m$$

i.e.

$$m \leqslant H_{\frac{\delta}{2}}(F)$$

Let e_α denote the projection of the family of functions $\{F_{\varepsilon, p}^{k, q}(x, y) = F_{\varepsilon, p, y}^{k, q}(x)\}$ into the space $E_m^C \supset f_\alpha$, i.e. the image of this family in the transformation which sets the function $F_{\varepsilon, p, y}^{k, q}(x)$ in correspondence with the point $t \in E_m^C$ with co-ordinates

$$t_i = F_{\varepsilon, p, y}^{k, q}(a_i) = r_i(y) \qquad (i = 1, 2, \ldots, m)$$

From the definition of $F_{\varepsilon, p}^{k, q}(x, y)$ it follows that e_α is a p-dimensional continuous piecewise rational surface of degree k with barrier $\{P^{q, x}(y) = 0\}$ of order q, which, generally speaking, depends on i.

Put

$$P^{mq}(y) = \prod_{i=1}^{m} P^{q, a_i}(y)$$

Taking the set $\{P^{mq}(y) = 0\}$ as the new barrier of the functions

$r_i(x)$, we will take e_α as a piecewise-rational surface of degree k and order mq .

As in the proof of Theorem 1, it is in this case not difficult to deduce from Theorem 2 § 27 that

$$3\varepsilon \geqslant \frac{2\delta}{3+\sqrt[m-p]{6^m (p+1)^2 (mq+1)^p (2mk+2k+mq+1)}}$$

where $m \geqslant AH_{B\delta}(F)$ (see the definition of a space of type C). But from this inequality we have

$$p \log [(mq+1)(2mk+2k+mq+1)] \geqslant$$
$$\geqslant (m-p) \log \left(\frac{2}{3} l - 3\right) - 3(m+3p+2)$$

Putting $l = 30$, we have

$$p \log [(mq+1)(2mk+2k+mq+1)] \geqslant m - 20p$$

i.e.

$$m - 20p \leqslant p \log [(mq+1)(2mk+2k+mq+1)] \leqslant$$
$$\leqslant p \log [(q+1)\, 8\, (m+1)^2 (k+q+1)] =$$
$$= p \log [(q+1)(k+q+1)] + p \log [8(m+1)^2]$$

But

$$\log [8(m+1)^2] \leqslant 8 \log (m+1) \leqslant 8 \log [1 + H_{15\varepsilon}(F)] \leqslant$$
$$\leqslant 8 \log \left[1 + \left(\frac{1}{15\varepsilon}\right)^s\right] \leqslant A' \log \frac{1}{\varepsilon},$$

where $A' \geqslant 1$ is a constant. Therefore

$$m - 20p \leqslant p \log [(q+1)(k+q+1)] + A'p \log \frac{1}{\varepsilon} \leqslant$$
$$\leqslant A'p \log \frac{(q+1)(k+q+1)}{\varepsilon}.$$

If $p \leqslant \frac{1}{40} m$, then

$$p \log \frac{(q+1)(k+q+1)}{\varepsilon} \geqslant \frac{1}{A'} (m - 20p) \geqslant \frac{m}{2A'} \geqslant$$
$$\geqslant \frac{A}{2A'} H_{B\delta}(F) = \frac{A}{2A'} H_{30B\varepsilon}(F)$$

While if $p \geqslant \frac{1}{40} m$, then

$$p \log \frac{(q+1)(k+q+1)}{\varepsilon} \geqslant p \geqslant \frac{1}{40} \dot{m} \geqslant \frac{1}{40} A H_{30 B_\varepsilon}(F)$$

Putting

$$A(F) = \min\left(\frac{1}{40} A, \frac{A}{2A'}\right)$$

and

$$B(F) = 30B$$

we obtain the result that in all cases

$$p \log \frac{(q+1)(k+q+1)}{\varepsilon} \geqslant A(F) H_{B(F)\varepsilon}(F)$$

Q.E.D.

§ 37. Tables of Differentiable Functions

We consider now the space $F_{s, L, c}^{\rho, n}$ $(s = p + \alpha)$ of functions p-times differentiable on the cube J_n^ρ , all of whose partial derivatives of order p satisfy the Golder condition with constant L and index α (see § 16).

Lemma 1. If $s > 0$, $c > 0$, $L > 0$, $\rho > 0$ and $n \geqslant 1$, then the family $F_{s, L, c}^{\rho, n}$ is a space of type C .

Proof. Let $a_1, a_2, \ldots, a_m$ all be points of the cube J_n^ρ all of whose co-ordinates are positive and multiples of some number $\delta > 0$ (which we shall fix below), and put $\alpha = \bigcup_{i=1}^{m} a_i$. Suppose that we are given some sufficiently small number $\varepsilon > 0$ (the bounds laid on ε will be set out below). We take the functions $f_\varepsilon(x)$ (see the definition in § 36) to be identically equal to zero. Let the numbers $\delta_1, \delta_2, \ldots, \delta_m$ such that

$$|\delta_i| \leqslant \varepsilon \qquad (i = 1, 2, \ldots, m)$$

be given. We show that there exists a function $f_{\delta_1, \delta_2, \ldots, \delta_m}(x)$ of the family $F_{s, L, c}^{\rho, n}$ such that

$$f_{\delta_1, \delta_2, \ldots, \delta_m}(a_i) = \delta_i = f_\varepsilon(a_i) + \delta_i \qquad (i = 1, 2, \ldots, m)$$

Let σ_i denote the n-dimensional closed sphere of $E_n \supset J_n^{\rho}$ of radius $\frac{\delta}{2}$ and centre at the point a_i, and let $f^i_{\delta_1, \delta_2, \ldots, \delta_m}(x)$ be the function, defined on J_n^{ρ}, which is identically zero but outside the sphere and equal to

$$\delta_i \left\{\cos\left[\frac{\pi}{\delta} \rho_{E_n}(x, a_i)\right]\right\}^s =$$

$$= A_i \delta^s \left\{\cos\left[\frac{\pi}{\delta} \sqrt{\sum_{j=1}^{n} (x_j - x_j(a_i))^2}\right]\right\}^s$$

when $x \in \sigma_i$. From Lemma 1 § 16 there exists a constant $A > 0$ such that when $A_i < A$ the corresponding function $f^i_{\delta_1, \delta_2, \ldots, \delta_m}(x)$ belongs to the family $F^{\rho, n}_{s, L, c}$.

Now put $\delta = \left(\frac{\varepsilon}{A}\right)^{\frac{1}{s}}$. Since

$$\delta_i = \delta_i \left\{\cos\left[\frac{\pi}{\delta} \cdot 0\right]\right\}^s = A_i \delta^s \left[\cos\left(\frac{\pi}{\delta} \cdot 0\right)\right]^s = A_i \delta^s$$

i.e.

$$A_i = \frac{\delta_i}{\delta^s} \leqslant \frac{\varepsilon}{\frac{\varepsilon}{A}} = A$$

from Lemma 1 § 16 $f^i_{\delta_1, \delta_2, \ldots, \delta_m}(x)$ belongs to the family $F^{\rho, n}_{s, L, c}$.

Put

$$f_{\delta_1, \delta_2, \ldots, \delta_m} = \sum_{i=1}^{m} f^i_{\delta_1, \delta_2, \ldots, \delta_m}(x)$$

Since for all i $f^i_{\delta_1, \delta_2, \ldots, \delta_m}(x) \in F^{\rho, n}_{s, L, c}$ and since the functions $\{f^i_{\delta_1, \delta_2, \ldots, \delta_m}(x)\}$ are different from zero on non-intersecting regions, then $f_{\delta_1, \delta_2, \ldots, \delta_m}(x)$ also belongs to the family $F^{\rho, n}_{s, L, c}$. On the other hand

$$f_{\delta_1, \delta_2, \ldots, \delta_m}(a_i) = f^i_{\delta_1, \delta_2, \ldots, \delta_m}(a_i) = \delta_i \qquad (i = 1, 2, \ldots. m)$$

To complete the proof of the lemma it remains only to evaluate the number m. We have

$$m \geqslant \left(\left[\frac{\rho}{\delta}\right]\right)^n$$

i.e. when $\varepsilon \leqslant A\left(\frac{\rho}{2}\right)^s$ we have

$$m \geqslant \left\{\left[\rho\left(\frac{A}{\varepsilon}\right)^{\frac{1}{s}}\right]\right\}^n \geqslant \left[\frac{\rho}{2}\left(\frac{A}{\varepsilon}\right)^{\frac{1}{s}}\right]^n \geqslant A'\left(\frac{1}{\varepsilon}\right)^{\frac{n}{s}} \geqslant$$
$$\geqslant A'' H_\varepsilon(F^{\rho, n}_{s, L, c})$$

(see Theorem 1 § 16).

Thus, we have proved that for any sufficiently small ε $\left(\varepsilon \leqslant A\left(\frac{\rho}{2}\right)^s\right)$ we can fix in the cube J^ρ_n a set $\alpha = (a_1, a_2, \ldots, a_m)$ consisting of $m \geqslant A'' H_\varepsilon(F^{\rho, n}_{s, L, c})$ points and such that for any $\delta_1, \delta_2, \ldots, \delta_m$ $(|\delta_i| \leqslant \varepsilon)$ in $F^{\rho, n}_{s, L, c}$ there exists $f_{\delta_1, \delta_2, \ldots, \delta_m}(x)$ taking the values $\delta_1, \delta_2, \ldots, \delta_m$ at the points $a_1, a_2, \ldots, a_m$ (respectively), i.e. we have proved that $F^{\rho, n}_{s, L, c}$ is a space of type C.

Theorem 1. If $F^{k, q}_{\varepsilon, p}(x, y)$ is a continuous ε-representation of the space $F^{\rho, n}_{s, L, c}$ with a barrier of order q not depending on x $(\varepsilon \leqslant 1)$ then

$$p \log [(q+1)(k+1)] \geqslant A(F) H_\varepsilon(F) \geqslant c(F)\left(\frac{1}{\varepsilon}\right)^{\frac{n}{s}}$$

where $A(F) > 0$ and $c(F) > 0$ are constants not dependent on ε, p, k and q.

Theorem 2. If $F^{k, q}_{\varepsilon, p}(x, y)$ is an ε-representation $(\varepsilon \leqslant 1)$ of the family $F^{\rho, n}_{s, L, c}$ then

$$p \log \frac{(q+1)(k+q+1)}{\varepsilon} \geqslant A(F) H_\varepsilon(F) \geqslant c(F)\left(\frac{1}{\varepsilon}\right)^{\frac{n}{s}}$$

where $A(F) > 0$ and $c(F) > 0$ are constants depending only on s, L, c, ρ, n.

These theorems are corollaries of Theorems 1 and 2 of § 36

and of Lemma 1 (see also Theorem 1 § 16).

In § 30 we gave two methods for constructing continuous ε-representations of the family $F^{\rho,n}_{s,L,c}$ with barrier of zero order, for which

$$p \log[(q+1)(k+1)] \leqslant B(F^{\rho,n}_{s,L,c}) H_\varepsilon(F^{\rho,n}_{s,L,c})$$

Moreover, for any ε, p, k and q satisfying the inequality

$$p \log[(q+1)(k+1)] \geqslant H_{\frac{\varepsilon}{2}}(F^{\rho,n}_{s,L,c})$$

we could construct for the family $F^{\rho,n}_{s,L,c}$ a continuous ε-representation (with p parameters) of degree k and barrier of order q, not dependent on x (see Theorem 2 § 36).

Thus, we can deduce the following result: the difficulty of constructing a table for an s-times differentiable function of n variables is determined essentially by the ratio $\frac{n}{s}$. This can be proved by Theorems 1 and 2 and the estimates for the volume of tables of such functions obtained from Theorem 2 § 4 and Theorem 1 § 16.

§ 38. Tables for Continuous Functions

We consider now the space $F^{G}_{\omega(\delta),c}$ of all real functions, defined on the connected compact metrical space G, uniformly bounded by the constant c and having a regular modulus of continuity $\omega(\delta)$ (see § 17).

Lemma 1. If G consists of more than one element, and $\omega(\delta)$ is not equal to zero for positive δ, then $F^{G}_{\omega(\delta),c}$ is a space of type C.

Proof. Let $\alpha = (a_1, a_2, \ldots, a_m)$ $(m = n_{\delta(4\varepsilon)}(G))$ denote the set consisting of the maximal number of elements $a_1, a_2, \ldots, a_m$ which are further apart than $2\delta(4\varepsilon)$ ($(\delta(\omega)$ is the inverse of $\omega(\delta)$). We take the function $f_\varepsilon(x)$ (see the definition in § 36) to be identically equal to zero. Suppose we are given numbers $\delta_1, \delta_2, \ldots, \delta_m$ such that

$$|\delta_i| \leqslant \varepsilon \qquad (i = 1, 2, \ldots, m)$$

Let σ_i denote the closed sphere of G $\{\rho_G(x, a_i) \leqslant \delta(\delta_i)\}$ of radius $\delta(\delta_i)$ with centre at the point a_i, and let $f^i_{\delta_1, \delta_2, \ldots, \delta_m}(x)$ be the function of $x \in G$ which is identically zero outside the sphere σ_i and equal to $\delta_i - \omega[\rho_G(x, a_i)]$ when $x \in \sigma_i$.

Put

$$f_{\delta_1, \delta_2, \ldots, \delta_m}(x) = \sum_{i=1}^{m} f^i_{\delta_1, \delta_2, \ldots, \delta_m}(x)$$

Since, when $i \neq j$

$$\rho_G(a_i, a_j) \geqslant 2\delta(4\varepsilon) > 2\delta(\varepsilon) \geqslant \delta(\delta_i) + \delta(\delta_j)$$

the spheres do not intersect one another. Therefore

$$f_{\delta_1, \delta_2, \ldots, \delta_m}(a_i) = f^i_{\delta_1, \delta_2, \ldots, \delta_m}(a_i) = \delta_i - \omega[\rho_G(a_i, a_j)] = \delta_i$$

We shall now prove that $f(x) = f_{\delta_1, \delta_2, \ldots, \delta_m}(x)$ has modulus of continuity $\omega(\delta)$. For, if $x \in \sigma_i$ and $y \in \sigma_j$ $(i \neq j)$

$$|f(x) - f(y)| \leqslant |f(a_i)| + |f(a_j)| = |\delta_i| + |\delta_j| \leqslant$$
$$\leqslant 2\varepsilon = \omega[\delta(2\varepsilon)] \leqslant \omega[\rho_G(\sigma_i, \sigma_j)] \leqslant \omega[\rho_G(a_i, a_j)]$$

since

$$\rho_G(\sigma_i, \sigma_j) \geqslant \rho_G(a_i, a_j) - \delta(\delta_i) - \delta(\delta_j) \geqslant$$
$$\geqslant 2\delta(4\varepsilon) - 2\delta(\varepsilon) \geqslant 4\delta(2\varepsilon) - 2\delta(\varepsilon) \geqslant \delta(2\varepsilon)$$

If $x \in \sigma_i$ and $y \in \sigma_i$ then

$$|f(x) - f(y)| = |\{\delta_i - \omega[\rho_G(x, a_i)]\} - \{\delta_i - \omega[\rho_G(y, a_i)]\}| =$$
$$= |\omega[\rho_G(y, a_i)] - \omega[\rho_G(x, a_i)]| \leqslant$$
$$\leqslant \omega[|\rho_G(y, a_i) - \rho_G(x, a_i)|] \leqslant \omega[\rho_G(x, y)]$$

(from the regularity of $\omega(\delta)$). If $x \in \sigma_i$ but $y \in G - \bigcup_{i=1}^{m} \sigma_i$, then

$$|f(x) - f(y)| = |f(x)| \leqslant \omega[\rho_G(x, g - \sigma_i)] \leqslant \omega[\rho_G(x, y)]$$

Thus we have shown that the modulus of continuity of the

function $f_{\delta_1, \delta_2, \ldots, \delta_m}(x)$ does not exceed $\omega(\delta)$, i.e. that

$$f_{\delta_1, \delta_2, \ldots, \delta_m}(x) \in F^G_{\omega(\delta), c}.$$

To complete the proof of the lemma we need only make a maximum estimate for the number m. We have

$$m = n_{\delta(4\varepsilon)}(G) = 2^{h_{\delta(4\varepsilon)}G} \geqslant 2^{H_{\delta(4\varepsilon)}G} \geqslant$$
$$\geqslant 2^{H_{4\delta(4\varepsilon)}G} \geqslant H_{8\varepsilon}\left(F^G_{\omega(\delta), c}\right) - \log\left(\frac{3c}{\varepsilon}\right)$$

(see Theorem 2 § 17). Since G is a connected set, consisting of more than one point, for sufficiently small ε

$$H_\varepsilon(G) \geqslant \log\left(\frac{d}{\varepsilon}\right)$$

($d > 0$ is a constant), i.e.

$$2^{H_\varepsilon(G)} \geqslant \frac{d}{\varepsilon}$$

Hence, for sufficiently small ε

$$m \geqslant H_{8\varepsilon}\left(F^G_{\omega(\delta), c}\right) - \log\left(\frac{3c}{\varepsilon}\right) \geqslant \frac{1}{2} H_{8\varepsilon}\left(F^G_{\omega(\delta), c}\right)$$

for $\log\left(\frac{3c}{\varepsilon}\right)$ is infinitely small in comparison with

$$H_{8\varepsilon}\left(F^G_{\omega(\delta), c}\right) \geqslant 2^{H_{4\delta(32\varepsilon)}}(G) + \log\left(\frac{c}{6\varepsilon}\right) \geqslant$$
$$\geqslant 2^{H_{k,\varepsilon}}(G) + \log\left(\frac{c}{6\varepsilon}\right) \geqslant \frac{d}{k\varepsilon}$$

since for sufficiently small ε

$$4\delta(32\varepsilon) \leqslant k\varepsilon$$

which k does not depend on ε. (This is so since, on account of its regularity $\omega(\delta)$ is a convex function).

Theorem 1. If $F^G_{\omega(\delta), c}$ satisfies the conditions of Lemma 1, and $F^{k,q}_{\varepsilon,p}(x, y)$ is a continuous ε-representation of the family $F^G_{\omega(\delta), c}$ with barrier of order q not depending on x, and ε is sufficiently small, then

$$p \log[(q+1)(k+1)] \geqslant AH_{B\varepsilon}\left(F^G_{\omega(\delta), c}\right) \geqslant A' 2^{H_{\delta(B'\varepsilon)}}(G)$$

where A, B, A' and B' are positive constants not depending on ε, p, k and q.

Theorem 2. If $F^{G}_{\omega(\delta), c}$ satisfies the conditions of Lemma 1, and $F^{k,q}_{\varepsilon,p}(x, y)$ is an arbitrary ε-representation of this space (ε being sufficiently small), then

$$p \log \frac{(q+1)(k+q+1)}{\varepsilon} \geqslant AH_{B\varepsilon}(F^{G}_{\omega(\delta), c}) \geqslant A' 2^{H_{\delta(B'\varepsilon)}(G)}$$

where A, B, A' B' are positive constants, not depending on ε, p, k and q.

These theorems follow from Theorems 1 and 3 of § 36 and Lemma 1 (see Theorem 2 § 17).

To emphasize the relative exactness of the result of Theorem 1, we shall give a method for constructing a table for a function $f(x) \in F^{G}_{\omega(\delta), c}$ for which the complexity of the table is

$$p \log [(q+1)(k+1)] \leqslant 2^{H_{\frac{1}{2}\delta(\varepsilon)}(G)}$$

To do this we choose the most economic δ-covering ($\delta = \delta(\varepsilon)$) $s_{\frac{\delta}{2}}(G)$ of the space G by sets $\sigma_1, \sigma_2, \ldots, \sigma_n$ $\left(n = N_{\frac{1}{2}\delta(\varepsilon)}(G)\right)$ and in each of the sets $\{\sigma_i\}$ we fix some point a_i. Put

$$\omega_i = \sigma_i - \bigcup_{j=1}^{i-1} \sigma_j$$

For $F^{k,q}_{\varepsilon,p}(x, y)$ we take the function of

$$x, y \quad (x \in G)(y = (y_1, y_2, \ldots, y_n))$$

which is equal to y_i when $x \in \omega_i$. The function $F^{k,q}_{\varepsilon,p}(x, y)$ is an ε-representation of the space $F^{G}_{\omega(\delta), c}$, since for any function $f(x)$ of this family we can find a point

$$y \in E_p \quad (p = n;\ y_i = f(a_i); \qquad i = 1, 2, \ldots, p)$$

such that

$$\left\| f(x) - F^{k,q}_{\varepsilon,p}(x, y) \right\| \leqslant \varepsilon$$
$$x \in G$$

The degree of this ε-representation is equal to 1, and the order of the barrier is 0. That is, in this case

$$p \log [(q+1)(k+1)] = n = N_{\frac{1}{2}\delta(\varepsilon)}(G) = 2^{H_{\frac{1}{2}\delta(\varepsilon)}(G)}$$

Moreover, for any given numbers $p \geqslant 0$, $q \geqslant 0$, $k \geqslant 0$ such that

$$p \log [(q+1)(k+1)] \geqslant H_{\frac{1}{2}\varepsilon}\left(F^{G}_{\omega(\delta),c}\right)$$

we can construct a continuous ε-representation of the family $F^{G}_{\omega(\delta),c}$ (with p parameters) of degree k with barrier of order q, not dependent on x.

Thus, we can deduce the following result: if we take as our measure of the complexity of a table the expression $p \log \frac{(q+1)(k+q+1)}{\varepsilon}$, then the complexity of any table which represents the element f of $F^{G}_{\omega(\delta),c}$ with an accuracy of ε cannot be less than $AH_{B\varepsilon}\left(F^{G}_{\omega(\delta),c}\right)$.

REFERENCES

[1] N.I. AKHIESER. Lectures in the Theory of Approximation, Gostekhizdat (1947).

[2] A.G. VITUSHKIN. On Hilbert's 13th Problem, Dokl. Akad. Nauk, SSSR 95, 4 (1954).

[3] A.N. KOLMOGOROV. On some Asymptotic Characteristics of Completely Bounded Metrical Spaces, Dokl. Akad. Nauk SSSR 108, 3 (1956).

[4] A.N. KOLMOGOROV. On the Representation of Continuous Functions of Several Variables by Superpositions of Continuous Functions of a Smaller Number of Variables, Dokl. Akad. Nauk SSSR 108, 2 (1956).

[5] A.S. KRONROD. On Functions of Two Variables, Usp. Mat. Nauk 5, 1 (35) (1950).

[6] I.P. NATANSON. The Constructive Theory of Functions, Moscow (1949).

[7] O.A. OLEINIK. Estimates of Betti numbers of Real Algebraic Hypersurfaces, Mat. Symposium: 28, 3 (1951).

[8] O.A. OLEINIK and I.G. PETROVSKII. On the Topology of Algebraic Surfaces, Izv. Akad. Nauk. ser. mat. 13, 5 (1949).

[9] C.E. SHANNON. The Statistical Theory of the Transmission of Electrical Signals, collection of Articles "The Theory of Transmission of Electrical Signals in the Presence of Noise". Translated into Russian (staticheskaya teoriya peredachi elektucheskikh signalov). Foreign Literature Publishing House 1953.

[10] D. HILBERT. Gesammelte Abhandlungen, 3, 17 (1935).

[11] L. TONELLI. Serie trigonometrische, Bologna (1924).

BASIC CONCEPTS AND NOTATION

Concept	Notation	Page
Aggregate in $F_s^{\sigma, c, n}$ of functions, real on the real part of the space E_n^z (the norm being the maximum of the absolute magnitude of the function on the cube $I_n \{-1 \leqslant u_k \leqslant 1\}, k = 1, 2, \ldots, n$)	$\Psi_s^{\sigma, c, n}$	64
Aggregate of functions $\varphi(x)$ representable on the segment r in the form $$\varphi(x) = L \int_0^x \varphi^*(t)\, dt$$ where $\varphi^*(t)$ is a function which takes the values $+1$ and -1 only, constant on each interval $$\frac{(k-1)\varepsilon}{L} < t < \frac{k\varepsilon}{L} \left(k = 1, 2, \ldots, \left[\frac{\rho L}{\varepsilon}\right]\right)$$	$\Phi^{\rho}_{L,\varepsilon}$	65
Algorithm, for decoding a table..	$\Gamma(t)$	1
Barrier of order q	$\{P^{q, x}(y) = 0\}$	154
Base, orthonormal, of space E_n ...	$x = (x_1, x_2, \ldots, x_n)$	101
Boundary of cube J_n	J_n^*	101
ε-capacity of space F	$h_\varepsilon(F)$	10

* This is the page on which the given concept is first introduced.

Concept	Notation	Page
Characteristic of representation of family of functions	$\delta(\varepsilon)$	163
2ε-covering of the space F containing the smallest number of covering elements	$s_\varepsilon(F)$	11
Depth of embedding of set e in cube J_n	$\Gamma(e, J_n)$	109
Deviation of function from its best approximation (in the class of all algebraic polynomials of degree p	l_p	18
Diameter, one-dimensional, of space F	$D(F)$	1
Distance between elements f_1 and f_2 in the metric sense of the space F	$\rho_F(f_1, f_2)$	27
Entropy of discrete set x	$H(x)$	4
ε-entropy of space F, absolute ..	$H_\varepsilon(F)$	7
ε-entropy of space F with respect to space Φ	$H_\varepsilon^\Phi(F)$	5
Expansion of space F, metrical...	Φ	1
Logarithm of a to base 2	$\log a$	4
Modulus of continuity	$\omega(\delta)$	94
ε-net of space Φ, minimal (in the number of elements), formed of elements of F....................	$S_\varepsilon^\Phi(F)$	8
Norm of function $f(x)$ (in the majority of cases the norm is taken to be the upper bound of values of the modulus of the function on some set or other	$\|f(x)\|$	-

Concept	Notation	Page
Number of elements of set e	$v_0(e)$	132
Number of elements of set $e \subset E_n$ lying strictly inside I_n	$v_0^{I_n}(e)$	101
Number of sets forming the covering $S_\varepsilon(F)$	$N_\varepsilon(F)$	7
Number of elements of the minimal set $\alpha = \alpha_\varepsilon^\delta$ for which the corresponding set $f_\varepsilon^\delta = \Phi_m^\alpha(F) \subset E_m^\sigma \left(m = 2\nu_\varepsilon^\delta(F)\right)$ is such that $H_\varepsilon\left(f_\varepsilon^\delta\right) \geqslant H_\delta(F)$	$\nu_\varepsilon^\delta(F)$	159
Number of elements of the set $S_\varepsilon^\Phi(F)$	$N_\varepsilon^\Phi(F)$	5
Number of elements of the set $s_\varepsilon(F)$	$n_\varepsilon(F)$	10
Parallelepiped of E_n^z, n-dimensional, given by the inequalities $a_k \leqslant x_k \leqslant b_k\ (k = 1, 2, \ldots, n)$	$J_n^{a,b}$	55
Part, integral, of A	$[A]$	-
Plane of E_n of dimension k, coordinate	τ_i^k	101
Plane of E_n of dimension $(n-k)$, orthogonal to the plane τ_i^k and passing through the point $q \in \tau_i^k$ ...	$\beta_i^{n-k}(q)$	101
Polynomial, Chebyshev, of order p	$t_p(x)$	17
Polynomial in n real variables $x_1, x_2, \ldots, x_n$ of degree not higher than k in these variables	$P_n^k(x)$	130
Product $\vartheta_{\rho_1}^{a_1, b_1} \times \vartheta_{\rho_2}^{a_2, b_2} \times \ldots \times \vartheta_{\rho_n}^{a_n, b_n}$	$\vartheta_\rho^{a, b}$	56
Projection, orthogonal, of set $E \subset E_n$ on the plane $\tau_i^k \subset E_n$	$\Psi_i^k(E)$	110

Concept	Notation	Page
Projection, orthogonal, of the set $E \subset E_n$ on the plane $\tau \subset E_n$	$\Psi_\tau(E)$	101
Region of complex plane z_k, bounded by the ellipse with semi-major axis ρ_k and with foci at the points a_k and b_k of real axis	$Э_{\rho_k}^{a_k, b_k}$	56
Regular n-dimensional closed cube of E_n given by the inequalities $0 \leqslant x_i \leqslant \rho$ $(i = 1, 2, \ldots, n)$	J_n^ρ	86
ε-representation of the space F (with p parameters) of degree k with barrier of order q	$F_{\varepsilon, p}^{k, q}(x, y)$	154
Ring of complex plane, given by $r_0 \leqslant \lvert z \rvert \leqslant \rho_0$	$B_{\rho_0}^{r_0}$	23
Segment, given by $a \leqslant x \leqslant b$	$[a, b]$	-
(Truncated) Chebyshev series, consisting of the first $(p+1)$ terms	$S_p(x)$	17
Set of F, consisting of the maximum number of elements which are further apart than 2ε	$S_\varepsilon(F)$	10
Space of complex functions, analytic in G_2, and bounded in G_2 by the constant c (the norm being the maximum modulus of the function in the region $G_1 \subset G_2$).........	$F_{G_2, c}^{G_1}$	45
Space of real functions, analytic in $I_n^{a, b}$, the modulus of the analytic continuations of which is bounded in the region $Э_\rho^{a, b}$ by the constant $c > 0$.....................	$F_{\rho, c}^{a, b}$	56

Concept	Notation	Page
Space of real analytic functions, bounded in the region $\mathcal{E}_\rho$ by the constant c	$F_{\rho, c}^{-1,1}$	16
Space of real functions of $2n$ real variables, $u_1, u_2, \ldots, u_n$ 2π-periodic (in each of the variables), analytic (in the space E_n), having analytic continuations in the region P_d bounded in P_d by the constant $c>0$	$F_{d, c, 2\pi}$	49
Space of real analytic functions, the analytic continuations of which are integral functions of order σ and type $s>0$ (the norm being the maximum of the absolute magnitude of the functions on the segment $[-1,1]$	$\Psi_s^{\sigma, c}$	63
Space of all functions analytic in the ring $B_{\rho_1}^{r_1}$ $\{r_1 \leqslant \lvert z \rvert \leqslant \rho_1\}$ bounded (in modulus) in this ring by the constant $c>0$ (the norm being the maximum modulus of the function on the ring $B_{\rho_0}^{r_0}$)	$\Phi_{\rho_0, \rho_1, c}^{r_0, r_1}$	36
Space of all complex functions, analytic inside the region $B_{\rho''}^{r''}$, bounded in this region (in modulus) by the constant $c>0$ (the norm being the maximum modulus of the function on $B_{\rho'}^{r'}$)	$F_{\rho, c}^{r, n}$	39
Space of all real functions $f(x)$ given on the compact metrical space G having modulus of continuity $\omega(\delta)$ and such that $\lvert f(x_0) \rvert \leqslant c$ where x_0 is some point of the space G constant for all functions of the family	$F_{\omega(\delta), c}^{G}$	94

Concept	Notation	Page
Space of all complex functions, analytic in the region $P^{\delta''}_{d''}$, $2n$-periodic in the variables $\{u_k\}$, bounded in the region $P^{\delta''}_{d''}$ in modu-less by the constant $c>0$ (the norm being the maximum modulus of the function in the region $P^{\delta'}_{d'}$)	$F^{\delta}_{d,\, c,\, 2n}$	47
Space of all real functions, continuous on the segment $[0,1]$ (the norm being the maximum modulus of the function on the segment)	C	8
Space of all functions, bounded on the segment $[0,1]$	$\Phi(0, 1)$	2
Space of real functions $f(x)=f(x_1, x_2, \ldots, x_n)$ defined on the cube I^{ρ}_{n}, all the pth order partial derivatives of which satisfy the Golder condition with constant $L>0$ and index α on the cube I^{ρ}_{n}, and such that $\left\| \frac{\partial^{k_1+k_2+\ldots+k_n} f(0)}{\partial x_1^{k_1} \partial x_2^{k_2} \ldots \partial x_n^{k_n}} \right\| \leqslant c \left(\sum_{i=1}^{n} k_i \leqslant p \right)$	$F^{\rho,\, n}_{\varkappa,\, L,\, c}$	86
Space, compact metrical	F	10
Space of n complex variables $z_1, z_2, \ldots, z_n$	E^{z}_{n}	37
Space of complex integral functions of order σ and type s_k $(k=1, 2, \ldots, n)$ in the variable z_k ..	$F^{\sigma,\, c,\, n}_{\rho}$	64
Space, Euclidean, of n dimensions	E_n	15

Concept	Notation	Page
Space of dimension n in which the norm is taken as the absolute magnitude of the maximum (in modulus) co-ordinate	E_n^C	123
Space of functions given on the segment $r\,(0 \leqslant x \leqslant \rho)$ of length ρ having everywhere on the segment r their $(s-1)$th partial derivative, satisfying on this segment the Lipschitz condition with constant L and such that $\lvert f^{(k)}(0) \rvert \leqslant c$ $(k = 0, 1, \ldots, s-1)$	$F^{\rho}_{s,\,L,\,c}$	71
Space of functions defined on segment r of length ρ satisfying on this segment the Lipschitz condition with constant L and not exceeding the constant c (in absolute magnitude)	$F^{\rho}_{L,\,c}$	68
Space of integral functions of order σ and type s	$F_s^{\sigma,\,c}$	61
Table of element $f \in F$ giving some element of the metrical expansion Φ of the space F, not further from f than ε	$T_{\varepsilon}^{\Phi}(f)$	1
Transformation $z = e^{iz'}$	Ψ	23
Transformation, projecting space orthogonally on k-dimensional coordinate plane τ_i^k	Ψ_i^k	110
Transformation, inverse to Ψ_i^k	Φ_i^k	110
Transformation, projecting the E_n space F_G on the m-dimensional Euclidean space E_m	Φ_m^{α}	159

Concept	Notation	Page
Transformation of the space E_n^w into the space E_n^z given by the equations $z_k = \cos \omega_k \ (k = 1, 2, \ldots, n)$	Ψ'	55
Variation of set e inside the cube J_n	$v^{J_n}(e)$	104
Variation of order k of the set e inside the cube J_n	$v_k^{J_n}(e)$	106
Variation of order k of the set e inside the cube J_n with respect to the plane τ_i^k	$v_{\tau_i^k}^{J_n}(e)$	107
Volume of the table $T_\varepsilon^\Phi(f)$	$P\left[T_\varepsilon^\Phi(f)\right]$	1